# Differential Equations

# Differential Equations

ALFRED L. NELSON, *Late Professor of Mathematics*
KARL W. FOLLEY, *Professor of Mathematics*
MAX CORAL, *Professor of Mathematics*
WAYNE STATE UNIVERSITY

## THIRD EDITION

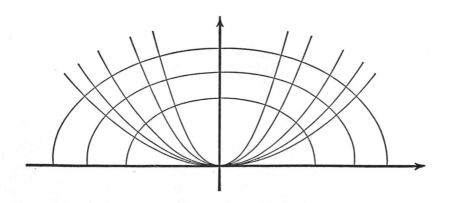

## D. C. HEATH AND COMPANY    BOSTON

Library of Congress Catalog Card Number: 64–14808

*Printed August 1968*

# PREFACE TO THE FIRST EDITION

A course in ordinary differential equations has become the conventional successor to a year's course in calculus. The present book is designed to serve as a text for such a course, to meet the needs both of students majoring in mathematics and of those whose interests lie in the physical sciences or engineering.

In fulfilling this dual purpose, attention is paid to the theory of the solution of ordinary differential equations and to the applications of such equations which arise in geometry, chemistry, and physics. In addition to the commoner types of first-order equations and certain types of second-order equations, whose solution can be easily reduced to quadratures, there is a full treatment of the linear equation of the $n$th order. Linear equations of the second order possessing singular points are solved by the method of Frobenius. As each type is introduced, the theoretical treatment is supplemented by worked examples, in order to strengthen the student's understanding of the material and prepare him to work independently the numerous well-graded exercises.

An exceptionally full discussion is given of the numerical approximation to solutions. Typical examples are worked by the methods of Runge-Kutta, Adams, and Milne, and by combinations of these methods.

Although the greater part of the book is devoted to ordinary differential equations, Chapters Nine and Ten give a brief but adequate introduction to the theory of partial differential equations of the first order, to completely integrable systems of such equations, and to total differential equations.

Enough material is provided for a one-semester course of three or four hours a week, covered at the rate of approximately one set of problems per meeting. For those institutions which, like the authors' own, prefer a sequence of two courses of two semester-hours each, the first course, intended primarily for engineering and science majors, can be devoted to the material treated in the first five chapters.

A. L. Nelson
K. W. Folley
M. Coral

v

# PREFACE TO THE SECOND EDITION

In the second edition of *Differential Equations* the following two significant additions will be noted:

1) A brief treatment of the Laplace Transformation is presented in the Appendix. This affords a useful supplement to the methods given in Chapter Four for solving linear differential equations with constant coefficients.

2) To the special methods for handling linear differential equations with constant coefficients when the right members are of the types $ke^{ax}$ and $kx^r$ has been added a treatment of the case in which sin $bx$ or cos $bx$ appears in the right member. Thus the evaluation of particular integrals of such equations has been made more routine for most cases which will arise.

Besides these more important changes, various alterations and improvements have been made in the text of the first edition, and in certain exercises some of the problems have been replaced.

# PREFACE TO THE THIRD EDITION

The present edition of *Differential Equations* incorporates the following changes:

1) The treatment of the Laplace Transformation, which appeared as an Appendix in the second edition, has been substantially enlarged and now forms Chapter Eleven of the book.

2) A new Chapter Twelve has been added, which offers a brief introduction to the subject of Fourier Series.

3) A few minor alterations have been made in the text of the first ten chapters which should contribute to greater clarity. In making these changes, the authors gratefully acknowledge the advice of those readers who brought the need for such alterations to their attention.

The present authors wish to record their belief that, although the untimely death of the senior author, Professor A. L. Nelson, has deprived them of his collaboration on the preparation of this edition, he would have approved of this revision of the text to which he contributed so largely.

K. W. FOLLEY
M. CORAL

# CONTENTS

## CHAPTER SEVEN
### DIFFERENTIAL EQUATIONS OF THE FIRST ORDER AND NOT OF THE FIRST DEGREE

## CHAPTER EIGHT
### SOLUTION IN SERIES

## CHAPTER NINE
### SYSTEMS OF PARTIAL DIFFERENTIAL EQUATIONS

CONTENTS

# Differential Equations

# CHAPTER ONE

# Preliminary concepts

**1. Introduction.** One of the fundamental types of problems of integral calculus may be illustrated by the following example: to find a function $y(x)$ such that

$$(1) \qquad \frac{dy}{dx} = 3x^2 + 2x$$

identically in $x$. The complete solution of this problem is, of course, readily found. It is $y = x^3 + x^2 + C$, where $C$ is an arbitrary constant.

More general problems of the same type as the preceding one can easily be formulated. Thus one may seek to determine a plane curve whose equation can be written in the form $y = f(x)$ and which has the property that at each point $(x, y)$ of the curve the condition

$$(2) \qquad \frac{dy}{dx} = x + y$$

is satisfied. The solution in this case is not immediately obvious.

A further example can be constructed by requiring that at each point of a curve the radius of curvature be equal to the distance of the point from the origin. From a formula of differ-

1

ential calculus this property can be expressed by means of the equation

$$(3) \qquad \frac{d^2y}{dx^2}(x^2+y^2)^{\frac{1}{2}} = \left[1+\left(\frac{dy}{dx}\right)^2\right]^{\frac{3}{2}}.$$

The equations (1), (2), and (3) are instances of *differential equations*, which express functional relations among an independent variable $x$, a function $y(x)$, and one or more of the derivatives $\frac{dy}{dx}$, $\frac{d^2y}{dx^2}$, etc. Such equations are encountered in many branches of both pure and applied mathematics.

**2. Ordinary differential equations.** A differential equation which involves functions depending upon only one independent variable is called an *ordinary* differential equation. By contrast, a *partial* differential equation is one which involves a function $u$ of several independent variables, together with the partial derivatives of $u$; e.g.:

$$x\frac{\partial u}{\partial x} + y\frac{\partial u}{\partial y} = u$$

$$\frac{\partial^2 u}{\partial x^2} + \frac{\partial^2 u}{\partial y^2} + \frac{\partial^2 u}{\partial z^2} = 0$$

Partial differential equations will be considered in Chapters Nine and Ten.

The *order* of a differential equation is the order of the derivative of highest order which appears in the equation. If a differential equation of order $n$ can be expressed as a polynomial * equation in all the derivatives which appear, then after it has been so expressed, the highest power of the $n$th derivative appearing in the equation is called the *degree* of the equation. Thus the equations (1) and (2) are each of the first order and first degree. Equation (3) is of the second order;

---

* It will be recalled that a *polynomial* in several variables $u$, $v$, $w$, . . . is a sum of terms, each term consisting of a product of non-negative integral powers of the variables, multiplied by a coefficient which is independent of the variables. The degree of any term is the sum of the exponents of the variables in the term. If all the terms in the polynomial have the same degree, the polynomial is said to be *homogeneous*.

it is of the second degree, as can be seen from the equation

$$\left(\frac{d^2y}{dx^2}\right)^2 (x^2 + y^2) = \left[1 + \left(\frac{dy}{dx}\right)^2\right]^3,$$

which is the polynomial equation obtained when (3) is rationalized. The word *degree* is not applied to differential equations which cannot be expressed as polynomial equations in the derivatives.

### EXERCISE 1

Determine the order of each of the following differential equations, and the degree, if the equation has a degree.

1. $y' + x + y = 0$
2. $xy' + y^2 = 0$
3. $y'' + xyy' + 2xy = \sin x$
4. $y'' + y'^2 = x^3$
5. $y = 2xy' + y^2y'^3$
6. $xy^2y'^2 - y^3y' + a^2x = 0$
7. $(xy' - y)^2 = x^2(2xy - x^2y')$
8. $(x^2 + y^2)(1 + y')^2 - 2(x + y)(x + yy') = 0$
9. $y\sqrt{1 + y'^2} = 2x + y$
10. $(1 + y'^2)^{\frac{3}{2}} = 4y''$
11. $\ln y' = xy$
12. $y \sin y' = x$
13. $e^{y'} = xy'$
14. $\ln(1 + y'^2) = 2xy + y'$
15. $(1 + y') \ln y' = x^2$
16. $y'''(1 + y'^2) = x + y''$

**3. Solution of a differential equation.** Consider a differential equation

(4) $$g(x, y, y') = 0$$

of the first order, involving the independent variable $x$, the

3

dependent variable $y$, and the derivative $y'$. A function $y = \phi(x)$ is a *solution* of the equation on an interval $(x_1, x_2)$ if

$$g[x, \phi(x), \phi'(x)] = 0$$

for all $x$ on $(x_1, x_2)$. A solution is frequently called an *integral* of the equation, and the process of finding a solution or integral is known as the *integration* of the equation.

The simple differential equation (1) displayed in Article 1 was shown to have the solution $y = x^3 + x^2 + C$, where $C$ is an arbitrary constant. For each value which is assigned to the constant $C$, the function $x^3 + x^2 + C$ is a solution of the equation (1), and every solution of (1) may be obtained by assigning to $C$ an appropriate value.

More generally, as will be seen in Article 6, a differential equation (4) of the first order possesses a solution $y = \phi(x, C)$ which depends upon one arbitrary constant (or *parameter*) $C$, provided the function $g(x, y, y')$ satisfies certain conditions. For each particular value of $C$ within an appropriate range of values, the function $\phi(x, C)$ is an integral of the differential equation. Further, every solution of the differential equation, with the possible exception of certain singular * solutions, can be obtained by assigning to $C$ an appropriately chosen value. Such a function $\phi(x, C)$ is called the *general solution* or *general integral* of the equation (4). Any solution which is obtained from the general solution by assigning to the parameter $C$ a fixed value is known as a *particular solution* or *particular integral*.

Similar remarks apply to a differential equation of the $n$th order. The equation

$$(5) \qquad g(x, y, y', y'', \ldots, y^{(n)}) = 0$$

of order $n$ will possess a *general solution*

$$y = \phi(x, c_1, c_2, \ldots, c_n),$$

which contains $n$ *independent* parameters $c_1, c_2, \ldots, c_n$. The meaning of the word *independent* will be clarified in Article 4. Every solution obtained from this general solution by assigning

---

* Singular solutions are discussed in Article 63.

fixed values to the parameters $c_i$ is a *particular integral* of equation (5), and every solution of the equation (5) (with the possible exception of certain singular solutions) can be obtained from the general solution by assigning appropriate values to the parameters $c_i$.

A particular integral $y(x)$ of the $n$th-order equation (5) can be determined so that $y(x)$ and its first $n - 1$ derivatives $y'$, $y''$, $\ldots$, $y^{(n-1)}$ have preassigned values at a given point $x = x_0$:

$$y(x_0) = a, \quad y'(x_0) = a_1, \quad \ldots, \quad y^{(n-1)}(x_0) = a_{n-1}$$

Such conditions are called *initial conditions* for the integral and serve to determine the integral uniquely, as will be seen in Article 6. A particular integral which satisfies given initial conditions may be found directly from the differential equation without first finding the general solution of the equation. Numerous illustrations of this will occur in the following chapters. However, if the general solution

$$y = \phi(x, c_1, c_2, \ldots, c_n)$$

of equation (5) is known, then the particular integral determined by given initial conditions can be found from the general solution by computing appropriate values for the constants $c_1, c_2, \ldots, c_n$.

EXAMPLE 1. Show that $y = \frac{1}{10} \sin x + \frac{3}{10} \cos x + \frac{1}{2}x + \frac{3}{4}$ is a solution of the equation $y'' - 3y' + 2y = x + \sin x$.

SOLUTION. We have:

$$y = \tfrac{1}{10} \sin x + \tfrac{3}{10} \cos x + \tfrac{1}{2}x + \tfrac{3}{4}$$
$$y' = \tfrac{1}{10} \cos x - \tfrac{3}{10} \sin x + \tfrac{1}{2}$$
$$y'' = -\tfrac{1}{10} \sin x - \tfrac{3}{10} \cos x$$

Substitution of these values into the left member of the differential equation gives

$$(-\tfrac{1}{10} \sin x - \tfrac{3}{10} \cos x) - 3(\tfrac{1}{10} \cos x - \tfrac{3}{10} \sin x + \tfrac{1}{2})$$
$$+ 2(\tfrac{1}{10} \sin x + \tfrac{3}{10} \cos x + \tfrac{1}{2}x + \tfrac{3}{4}),$$

which reduces to $x + \sin x$, so that the differential equation is satisfied.

**5**

EXAMPLE 2. The differential equation $y'' + y = \cos 2x$ has the general solution $y = c_1 \cos x + c_2 \sin x - \frac{1}{3} \cos 2x$. Find the particular integral satisfying the initial conditions

$$y = 1, \; y' = 0, \text{ at } x = \frac{\pi}{4}.$$

SOLUTION. Let $y = \phi(x)$ denote the particular solution to be found. The problem is to determine the constants $c_1$, $c_2$ so that

$$\phi(x) = c_1 \cos x + c_2 \sin x - \tfrac{1}{3} \cos 2x$$

and $\phi\left(\dfrac{\pi}{4}\right) = 1$, $\phi'\left(\dfrac{\pi}{4}\right) = 0$. Since

$$\phi'(x) = -c_1 \sin x + c_2 \cos x + \tfrac{2}{3} \sin 2x,$$

we have:

$$\phi\left(\frac{\pi}{4}\right) = c_1 \cos \frac{\pi}{4} + c_2 \sin \frac{\pi}{4} - \frac{1}{3} \cos \frac{\pi}{2} = \frac{\sqrt{2}}{2} (c_1 + c_2)$$

$$\phi'\left(\frac{\pi}{4}\right) = -c_1 \sin \frac{\pi}{4} + c_2 \cos \frac{\pi}{4} + \frac{2}{3} \sin \frac{\pi}{2} = -\frac{\sqrt{2}}{2} (c_1 - c_2) + \frac{2}{3}$$

Hence $c_1$ and $c_2$ must satisfy the equations:

$$\frac{\sqrt{2}}{2} (c_1 + c_2) = 1$$

$$-\frac{\sqrt{2}}{2} (c_1 - c_2) + \frac{2}{3} = 0$$

The solution of this pair of linear equations is readily found to be $c_1 = \frac{5}{6}\sqrt{2}$, $c_2 = \frac{1}{6}\sqrt{2}$ and hence the desired integral is

$$\phi(x) = \tfrac{5}{6}\sqrt{2} \cos x + \tfrac{1}{6}\sqrt{2} \sin x - \tfrac{1}{3} \cos 2x.$$

## EXERCISE 2

In each of Problems 1–10 verify that the function $y$ defined by the given equation is a solution of the differential equation.

1. $x^2 - xy + 2x + 1 = 0$; $xy' + y = 2\sqrt{xy}$
2. $x^2 + y = xy$; $x^3 y' - x^2 y + y^2 = 0$
3. $y = \tan x - x$; $y' = (x + y)^2$

4. $y = x - x \ln x$; $xy' + x - y = 0$
5. $y = e^x + e^{2x}$; $y'' - 3y' + 2y = 0$
6. $y = 2e^{2x} + e^{-3x}$; $y'' + y' - 6y = 0$
7. $y = xe^x + e^{2x} - \frac{1}{4}(2x + 5)$; $y''' - 4y'' + 5y' - 2y = x$
8. $y = e^{-x} + e^{3x} + \frac{1}{27}(9x^2 + 6x + 20)$; $y''' - 3y'' - y' + 3y = x^2$
9. $y = - e^x \ln (1 - x)$; $y'' - 2y' + y = \dfrac{e^x}{(1 - x)^2}$
10. $y = \frac{1}{3}e^{2x} - \frac{1}{2} \sin x$; $y'' + 2y' + y = 3e^{2x} - \cos x$

In each of the following problems the general solution of some differential equation is given. Find the particular solution which satisfies the stated initial condition or conditions.

11. $xy = C$; $y = 1$ at $x = 2$
12. $x^2 + Cy^2 = C - 1$; $y = 2$ at $x = 1$
13. $\sin (xy) + y = C$; $y = 1$ at $x = \dfrac{\pi}{4}$
14. $y \sin x = \ln \sec x + C$; $y = 0$ at $x = 1$
15. $y = c_1 e^{\frac{x}{3}} + c_2 e^{-\frac{x}{2}}$; $y = 2$, $y' = 1$ at $x = 0$
16. $y = c_1 + c_2 e^{2x}$; $y = 0$, $y' = 2$ at $x = 1$
17. $y = c_1 \cos 2x + c_2 \sin 2x$; $y = \sqrt{2}$, $y' = 1$ at $x = 0$
18. $y = c_1 \cos (x + c_2)$; $y = 1$, $y' = \sqrt{3}$ at $x = 0$
19. $y = c_1 + (c_2 + c_3 x)e^{3x}$; $y = 0$, $y' = 1$, $y'' = - 1$ at $x = 0$
20. $y = (c_1 + c_2 x)e^x + c_3 e^{-x}$; $y = 1$, $y' = 0$, $y'' = 1$ at $x = 0$

**4. Primitives.** In the preceding article the general integral of a differential equation of order $n$ was defined to be one involving $n$ independent arbitrary constants. The concept of independent constants requires elucidation at this point.

Consider the differential equation

$$(6) \qquad\qquad y'' - 2y' + y = 0.$$

It is easily verified that

$$(7) \qquad\qquad y = c_1 e^{x + c_2}$$

is a solution for any choice of the constants $c_1$, $c_2$. However, it would be an error to suppose that the solution (7), which

7

contains two arbitrary constants, is the general integral of the equation (6). In fact, the solution (7) may readily be written in a form which makes it apparent that there is essentially only one arbitrary constant present:

$$y = c_1 e^{x+c_2} = c_1 e^{c_2} e^x = Ce^x,$$

where the substitution $C = c_1 e^{c_2}$ has been made. It is evident that every particular solution of the equation (6), obtained from $y = c_1 e^{x+c_2}$ by giving special values to $c_1$ and $c_2$, can be obtained from $y = Ce^x$ by giving to $C$ the value $C = c_1 e^{c_2}$; and conversely, every particular solution obtained from $y = Ce^x$ for a special value of $C$ can be secured from (7) by putting $c_2 = 0$, $c_1 = C$. However, $y = Ce^x$, which contains only one arbitrary constant, cannot be the general solution of the second-order equation (6). In fact, by methods given later in this text the general integral of (6) may be shown to be

$$y = (c_1 + c_2 x)e^x.$$

Consider a function

(8) $$y = \phi(x, c_1, c_2, \ldots, c_n),$$

which contains $n$ arbitrary constants $c_1, c_2, \ldots, c_n$, and which is a solution of the differential equation

(9) $$g(x, y, y', y'', \ldots, y^{(n)}) = 0.$$

The constants $c_1, c_2, \ldots, c_n$ are said to be *independent* in case the determinant

(10)
$$\begin{vmatrix} \dfrac{\partial \phi}{\partial c_1} & \dfrac{\partial \phi}{\partial c_2} & \cdots & \dfrac{\partial \phi}{\partial c_n} \\[2ex] \dfrac{\partial \phi'}{\partial c_1} & \dfrac{\partial \phi'}{\partial c_2} & \cdots & \dfrac{\partial \phi'}{\partial c_n} \\[2ex] \dfrac{\partial \phi''}{\partial c_1} & \dfrac{\partial \phi''}{\partial c_2} & \cdots & \dfrac{\partial \phi''}{\partial c_n} \\[2ex] \cdot & \cdot & \cdots & \cdot \\[1ex] \dfrac{\partial \phi^{(n-1)}}{\partial c_1} & \dfrac{\partial \phi^{(n-1)}}{\partial c_2} & \cdots & \dfrac{\partial \phi^{(n-1)}}{\partial c_n} \end{vmatrix}$$

is different from zero for some ranges of values of $x, c_1, c_2, \ldots, c_n$.

8

If the function (8) is differentiated $n - 1$ times with respect to $x$, the following equations result:

(11)
$$y = \phi(x, c_1, c_2, \ldots, c_n)$$
$$y' = \phi'(x, c_1, c_2, \ldots, c_n)$$
$$y'' = \phi''(x, c_1, c_2, \ldots, c_n)$$
$$\cdot \quad \cdot \quad \cdot \quad \cdot \quad \cdot \quad \cdot$$
$$y^{(n-1)} = \phi^{(n-1)}(x, c_1, c_2, \ldots, c_n)$$

It is shown in more advanced treatises that the nonvanishing of the determinant (10) is sufficient to insure that the equations (11) can be solved for the parameters $c_1, c_2, \ldots, c_n$ as functions of $x, y, y', y'', \ldots, y^{(n-1)}$:

(12)   $c_i = c_i(x, y, y', y'', \ldots, y^{(n-1)}), \quad i = 1, 2, \ldots, n$

When the functions (12) are substituted for the parameters $c_i$ in the equation

$$y^{(n)} = \phi^{(n)}(x, c_1, c_2, \ldots, c_n),$$

which is obtained by differentiating $\phi(x, c_1, c_2, \ldots, c_n)$ $n$ times with respect to $x$, there results a differential equation of order $n$:

(13)   $y^{(n)} = \phi^{(n)}[x, c_1(x, y, y', \ldots, y^{(n-1)}), \ldots,$
$$c_n(x, y, y', \ldots, y^{(n-1)})]$$
$$= \psi(x, y, y', \ldots, y^{(n-1)}),$$

of which $y = \phi(x, c_1, c_2, \ldots, c_n)$ will be the general integral. This general integral is called the *primitive* of the differential equation (13) which has been derived therefrom.

EXAMPLE 1. Derive the first-order equation which has $y = C \sin x$ as its primitive.

SOLUTION. Differentiating

(a)                    $y = C \sin x$

once with respect to $x$, we have

(b)                    $y' = C \cos x.$

The elimination of $C$ between (a) and (b) can be accomplished by solving (a) for $C$ and substituting this solution into (b). The resulting differential equation is

$$y' = y \cot x.$$

EXAMPLE 2. Derive the second-order equation which has

$$y = c_1 \sin (x + c_2)$$

as its primitive.

SOLUTION. Differentiating

$(a)$ $$y = c_1 \sin (x + c_2)$$

twice with respect to $x$, we have:

$(b)$ $$y' = c_1 \cos (x + c_2)$$
$(c)$ $$y'' = - c_1 \sin (x + c_2)$$

The parameters $c_1$, $c_2$ are readily eliminated by adding equations $(a)$ and $(c)$. The resulting differential equation is

$$y'' + y = 0.$$

EXAMPLE 3. Verify that the primitive

$$y = c_1 x + c_2 e^x$$

contains two independent parameters, and find the second-order differential equation of which this function is the general solution.

SOLUTION. We have

$(a)$ $$y = c_1 x + c_2 e^x$$
$(b)$ $$y' = c_1 + c_2 e^x$$

so that for this case the determinant (10) has the value

$$\begin{vmatrix} x & e^x \\ 1 & e^x \end{vmatrix} = e^x(x - 1),$$

which does not vanish for $x \neq 1$. Thus $c_1$ and $c_2$ are independent. The solution of equations $(a)$ and $(b)$ for $c_1$ and $c_2$ is

$$c_1 = \frac{y - y'}{x - 1},$$

$$c_2 = \frac{y'x - y}{e^x(x - 1)},$$

and substitution into the equation

$$y'' = c_2 e^x$$

gives the desired equation

$$y''(x - 1) = y'x - y.$$

## EXERCISE 3

In each of Problems 1–12 derive the differential equation which has as primitive the function $y$ defined by the given equation.

1. $x^2 - 2Cy - C^2 = 0$
2. $x = y^4 + Cy^3$
3. $x + y = \tan{(x + C)}$
4. $y = x + C\sqrt{x^2 + 1}$
5. $x^3 - y^2 = Cy$
6. $x^2y + 2x = Cy$
7. $x \sin y = e^{Cx}$
8. $y = c_1 e^x + c_2 e^{-x} + x$
9. $y = c_1 e^x + c_2 e^{2x} - xe^x$
10. $y = c_1 \cos 2x + c_2 \sin 2x$
11. $y = e^x(c_1 \cos x + c_2 \sin x)$
12. $y = x(c_1 \cos x + c_2 \sin x)$

13. Verify that the primitive in each of Problems 8–12 contains two independent arbitrary constants.

In each of the following problems, find the differential equation which has the given family of integral curves.

14. The family of equilateral hyperbolas whose asymptotes are the coordinate axes.
15. The family of circles with centers on the $x$-axis.
16. The family of circles through the origin, with centers on the $x$-axis.
17. The family of straight lines for each of which the measure of the $y$-intercept equals the slope.
18. The family of straight lines for each of which the measure of the $y$-intercept is a given function of the slope.
19. The family of tangents to the circle $x^2 + y^2 = 25$.
20. The family of tangents to the parabola $y = x^2$.
21. The family of parabolas each of which has vertex and focus on the $x$-axis.
22. The family of parabolas each with axis parallel to the $x$-axis, the distance between the vertex and focus being 1.

**11**

**5. Slope fields.** A differential equation of the first order

$$(14) \qquad\qquad g(x, y, y') = 0$$

can be given a geometrical interpretation which is illuminating. For this purpose, we shall consider the case in which (14) can be put in the explicit form

$$(15) \qquad\qquad y' = f(x, y).$$

It will be supposed that the function $f(x, y)$ is single valued and continuous in a region $R$ of the $xy$-plane.

At each point $(x, y)$ of the region $R$ a slope $y'$ is determined by the equation $y' = f(x, y)$. A line segment drawn through the point $(x, y)$ with slope $y' = f(x, y)$ will be called the *line element* at the point $(x, y)$, determined by the equation (15). The entire region $R$ may then be thought of as covered by line elements determined by the differential equation. The resulting aggregation of line elements is the *slope field* of the differential equation.

A curve in the region $R$ whose tangent at each point coincides with the line element at that point is called an *integral curve* of the equation (15). If $\phi(x, C)$ is the general solution of (15), then the equation $y = \phi(x, C)$ represents a one-parameter family of integral curves for (15).

EXAMPLE. Construct the slope field for the differential equation

$$y' = \frac{y^2 - y}{x}.$$

SOLUTION. The right member of the equation is continuous in any region $R$ of the $xy$-plane which does not contain the $y$-axis. Figure 1 is a representation of that portion of the slope field which lies to the right of the $y$-axis. A curve drawn in this region, so as to be tangent at each of its points to the line element of the slope field drawn through this point, resembles a branch of a hyperbola. The integral curves are in fact hyperbolas since the general solution of the differential equation is

$$y - 1 = Cxy,$$

as is readily verified.

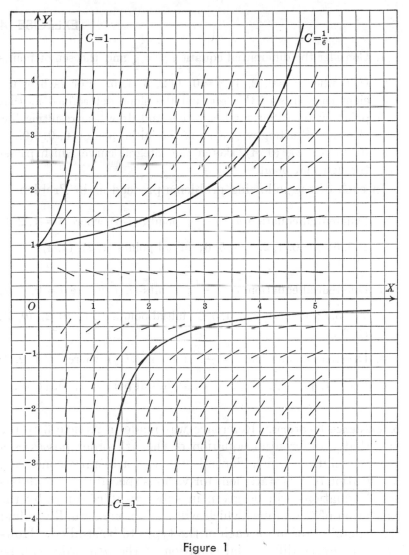

Figure 1

13

## EXERCISE 4

1. Consider the differential equation $y' = \dfrac{x}{2}$ and the set of points $(i, j)$ where $i = 0$, 2, 4; $j = 0$, 1, 2, 3, 4, 5. For each of the eighteen points of this set find the slope determined at that point by the differential equation and draw the resulting line element. Starting with each of the initial points $(0, 0)$, $(0, 1)$, $(0, 2)$, $(0, 3)$, $(0, 4)$, sketch the integral curve which passes through that point.

In each of the following problems proceed as in Problem 1.

2. Differential equation $y' = -\dfrac{y}{x}$; points $(i, j)$ where $i = 1, 2, 3,$ 4, 5, 6; $j = 0$, 1, 2, 3, 4, 5, 6; initial points $(1, 2)$, $(1, 4)$, $(1, 6)$, $(2, 6)$.

3. Differential equation $y' = -\dfrac{x}{y}$; points $(i, j)$ where $i = 0$, 1, 2, 3, 4, 5, 6; $j = 0, 1, 2, 3, 4, 5, 6$; initial points $(0, 1)$, $(0, 2)$, $(0, 5)$, $(1, 3)$.

4. Differential equation $y' = -\dfrac{8}{x^3}$; points $(i, j)$ where $i = 1$, 2, 4; $j = \frac{1}{4}$, 1, $\frac{7}{4}$, 2, $\frac{11}{4}$, 3, $\frac{15}{4}$, 4, $\frac{19}{4}$, 5; initial points $(1, 4)$, $(1, 5)$.

**6. Existence theorems.** Reference was made in Article 3 to the fact that a differential equation of the $n$th order possesses a general solution which depends upon $n$ arbitrary constants. Verification of this statement for various special types of differential equations will be given in subsequent chapters by the exposition of techniques which will enable one actually to find the general solution for each of the types to be studied. However, not every differential equation of the $n$th order can be included under these types; for some equations, indeed, no technique exists for expressing the solution in terms of simple functions and resort must be had to methods of approximation such as will be described in Chapters Five and Eight. It would be useful, therefore, to be assured in advance that the differential equation under study does indeed possess a solution.

Such assurance is furnished by well-known existence theorems. We shall content ourselves here with stating without proof two such theorems which will be adequate for the purposes of this book.

*Theorem 1.* Let $g(x, u, u_1)$ be a function which is defined for values of $x$, $u$, $u_1$ satisfying conditions of the form

(16)　　$|x - a| < A, \quad |u - b| < B, \quad |u_1 - c_1| < C_1,$

where $a$, $b$, $c_1$ and $A$, $B$, $C_1$ are given constants, the latter three being positive. For such values of $x$, $u$, $u_1$ let the function $g(x, u, u_1)$ be continuous and have continuous partial derivatives of the first order. Suppose further that for these values the derivative

$$\frac{\partial}{\partial u_1} g(x, u, u_1)$$

is never zero. Let $x_0, a_0, a_1$ be values satisfying the following conditions:

$$|x_0 - a| < A, \quad |a_0 - b| < B, \quad |a_1 - c_1| < C_1$$
$$g(x_0, a_0, a_1) = 0$$

Then the first-order differential equation

(17)　　　　　　$g(x, y, y') = 0$

has a unique solution $y = \phi(x)$, which is defined on a suitably chosen interval $x_1 \leqq x \leqq x_2$ containing the value $x_0$, and which is such that

(18)　　　　$\phi(x_0) = a_0, \quad \phi'(x_0) = a_1.$

The equation (17) possesses a general solution $y = \phi(x, C)$ containing one independent arbitrary constant $C$, and each solution satisfying conditions of the form (18) can be obtained from the general solution by assigning an appropriate value to the constant $C$. If the function $g(x, u, u_1)$ is *analytic* in the neighborhood of the values $(a, b, c_1)$, i.e., if $g(x, u, u_1)$ can be expressed as a power series in powers of $x - a$, $u - b$, $u_1 - c_1$ which is absolutely convergent for values of $x$, $u$, $u_1$ satisfying the conditions (16), then the solution satisfying (18) is also expressible as a power series in powers of $x - a$ which converges for values of $x$ in a non-vanishing interval with center at $x = a$.

The proof of this theorem is beyond the scope of this book.* However, indications will be given in Article 46 of one possible method of proof. An extension of the results of Theorem 1 to differential equations of order higher than the first is contained in the following theorem.

*Theorem 2.* Let $g(x, u, u_1, u_2, \ldots, u_n)$ be a function which is defined for values $x, u, u_1, u_2, \ldots, u_n$ satisfying conditions of the form

(19) $\qquad \begin{aligned} &| x - a | < A, \quad | u - b | < B, \\ &| u_i - c_i | < C_i, \quad i = 1, 2, \ldots, n, \end{aligned}$

where $a, b, c_i$, and $A, B, C_i$ are constants, the latter set being positive. For such values of $x, u, u_1, u_2, \ldots, u_n$ let the function $g(x, u, u_1, u_2, \ldots, u_n)$ be continuous and have continuous partial derivatives of the first order. Suppose further that for these values the derivative

$$\frac{\partial}{\partial u_n} g(x, u, u_1, u_2, \ldots, u_n)$$

is never zero. Let $x_0, a_0, a_1, \ldots, a_n$ be values satisfying the following conditions:

$$\begin{aligned} | x_0 - a | &< A, \quad | a_0 - b | < B, \\ | a_i - c_i | &< C_i, \quad i = 1, 2, \ldots, n, \\ g(x_0, a_0, a_1, \ldots, a_n) &= 0 \end{aligned}$$

Then the differential equation

(20) $\qquad g(x, y, y', \ldots, y^{(n)}) = 0$

of the $n$th order has a unique solution $y = \phi(x)$, which is defined on a suitably chosen interval $x_1 \leq x \leq x_2$ containing $x_0$, and which is such that

(21) $\qquad \phi(x_0) = a_0, \quad \phi'(x_0) = a_1, \ldots, \quad \phi^{(n-1)}(x_0) = a_{n-1}.$

* See E. J. B. Goursat, *A Course in Mathematical Analysis*, Vol. II, Pt. II, trans. by E. R. Hedrick and O. Dunkel (Boston: Ginn and Co., 1917), pp. 45 ff.

The equation (20) possesses a general solution

$$y = \phi(x, c_1, c_2, \ldots, c_n)$$

containing $n$ independent arbitrary constants, and each solution satisfying conditions of the form (21) can be obtained from the general solution by assigning appropriate values to the constants $c_1, c_2, \ldots, c_n$. If the function $g(x, u, u_1, u_2, \ldots, u_n)$ is analytic in the neighborhood of the values $(a, b, c_1, c_2, \ldots, c_n)$, i.e., can be expressed as a power series in powers of $x - a$, $u - b$, $u_1 - c_1, \ldots, u_n - c_n$ which converges absolutely for values of $x, u, u_1, \ldots, u_n$ satisfying the conditions (19), then the solution $y = \phi(x)$ which satisfies the conditions (21) can be expressed as a power series in powers of $x - a$, which converges for $x$ on a nonvanishing interval with center at $x = a$.

17

# CHAPTER TWO

# Differential equations of the first order and first degree

**7. Introduction.** A differential equation of the first order and first degree can be written in the form

$$(1) \qquad \frac{dy}{dx} = F(x, y).$$

An alternative form, found to be more useful in the greater part of this chapter, is

$$(2) \qquad M(x, y)\, dx + N(x, y)\, dy = 0.$$

One difference between these two equations should be noted. In equation (1) it is clear that $x$ is the independent variable and that the general solution of (1) will be a function $y = \phi(x, C)$, as explained in Article 3. In equation (2), however, the independent variable may be either $x$ or $y$, according as $N$ or $M$ is different from zero in the region of values $(x, y)$ being considered. The general solution of (2), in a sense somewhat broader than that of Article 3, is given by an equation $\Phi(x, y, C) = 0$ such that the partial derivatives $\Phi_x(x, y, C)$ and $\Phi_y(x, y, C)$ are proportional to $M(x, y)$ and $N(x, y)$ for each set of values $x$, $y$, and $C$ under consideration. If $N$ (and hence $\Phi_y$) is not zero, one may solve the equation $\Phi(x, y, C) = 0$ and obtain a function $y = \phi(x, C)$ which is the general solution of $dy/dx = -M/N$.

18

Certain especially simple cases of these equations may be given passing notice. If in (1) the right member is a constant or a function of $x$ alone, solving the equation reduces to an exercise in indefinite integration. In equation (2), whenever $M$ is a function of $x$ alone and $N$ a function of $y$ alone, the variables are said to be *separated*. The function

$$\Phi(x, y) = \int M(x) \, dx + \int N(y) \, dy$$

has the partial derivatives $\Phi_x = M$ and $\Phi_y = N$. Hence $d\Phi = M \, dx + N \, dy = 0$ and $\Phi(x, y) = C$ is the solution of (2) in this case.

In this chapter various special cases of equations (1) and (2) will be considered, and devices for solving them will be explained. Facility in solving will depend to a large extent on a correct classification of the differential equation to be solved.

**8. Variables separable.** While in the differential equation

$$(3) \qquad x \sec y \, dx + (1 + x) \, dy = 0$$

the variables are not separated, it is easily seen that division by $(1 + x) \sec y$ replaces (3) by an equation having this desirable property. The original equation is described as one whose variables are *separable*. An inspection is sufficient to show whether the variables are separable in a given differential equation.

EXAMPLE 1. Obtain the general solution of equation (3).
SOLUTION. As a result of division by $(1 + x) \sec y$, the given differential equation is replaced by

$$\frac{x \, dx}{1 + x} + \cos y \, dy = 0 \quad \text{or} \quad \left(1 - \frac{1}{1 + x}\right) dx + \cos y \, dy = 0.$$

Integrating each term with respect to its variable, we see that the function

$$x - \ln (1 + x) + \sin y$$

has its total differential equal to the left member of the preceding equation. Hence the solution sought is

$$x - \ln (1 + x) + \sin y = C.$$

19

It should be noted that division by $(1 + x) \sec y$ in Example 1 is permissible only for those values of $x$ and $y$ for which the divisor does not vanish. The factor $\sec y$ is never zero; the factor $1 + x$ vanishes for $x = -1$, and it is readily seen that $x = -1$ is indeed a solution if $y$ is considered to be the independent variable.

A remark concerning the logarithmic term of the solution of Example 1 is also in order. Strictly speaking, the indefinite integral of the term $\dfrac{dx}{1 + x}$ should have been written $\ln |\, 1 + x\, |$. However, no ambiguity can arise from the omission of the symbol for absolute value provided it is assumed that the variables are so restricted as to make the argument of the logarithm positive.

EXAMPLE 2. For the differential equation

$$(1 - y)\, \frac{dy}{dx} = y(1 - x),$$

find the particular solution $y(x)$ for which $y(2) = -1$.

SOLUTION. When the variables are separated, the given differential equation takes the form

$$(1 - x)\, dx = \frac{(1 - y)\, dy}{y},$$

whose general solution is

$$x - \frac{x^2}{2} = \ln\,(-y) - y + C.$$

The use of the argument $-y$ in the logarithmic term is dictated by the fact that the initial value of $y$ is negative. Substituting $x = 2$, $y = -1$, we find $C = -1$. Hence the particular solution desired is

$$\ln\,(-y) = x - \frac{x^2}{2} + y + 1.$$

It should be remarked that the particular solution $y = 0$, lost by dividing the original equation by $y$, is not of interest, since it cannot satisfy the given initial condition.

$odd$

In Problems 1–20 find the general solution of each of the differential equations.

1. $xy\, dx + (x^2 + 1)\, dy = 0$
2. $(xy^2 + x)\, dx + (y - x^2 y)\, dy = 0$
3. $(1 + y^2)\, dx + (1 + x^2)\, dy = 0$
4. $y\, dx + x\, dy = 0$
5. $dy = 2xy\, dx$
6. $(xy^2 + x)\, dx + (x^2 y - y)\, dy = 0$
7. $\sqrt{1 - x^2}\, dy + \sqrt{1 - y^2}\, dx = 0$
8. $(1 + x)\, dy - (1 - y)\, dx = 0$
9. $y' \tan x - y = 1$
10. $(y + 3)\, dx + \cot x\, dy = 0$
11. $\dfrac{dy}{dx} = \dfrac{x}{y}$
12. $\dfrac{dx}{dt} = 1 - \sin 2t$
13. $x\dfrac{dy}{dx} + y = y^2$
14. $\sin x \cos^2 y\, dx + \cos^2 x\, dy = 0$
15. $\sec x \cos^2 y\, dx = \cos x \sin y\, dy$
16. $y\, dx + x\, dy = xy(dy - dx)$
17. $xy\, dx + \sqrt{1 + x^2}\, dy = 0$
18. $y\, dx = xy\, dx + x^2\, dy$
19. $\tan x \sin^2 y\, dx + \cos^2 x \cot y\, dy = 0$
20. $y^2\, dx + y\, dy + x^2 y\, dy - dx = 0$

For each of the differential equations in Problems 21–30, find the particular solution corresponding to the given values of the variables.

21. $\dfrac{dy}{dx} = \dfrac{y}{x};\ y = 3$ when $x = 1$
22. $x\, dy + 2y\, dx = 0;\ y = 1$ when $x = 2$
23. $\sin x \cos y\, dx + \cos x \sin y\, dy = 0;\ y = 0$ when $x = 0$
24. $x^2\, dy + y^2\, dx = 0;\ y = 1$ when $x = 3$
25. $\dfrac{dy}{dx} = e^y;\ y = 0$ when $x = 0$

21

26. $e^y \left( \dfrac{dy}{dx} + 1 \right) = 1$; $y = 1$ when $x = 0$

27. $(1 + y^2) \, dx = \dfrac{dy}{x^3(x - 1)}$; $y = 0$ when $x = 2$

28. $(x^2 + 3x) \, dy = (y^3 + 2y) \, dx$; $y = 1$ when $x = 1$

29. $(x^2 + x + 1) \, dy = (y^2 + 2y + 5) \, dx$; $y = 1$ when $x = 1$

30. $(x^2 - 2x - 8) \, dy = (y^2 + y - 2) \, dx$; $y = 0$ when $x = 0$

**9. M, N homogeneous and of the same degree.** Consider the differential equation

(4) $$(x - y) \, dx + (x + 2y) \, dy = 0,$$

a simple example of a differential equation in which $M$ and $N$ are homogeneous polynomials, each of degree unity. We proceed to indicate how (4) can be replaced by an equivalent equation whose variables are separable. Substituting $y = vx$, which implies $dy = v \, dx + x \, dv$, into (4), we have

$$(x - vx) \, dx + (x + 2vx)(v \, dx + x \, dv) = 0.$$

If the factor $x$ is removed,* the new equation takes the form

$$(1 + 2v^2) \, dx + x(1 + 2v) \, dv = 0,$$

in which the variables are separable.

Before undertaking an argument to support the general applicability of the method used in treating equation (4), an extension of the notion of homogeneity is desirable. A homogeneous polynomial $f(x, y)$ is characterized by the property

(5) $$f(tx, ty) = t^n f(x, y),$$

where $n$ is the degree of $f(x, y)$, and $t$ is arbitrary. For the purpose of the present discussion we wish to consider *all* functions, not necessarily polynomials or even algebraic functions, which satisfy (5), and we shall term such functions *homogeneous of degree n* in the extended sense. For example, if we replace $x$ and $y$ by $tx$ and $ty$ respectively, then the function

---

* The equation $x = 0$ does not satisfy (4) for all values of $y$.

$x + y \sin \dfrac{y}{x}$ is replaced by $tx + ty \sin \dfrac{ty}{tx} = t\left[x + y \sin \dfrac{y}{x}\right]$. Hence the function is homogeneous of degree unity in the sense just defined.

**10. Separation of variables effected by substitution.** Now consider a differential equation (2) in which $M$ and $N$ are homogeneous of the same degree $n$. If $N \neq 0$, the equation can be written

$$\frac{dy}{dx} = -\frac{M(x, y)}{N(x, y)} = -\frac{M(tx, ty)}{t^n} \cdot \frac{t^n}{N(tx, ty)} = -\frac{M(tx, ty)}{N(tx, ty)}$$

for any value of $t$. If we take $t = \dfrac{1}{x}$, the last fraction can be written

$$-\frac{M\left(1, \dfrac{y}{x}\right)}{N\left(1, \dfrac{y}{x}\right)}$$

in which $x$ and $y$ occur only in the combination $\dfrac{y}{x}$. Hence the differential equation takes the form

(6) $$\frac{dy}{dx} = F\left(\frac{y}{x}\right).$$

The substitution of $y = vx$, $\dfrac{dy}{dx} = v + x \dfrac{dv}{dx}$, enables us to reduce (6) as follows:

$$v + x \frac{dv}{dx} = F(v)$$

$$[v - F(v)] \, dx + x \, dv = 0$$

$$\frac{dx}{x} + \frac{dv}{v - F(v)} = 0$$

This demonstrates the separability of the variables $v$ and $x$. If $v - F(v) = 0$ identically in $v$, then $\dfrac{y}{x} = \dfrac{dy}{dx}$ and the equation (2) has the simple form $y \, dx - x \, dy = 0$.

The argument just given can be readily modified to show that the substitution $x = vy$ also leads to a new equation in which the variables are separable.

EXAMPLE 1. Complete the solution of equation (4).

SOLUTION. It was shown in Article 9 that the substitution $y = vx$ results in the new equation

$$(1 + 2v^2) \, dx + x(1 + 2v) \, dv = 0.$$

Separating the variables, we have

$$\frac{dx}{x} + \frac{(1 + 2v) \, dv}{1 + 2v^2} = 0.$$

A rearrangement of the second fraction enables us to solve as follows:

$$\frac{dx}{x} + \frac{2v \, dv}{1 + 2v^2} + \frac{dv}{1 + 2v^2} = 0$$

$$\ln x + \tfrac{1}{2} \ln (1 + 2v^2) + \frac{\sqrt{2}}{2} \text{ Arc tan } \sqrt{2}v = \ln C$$

$$\ln [C'x^2(1 + 2v^2)] + \sqrt{2} \text{ Arc tan } \sqrt{2}v = 0,$$

where $C' = \dfrac{1}{C^2}.$ Since $v = \dfrac{y}{x}$, the solution takes the form

$$\ln [C'(x^2 + 2y^2)] + \sqrt{2} \text{ Arc tan } \frac{\sqrt{2}y}{x} = 0.$$

As in the example just solved, we shall use capital letters to indicate principal values of inverse trigonometric functions. Thus in the general solution of the example, it is understood that Arc tan $\dfrac{\sqrt{2}y}{x}$ is restricted to the range

$$-\frac{\pi}{2} < \text{Arc tan } \frac{\sqrt{2}y}{x} < \frac{\pi}{2}.$$

EXAMPLE 2. Find the particular solution $y(x)$ of the equation $y^2 \, dx + (x^2 + xy + y^2) \, dy = 0$ for which $y(1) = 1$.

SOLUTION. The substitution of

$$x = vy, \quad dx = v \, dy + y \, dv$$

into the equation results in an equation in $v$ and $y$ whose general solution may be found as follows:

$$(v^2 + 2v + 1)\, dy + y\, dv = 0$$

$$\frac{dy}{y} + \frac{dv}{(v+1)^2} = 0$$

$$\ln y - \frac{1}{v+1} = \ln C$$

$$\ln \frac{y}{C} = \frac{1}{\dfrac{x}{y}+1} = \frac{y}{x+y}$$

$$y = Ce^{\frac{y}{x+y}}$$

The particular solution for which $y = 1$ when $x = 1$ is

$$y = e^{\frac{y-x}{2(y+x)}}.$$

**EXERCISE 6**

Find the general solution of each of the differential equations in Problems 1–14.

1. $(x + y)\, dx = x\, dy$
2. $(x + y)\, dy + x\, dx = y\, dx$
3. $x\, dy - y\, dx = \sqrt{xy}\, dx$
4. $\dfrac{dy}{dx} = \dfrac{2x - y}{x + 4y}$
5. $x\, dy - y\, dx = \sqrt{x^2 - y^2}\, dx$
6. $x\, dx + y\, dy = 2y\, dx$
7. $\dfrac{x\, dy}{dx} - y + \sqrt{y^2 - x^2} = 0$
8. $(x^2 + y^2)\, dx = xy\, dy$
9. $(xy - x^2)\, dy - y^2\, dx = 0$
10. $x\dfrac{dy}{dx} + y = 2\sqrt{xy}$
11. $(x + y)\, dx + (x - y)\, dy = 0$
12. $y(x^2 - xy + y^2) + xy'(x^2 + xy + y^2) = 0$
13. $y'x - y - x \sin \dfrac{y}{x} = 0$
14. $y' = \dfrac{y}{x} + \cosh \dfrac{y}{x}$

25

Solve each of the following equations subject to the given condition.

15. $(x^2 + y^2)\, dx = 2xy\, dy$; $y = 0$ when $x = -1$

16. $\left(\dfrac{x}{y} + \dfrac{y}{x}\right) dy + dx = 0$; $y = -1$ when $x = 0$

17. $(xe^{\frac{y}{x}} + y)\, dx = x\, dy$; $y = 0$ when $x = 1$

18. $\dfrac{dy}{dx} = \dfrac{x+y}{x-y}$; $y = 0$ when $x = 1$

19. $\dfrac{dy}{dx} = \dfrac{y}{x} + \tan\dfrac{y}{x}$; $y = \pi$ when $x = 6$

20. $(3xy - 2x^2)\, dy = (2y^2 - xy)\, dx$; $y = -1$ when $x = 1$

21. $\dfrac{dy}{dx} = \dfrac{y}{x - k\sqrt{x^2 + y^2}}$; $y = 1$ when $x = 0$

22. $y^2(y\, dx - x\, dy) + x^3\, dx = 0$; $y = 3$ when $x = 1$

23. $y' = \dfrac{y}{x} + \tanh\dfrac{y}{x}$; $y = .376$ when $x = .301$

## 11. M, N linear, nonhomogeneous.

If $M = a_1x + b_1y + c_1$ and $N = a_2x + b_2y + c_2$, the substitution of new variables for these linear expressions leads to the solution of the differential equation. The modification which is necessary when the coefficients of $x$ and $y$ in $M$ and $N$ are proportional is shown in Example 2.

EXAMPLE 1. Solve the differential equation

$$(x - y + 1)\, dx + (x + y)\, dy = 0.$$

SOLUTION. Let

$$u = x - y + 1, \quad v = x + y.$$

Then

$$x = \tfrac{1}{2}(u + v - 1), \quad y = -\tfrac{1}{2}(u - v - 1).$$

Hence

$$dx = \tfrac{1}{2}(du + dv), \quad dy = -\tfrac{1}{2}(du - dv).$$

The differential equation is transformed as follows:

$$u(du + dv) + v(dv - du) = 0$$
$$(u - v)\, du + (u + v)\, dv = 0$$

Following the method explained in the preceding article, the further substitution

$$u = tv, \quad du = t\, dv + v\, dt$$

is made. The resulting equation, after reduction, becomes

$$\frac{dv}{v} + \frac{(t-1)\, dt}{t^2 + 1} = 0,$$

for which we have the solution

$$\ln\left(v^2 t^2 + v^2\right) = 2 \text{ Arc tan } t + C.$$

Replacing $t$ by $\dfrac{u}{v}$, we have

$$\ln\left(u^2 + v^2\right) = 2 \text{ Arc tan } \frac{u}{v} + C.$$

In terms of the original variables, the solution is

$$\ln\left[(x - y + 1)^2 + (x + y)^2\right] = 2 \text{ Arc tan } \frac{x\ \ y + 1}{x + y} + C.$$

EXAMPLE 2. Solve the equation $(x - 2y + 1)\, dx = (x - 2y)\, dy$. SOLUTION. Since the coefficients of $x$ and $y$ in the expressions $x - 2y + 1$ and $x - 2y$ are proportional, the technique employed in Example 1 will fail. In this case the introduction of the single new variable $u = x - 2y + 1$ will serve. It follows that

$$x = u + 2y - 1,$$

so that $dx = du + 2\, dy$. Hence the differential equation takes the successive forms:

$$u(du + 2\, dy) = (u - 1)\, dy$$

$$u\, du + (u + 1)\, dy = 0$$

$$\frac{u\, du}{u + 1} + dy = 0$$

$$\left(1 - \frac{1}{u + 1}\right) du + dy = 0$$

The general solution is

$$u - \ln(u + 1) + y = C,$$

or, in terms of the original variables,

$$x - y + 1 = C + \ln(x - 2y + 2).$$

*odd thru 9*

Find the general solutions in Problems 1–10.

1. $(x + y) \, dx - (x - y + 2) \, dy = 0$
2. $x \, dx + (x - 2y + 2) \, dy = 0$
3. $(2x - y + 1) \, dx + (x + y) \, dy = 0$
4. $(x - y + 2) \, dx + (x + y - 1) \, dy = 0$
5. $(x - y) \, dx + (y - x + 1) \, dy = 0$
6. $\dfrac{dy}{dx} = \dfrac{x + y - 1}{x - y - 1}$
7. $(x + y) \, dx + (2x + 2y - 1) \, dy = 0$
8. $(x - y + 1) \, dx + (x - y - 1) \, dy = 0$
9. $(x + 2y) \, dx + (3x + 6y + 3) \, dy = 0$
10. $(x + 2y + 2) \, dx = (2x + y - 1) \, dy$

In each of Problems 11–20 find the particular solution determined by the given conditions.

11. $(3x - y + 1) \, dx + (x - 3y - 5) \, dy = 0$
    $y = 0$ when $x = 0$
12. $3(2x - y + 2) \, dx + (2x - y + 5) \, dy = 0$
    $y = 1$ when $x = -1$
13. $(2x + 3y + 2) \, dx + (y - x) \, dy = 0$
    $y = -2$ when $x = 0$
14. $(x + y + 4) \, dx = (2x + 2y - 1) \, dy$
    $y = 0$ when $x = 0$
15. $(2x + 3y - 1) \, dx + (2x + 3y + 2) \, dy = 0$
    $y = 1$ when $x = 3$
16. $(3x - y + 2) \, dx + (x + 2y + 1) \, dy = 0$
    $y = 0$ when $x = 0$
17. $(3x + 2y + 3) \, dx - (x + 2y - 1) \, dy = 0$
    $y = 1$ when $x = -2$
18. $(x - 2y + 3) \, dx + (1 - x + 2y) \, dy = 0$
    $y = 2$ when $x = -4$
19. $(2x + y) \, dx + (4x + 2y + 1) \, dy = 0$
    $y = 0$ when $x = -\frac{1}{6}$
20. $(2x + y) \, dx + (4x - 2y + 1) \, dy = 0$
    $y = \frac{1}{2}$ when $x = 0$

**12. Exact differential equations.** Recalling from calculus the formula for the total differential of a function of $x$ and $y$

(7) $$df(x, y) = f_x \, dx + f_y \, dy,$$

in which $f_x$ and $f_y$ are partial derivatives with respect to the indicated variables, we see that the differential equation

$$f_x \, dx + f_y \, dy = 0$$

has the general solution

$$f(x, y) = C.$$

A differential expression

(8) $$M \, dx + N \, dy$$

which is equal to the total differential of some function of $x$ and $y$ is said to be *exact*, as is also the equation obtained by equating (8) to zero. An exact differential expression (8) is therefore one in which $M, N$ are respectively the partial derivatives $f_x, f_y$ of some function $f(x, y)$. It is known that

$$\frac{\partial}{\partial y} f_x = \frac{\partial}{\partial x} f_y$$

if these second-order partial derivatives exist and are continuous. It follows that if the expression (8) (or the equation $M \, dx + N \, dy = 0$) is exact, then

(9) $$M_y = N_x.$$

**13. Sufficiency of the condition for exactness.** It will be useful first to examine some particular differential equations for which the condition $M_y = N_x$ is satisfied. The method used in these cases to establish the existence of a function $f(x, y)$ whose total differential is identical with the left member of the given differential equation will indicate the nature of the general proof that the condition $M_y = N_x$ is sufficient for the expression $M \, dx + N \, dy$ to be exact. In addition to providing a suitable approach to the argument for sufficiency, the following examples will serve as a pattern to be followed in solving those exact differential equations whose integration cannot be performed more simply.

EXAMPLE 1. Show that the condition $M_y = N_x$ is satisfied by the differential equation

(a) $$e^{-x} \sin y \, dx - (e^{-x} \cos y + y) \, dy = 0,$$

and find a function $f(x, y)$ whose total differential equals the left member of (a).

SOLUTION. Since $M = e^{-x} \sin y$ and $N = - e^{-x} \cos y - y$, it follows that the partial derivatives $M_y$ and $N_x$ have the common value $e^{-x} \cos y$. We seek to determine a function $f(x, y)$ such that

$$df = f_x \, dx + f_y \, dy = e^{-x} \sin y \, dx - (e^{-x} \cos y + y) \, dy.$$

This requires:

(b) $$f_x = e^{-x} \sin y, \quad f_y = - e^{-x} \cos y - y$$

Since $f_x$ is the derivative of the undetermined function $f$ calculated under the supposition that $y$ is held fixed, $f$ must be the result of integrating $e^{-x} \sin y$ with respect to $x$ while $y$ behaves as a constant. That is,

(c) $$f = - e^{-x} \sin y + Y(y),$$

where the customary arbitrary constant of integration is in this case replaced by a function $Y(y)$ of $y$ alone. Equating $f_y$ as determined from (c) to its expression given by (b), we have

$$f_y = - e^{-x} \cos y + Y'(y) = - e^{-x} \cos y - y,$$

so that $Y'(y) = - y$, and $Y(y) = - \frac{1}{2}y^2$. The function $f$ then takes the form

$$f(x, y) = - e^{-x} \sin y - \tfrac{1}{2}y^2,$$

and the general solution of (a) may be written

$$- e^{-x} \sin y - \tfrac{1}{2}y^2 = C.$$

It will be noted that no greater generality would have resulted from the addition of an arbitrary constant to the function $Y(y)$.

EXAMPLE 2. Find the general solution of the equation

$$(x^2 + xy \sin 2x + y \sin^2 x) \, dx + x \sin^2 x \, dy = 0.$$

SOLUTION. Since $M_y = x \sin 2x + \sin^2 x = N_x$, the equation satisfies the necessary condition (9) for exactness, and we seek a function $f(x, y)$ such that:

$$f_x = x^2 + xy \sin 2x + y \sin^2 x, \quad f_y = x \sin^2 x.$$

In this example, it is simpler to start with the second of the conditions on the partial derivatives of $f$. We have:

$$f_y = x \sin^2 x$$
$$f = xy \sin^2 x + X(x)$$
$$f_x = 2xy \sin x \cos x + y \sin^2 x + X'(x)$$

By comparison with the earlier condition on $f_x$, it is seen that $X'(x) = x^2$, so that $X(x) = \frac{1}{3}x^3$, and the general solution is

$$xy \sin^2 x + \frac{1}{3}x^3 = C.$$

In the general situation, suppose that $M$ and $N$ and their partial derivatives $M_y$ and $N_x$ are continuous and satisfy the condition (9). Following the line of reasoning used in the preceding examples, we wish to demonstrate the existence of a function $f(x, y)$ such that $df = M \, dx + N \, dy$.

By comparison with $df = f_x \, dx + f_y \, dy$, two conditions on $f$ are apparent. They are:

$$(10) \qquad f_x = M(x, y), \quad f_y = N(x, y)$$

As in Example 1, the integration of the first of these equations partially with respect to $x$ shows that $f$ must have the form

$$(11) \qquad f(x, y) = \int M(x, y) \, dx + Y(y).$$

Comparing the expression for $f_y$ as derived from (11) with that given by the second equation of (10), we see that the function $Y(y)$ must satisfy the condition

$$\frac{\partial}{\partial y} \int M \, dx + \frac{dY}{dy} = N.$$

From this we find

$$\frac{dY}{dy} = N - \frac{\partial}{\partial y} \int M \, dx.$$

We are thus led to define the function $f(x, y)$ as

$$(12) \qquad f(x, y) = \int M \, dx + \int \left( N - \frac{\partial}{\partial y} \int M \, dx \right) dy.$$

31

Since $\dfrac{\partial}{\partial x}\left(N - \dfrac{\partial}{\partial y}\displaystyle\int M\, dx\right) = N_x - \dfrac{\partial}{\partial y}\left(\dfrac{\partial}{\partial x}\displaystyle\int M\, dx\right) = N_x - M_y$

and $N_x - M_y = 0$ by hypothesis, it is seen that the term

$$\int\left(N - \frac{\partial}{\partial y}\int M\, dx\right)dy$$

in the right member of (12) is a function of $y$ alone, and

$$f_x = M, \quad f_y = \frac{\partial}{\partial y}\int M\, dx + N - \frac{\partial}{\partial y}\int M\, dx = N.$$

Thus the function $f(x, y)$ given by (12) has as its total differential

$$f_x\, dx + f_y\, dy = M\, dx + N\, dy.$$

**14. Integration of exact equations.** As was suggested at the beginning of Article 13, if the equation $M\, dx + N\, dy = 0$ is known to be exact and its solution is not apparent by inspection, the key to the solution is the identification of the partial derivatives $f_x$ and $f_y$ with $M$ and $N$ respectively. The steps of the process, illustrated by the examples of that article, are the following. Integrate the equation $f_x = M$ partially with respect to $x$, using an arbitrary function of $y$ in the place of the arbitrary constant of integration. Substitute the resulting expression for $f$ into the equation $f_y = N$ and determine the arbitrary function. The solution is then $f(x, y) = C$. The modification necessary if one starts with the equation $f_y = N$ is obvious. A rearrangement of the terms of the differential equation is sometimes of assistance in testing for exactness or in finding the solution.

EXAMPLE 1. Show that the equation

$$(x^2 - x + y^2)\, dx - (ye^y - 2xy)\, dy = 0.$$

is exact, and find its general solution.

SOLUTION. Among the terms of the differential equation are three which are manifestly individually exact, i.e., $x^2\, dx$, $- x\, dx$, and $- ye^y\, dy$. A rearrangement which effects a segregation of the remaining terms results in the equation

$$(x^2 - x)\, dx - ye^y\, dy + (y^2\, dx + 2xy\, dy) = 0.$$

It is now necessary to test for exactness only the expression

(a) $$y^2 \, dx + 2xy \, dy.$$

The condition for exactness is satisfied, since

$$\frac{\partial}{\partial y} (y^2) = \frac{\partial}{\partial x} (2xy) = 2y.$$

In this case the technique indicated at the beginning of this article is not necessary, since one can see directly that the expression (a) is the total differential of the function $xy^2$. Hence the general solution is

$$\tfrac{1}{3}x^3 - \tfrac{1}{2}x^2 - (y - 1)e^y + xy^2 = C.$$

When the equation $M \, dx + N \, dy = 0$ is exact and the coefficients $M$ and $N$ are sums of terms of the type $f(x) \cdot g(y)$ where $f(x)$ and $g(y)$ are differentiable, a method * based on integration by parts can be applied. The method will be illustrated by means of the differential equation discussed in Example 1 of Article 13.

EXAMPLE 2. Solve the differential equation

$$e^{-x} \sin y \, dx - (e^{-x} \cos y + y) \, dy = 0$$

by the method of integration by parts.

SOLUTION. This equation has been shown to be exact, and $M$ and $N$ have the necessary properties. We first indicate the integration

(a) $$\int e^{-x} \sin y \, dx - \int e^{-x} \cos y \, dy - \int y \, dy = 0.$$

Next the formula $\int u \, dv = uv - \int v \, du$ is applied to the first integral, taking $u = \sin y$, $dv = e^{-x} \, dx$. Equation (a) then takes the form

$$-e^{-x} \sin y + \int e^{-x} \cos y \, dy - \int e^{-x} \cos y \, dy - \int y \, dy = 0,$$

so that the general solution is

$$- e^{-x} \sin y - \tfrac{1}{2}y^2 = C.$$

* C. R. Phelps, "Integration by Parts as a Method in the Solution of Exact Differential Equations," *American Mathematical Monthly*, Vol. 56, No. 5 (May, 1949), p. 335.

*old*

Test the following differential equations for exactness and solve those which are exact.

1. $(x + y)\, dx + (x - 2y)\, dy = 0$
2. $(3x - y)\, dx + (x + 3y)\, dy = 0$
3. $(a_1x + b_1y + c_1)\, dx + (b_1x + b_2y + c_2)\, dy = 0$
4. $x(6xy + 5)\, dx + (2x^3 + 3y)\, dy = 0$
5. $(3x^2y + xy^2 + e^x)\, dx + (x^3 + x^2y + \sin y)\, dy = 0$
6. $2xy\, dx - (x^2 + y^2)\, dy = 0$
7. $(y \cos x - 2 \sin y)\, dx = (2x \cos y - \sin x)\, dy$
8. $\dfrac{2xy - 1}{y}\, dx + \dfrac{x + 3y}{y^2}\, dy = 0$
9. $(a + r \cos \theta)\, dr + r^2 \sin \theta\, d\theta = 0$
10. $(ye^x - 2x)\, dx + e^x\, dy = 0$
11. $(3y \sin x - \cos y)\, dx + (x \sin y - 3 \cos x)\, dy = 0$
12. $(xy^2 + 2y)\, dx + (2y^3 - x^2y + 2x)\, dy = 0$
13. $\left(\dfrac{2}{y} - \dfrac{y}{x^2}\right) dx + \left(\dfrac{1}{x} - \dfrac{2x}{y^2}\right) dy = 0$
14. $\dfrac{xy + 1}{y}\, dx + \dfrac{2y - x}{y^2}\, dy = 0$
15. $\dfrac{y(2 + x^3y)}{x^3}\, dx = \dfrac{1 - 2x^3y}{x^2}\, dy$
16. $(y^2 \csc^2 x + 6xy - 2)\, dx = (2y \cot x - 3x^2)\, dy$
17. $2\left(\dfrac{y}{x^3} + \dfrac{x}{y^2}\right) dx = \left(\dfrac{1}{x^2} + \dfrac{2x^2}{y^3}\right) dy$
18. $\cos y\, dx - (x \sin y - y^2)\, dy = 0$
19. $2y \sin xy\, dx + (2x \sin xy + y^3)\, dy = 0$
20. $\left(\dfrac{x}{y} \cos \dfrac{x}{y} + \sin \dfrac{x}{y} + \cos x\right) dx - \dfrac{x^2}{y^2} \cos \dfrac{x}{y}\, dy = 0$
21. $(ye^{xy} + 2xy)\, dx + (xe^{xy} + x^2)\, dy = 0$
22. $\dfrac{x^2 + 3y^2}{x(3x^2 + 4y^2)}\, dx + \dfrac{2x^2 + y^2}{y(3x^2 + 4y^2)}\, dy = 0$
23. $\dfrac{x^2 - y^2}{x(2x^2 + y^2)}\, dx + \dfrac{x^2 + 2y^2}{y(2x^2 + y^2)}\, dy = 0$
24. $\left[\dfrac{2x^2}{x^2 + y^2} + \ln (x^2 + y^2)\right] dx + \dfrac{2xy}{x^2 + y^2}\, dy = 0$

**15. Integrating factors.** The process of separating variables, which was discussed in Article 8, is an instance of the technique of multiplying a nonexact differential equation by a factor in order to convert it into an exact equation. Such a factor is called an *integrating factor*. However, it must not be supposed that an integrating factor must effect a separation of the variables. In order to throw more light on the subject, let us consider the following example.

EXAMPLE 1. Find several integrating factors of the equation

(a) $$2y\, dx + x\, dy = 0.$$

SOLUTION. One integrating factor of (a) is of course the factor $\dfrac{1}{xy}$ which results in a separation of the variables. Multiplication of (a) by this factor produces the equation

$$2\frac{dx}{x} + \frac{dy}{y} = d\,(\ln x^2 y) = 0.$$

A second simple integrating factor is seen to be $x$. If (a) is multiplied by $x$, we have the equation

$$2xy\, dx + x^2\, dy = d(x^2 y) = 0.$$

An infinite number of integrating factors of the equation (a) can be found as follows. Multiply (a) by $x^p y^q$ to convert it into the equation

(b) $$2x^p y^{q+1}\, dx + x^{p+1} y^q\, dy = 0.$$

The condition that (b) shall be exact is that $p$, $q$ shall identically satisfy the equation:

$$\frac{\partial}{\partial y}\,(2x^p y^{q+1}) = \frac{\partial}{\partial x}\,(x^{p+1} y^q)$$

$$2(q + 1)x^p y^q = (p + 1)x^p y^q$$

Hence $x^p y^q$ will be an integrating factor of (b) if $2(q + 1) = p + 1$, that is, if $p = 2q + 1$. Two special cases of the integrating factor $x^p y^q$ have already been noted, namely, those for which

$$p = -1,\ q = -1 \quad \text{and} \quad p = 1,\ q = 0.$$

Any real number $q$ and that value of $p$ given by the equation $p = 2q + 1$ determine an integrating factor of (a).

It may be noted that the device just used to discover integrating factors for the equation (a) is effective for any equation of the type

$$(Ax^k y^l + Bx^m y^n)y \, dx + (Cx^k y^l + Dx^m y^n)x \, dy = 0,$$

where $A, B, C, D$ are constants.

It is possible to prove (see Article 85) that every equation $M \, dx + N \, dy = 0$ which has a solution possesses an infinite number of integrating factors, although their discovery may be difficult. However, as will be shown in the examples which follow, integrating factors can be found for some differential equations by noting the occurrence of simple differential expressions, such as $y \, dx + x \, dy$ and $y \, dx - x \, dy$. The first of these is equal to $d(xy)$, while the second is converted into $d\left(\dfrac{x}{y}\right)$ or $- d\left(\dfrac{y}{x}\right)$ by division by $y^2$ or $x^2$ respectively. The rearrangement of the terms of a differential equation in such a way as to establish the presence of one of these differentials in the equation sometimes points the way to the completion of the solution.

EXAMPLE 2. Solve the equation $xy' = y + y^2$.

SOLUTION. In differential notation the equation may be written

$$x \, dy - y \, dx = y^2 \, dx.$$

The left member can be converted into an integrable combination if we divide either by $x^2$ or by $y^2$. A glance at the right member shows that the latter divisor must be chosen. The integration of the equation is completed as follows.

$$\frac{x \, dy - y \, dx}{y^2} = dx$$

$$- d\left(\frac{x}{y}\right) = dx$$

$$- \frac{x}{y} = x - C$$

$$- x = xy - Cy$$

$$x + xy = Cy$$

EXAMPLE 3. Find the particular solution $y(x)$ of the equation $y\,dx = x\,dy + \sqrt{x^2 - y^2}\,dx$ consistent with the condition $y(1) = 0$.
SOLUTION. We transpose terms and divide by $x^2$:

$$\frac{y\,dx - x\,dy}{x^2} = -d\left(\frac{y}{x}\right) = \frac{1}{x}\sqrt{1 - \frac{y^2}{x^2}}\,dx$$

At this stage we notice that division by the radical will effect a separation of variables, if the independent variables are taken to be $x$ and $\frac{y}{x}$.

$$\frac{-d\left(\frac{y}{x}\right)}{\sqrt{1 - \left(\frac{y}{x}\right)^2}} = \frac{dx}{x}$$

$$-\text{Arc sin}\,\frac{y}{x} = \ln x + C$$

The condition $y(1) = 0$ implies $C = 0$. Hence the particular solution required is

$$\text{Arc sin}\,\frac{y}{x} + \ln x = 0.$$

It is not difficult to make slight generalizations of the key expressions $y\,dx + x\,dy$, $y\,dx - x\,dy$. For example, the expression $x\,dy + 2y\,dx$ suggests multiplication by $x$ so as to produce $x^2\,dy + 2xy\,dx = d(x^2y)$. Similarly, the expression $x\,dy - 3y\,dx$ suggests a preliminary multiplication by $x^2$, which converts it into $x^3\,dy - 3x^2y\,dx$. The new expression may be divided by $x^6$ to form $d\left(\frac{y}{x^3}\right)$ or by $y^2$ to form $-d\left(\frac{x^3}{y}\right)$.

EXAMPLE 4. Solve the equation $y\,dx - 2x\,dy = xy\,dy$.
SOLUTION. Multiplication by $y$ produces the equation

$$y^2\,dx - 2xy\,dy = xy^2\,dy.$$

The left member suggests one of the divisors $x^2$ or $y^4$. Using the latter, we have

$$d\left(\frac{x}{y^2}\right) = \frac{x\,dy}{y^2}.$$

37

Dividing once more, this time by $\dfrac{x}{y^2}$, we separate the variables $\dfrac{x}{y^2}$ and $y$, and complete the solution.

$$\frac{d\left(\dfrac{x}{y^2}\right)}{\dfrac{x}{y^2}} = dy$$

$$\ln \frac{x}{y^2} = y + \ln C$$

$$\frac{x}{Cy^2} = e^y$$

$$x = Cy^2 e^y$$

## EXERCISE 9

Find the general solutions of the differential equations of Problems 1–19.

1. $x\,dy - y\,dx + \ln x\,dx = 0$
2. $xy\,dx + (x^2 + y)\,dy = 0$
3. $x\,dy + 2y\,dx = 2xy\,dy$
4. $(x^2y + y^2)\,dx + x^3\,dy = 0$
5. $(xy^3 - 1)\,dx + x^2y^2\,dy = 0$
6. $(x^3y^3 - 1)\,dy + x^2y^4\,dx = 0$
7. $y(y - x^2)\,dx + x^3\,dy = 0$
8. $y\,dx + x\,dy + xy\,(y\,dx - x\,dy) = 0$
9. $x\,dy - y\,dx = x\sqrt{x^2 - y^2}\,dy$
10. $2xy\,dx + (y - x^2)\,dy = 0$
11. $y\,dx = x(x^2y - 1)\,dy$
12. $e^x\,(dy - y\,dx) = 2xy^2\,dx$
13. $(x^2 + y^2)\,dy + x\,dy - y\,dx = 0$
14. $y\,dx + 2x\,dy + xy(2y\,dx + 3x\,dy) = 0$
15. $(x^4e^x - 2xy^2)\,dx + 2x^2y\,dy = 0$
16. $x^3y^5(2y\,dx + 3x\,dy) + x^2y^3(3y\,dx + 4x\,dy) = 0$
17. $(2x^3y - y^2)\,dx = (2x^4 + xy)\,dy$
18. $y(2x + y^2)\,dx + x(x + 2y^2)\,dy = 0$
19. $(xy + y^2)\,dx + (x^2 - xy)\,dy = 0$

In each of the following problems, find the particular solution determined by the given condition.

20. $y(1 - x^4y^2) \, dx + x \, dy = 0$; $y = -1$ when $x = 1$

21. $y(x^2 - 1) \, dx + x(x^2 + 1) \, dy = 0$; $y = 2$ when $x = 1$

22. $x^2y^2 \, dx + 2x^3y \, dy = y \, dx - x \, dy$; $y = -2$ when $x = 2$

23. $(x^2 + y^2 - 2y) \, dy = 2x \, dx$; $y = 0$ when $x = 1$

24. $y \, dx - x \, dy = x^2\sqrt{x^2 - y^2} \, dx$; $y = 1$ when $x = 1$

25. $y(x + y^2) \, dx + x(x - y^2) \, dy = 0$; $y = 2$ when $x = 2$

## 16. Linear differential equations.  The equation

$$(13) \qquad A \frac{dy}{dx} + By = C, \quad A \neq 0,$$

where $A$, $B$, and $C$ are functions of $x$, is of the first degree in the variables $y$ and $\dfrac{dy}{dx}$.  Such an equation is said to be a *linear differential equation* of the first order.  In Chapter Four this definition will be generalized to apply to differential equations of higher order.  Upon division by $A$, equation (13) is reduced to the standard form

$$(14) \qquad \frac{dy}{dx} + Py = Q,$$

where $P$ and $Q$ are functions of $x$.

We consider first the *homogeneous* linear differential equation

$$(15) \qquad \frac{dy}{dx} + Py = 0,$$

the special case of (14) in which the right member is zero. Since $P$ does not involve $y$, multiplication of (15) by $\dfrac{dx}{y}$ separates the variables, giving

$$\frac{dy}{y} + P(x) \, dx = 0.$$

Hence

$$\ln y + \int P(x) \, dx = \ln C$$

$(16)$  take ln of both sides  $\left( ye^{\int P \, dx} = C \right)$

$\ln \left( y \cdot e^{\int P \, dx} \right) = \ln C$

$\ln y + \int P \, dx = \ln C$

If we differentiate both members of (16), we expect to obtain an equation equivalent to (15), since by this differentiation the arbitrary constant is eliminated. We have

$$d(ye^{\int P\,dx}) = e^{\int P\,dx}\,dy + Pye^{\int P\,dx}\,dx = 0.$$

Comparison of this equation with (15) reveals the fact that $e^{\int P\,dx}$ is an integrating factor of the homogeneous equation (15). Further, since this factor is independent of $y$, its multiplication into the right member of the nonhomogeneous equation (14) will convert the right member into a function of $x$ alone. Consequently we have discovered the important fact that *the linear differential equation*

$$\frac{dy}{dx} + Py = Q$$

*possesses* $e^{\int P\,dx}$ *as an integrating factor.* This fact is sufficient to enable us to find the general solution of any equation of this type.

EXAMPLE 1. Solve the equation $xy' - 2y = x^3e^{-2x}$.
SOLUTION. The standard form of the equation is

$(a)$ 
$$y' - \frac{2}{x}\,y = x^2e^{-2x}.$$

Since $P = -\dfrac{2}{x}$, an integrating factor is

$$e^{\int P\,dx} = e^{\int \frac{-2\,dx}{x}} = e^{-2\ln x} = x^{-2}.$$

The equation obtained by multiplying the standard form $(a)$ by this factor is

$$x^{-2}y' - 2x^{-3}y = e^{-2x}.$$

The first term indicates that the left member is the derivative of $x^{-2}y$, and this may be checked by examining the second term. It follows that the general solution sought is

$$x^{-2}y = \int e^{-2x}\,dx = -\tfrac{1}{2}e^{-2x} + C,$$

which can be put in the form

$$2y + x^2e^{-2x} = C'x^2.$$

On occasion it is useful to interchange the roles of $x$ and $y$. The following example exhibits such a situation.

EXAMPLE 2. Solve the equation

$$\sin y \, dx + 2x \cos y \, dy = \sin 2y \, dy.$$

SOLUTION. Division by $dx$ shows that the equation is not linear in $y$ and $\dfrac{dy}{dx}$. However, division by $dy$ results in the equation

$$\sin y \frac{dx}{dy} + 2x \cos y = \sin 2y,$$

which is linear if we consider $x$ to be the dependent variable. The standard form of this equation is

$$\frac{dx}{dy} + 2x \cot y = 2 \cos y,$$

from which we deduce that the integrating factor is

$$e^{\int P \, dy} = e^{\int 2 \cot y \, dy} = e^{2 \ln \sin y} = \sin^2 y.$$

Multiplying by this factor, we have

$$\sin^2 y \frac{dx}{dy} + 2x \sin y \cos y = 2 \sin^2 y \cos y.$$

The first term shows that $x \sin^2 y$ is the integral of the left member, and this is checked by means of the second term. Hence the solution can be written:

$$x \sin^2 y = \int 2 \sin^2 y \cos y \, dy$$

$$x \sin^2 y = \tfrac{2}{3} \sin^3 y + C$$

## EXERCISE 10

*1 – 17 odd*

In Problems 1–18, find the general solutions.

1. $xy' + 2y = x^2$
2. $y' - xy = e^{\frac{1}{2}x^2} \cos x$
3. $y' + 2xy = 2xe^{-x^2}$
4. $y' = y + 3x^2 e^x$
5. $\dfrac{dx}{dy} + x = e^{-y}$

6. $y \dfrac{dx}{dy} + (1 + y)x = e^y$

7. $y\, dx + (2x - 3y)\, dy = 0$

8. $x\, dy - 2(x^4 + y)\, dx = 0$

9. $dx = (x + e^y)\, dy$

10. $y^2 \dfrac{dx}{dy} + (y^2 + 2y)x = 1$

11. $x\, dy = (5y + x + 1)\, dx$

12. $x^2\, dy + (y - 2xy - 2x^2)\, dx = 0$

13. $(x + 1)y' + 2y = e^x(x + 1)^{-1}$

14. $\cos^2 y\, dx + (x - \tan y)\, dy = 0$

15. $2y\, dx = (y^4 + x)\, dy$

16. $\cos \theta \dfrac{dr}{d\theta} = 2 + 2r \sin \theta$

17. $\sin \theta \dfrac{dr}{d\theta} + 1 + r \tan \theta = \cos \theta$

18. $y \dfrac{dx}{dy} = 2ye^{3y} + x(3y + 2)$

In each of the following problems find the particular solution which satisfies the given condition.

19. $(y^2 + 1) \dfrac{dx}{dy} + 2xy = y^2$; $y = -1$ when $x = 0$

20. $dy + (y \cot x - \sec x)\, dx = 0$; $y = 1$ when $x = 0$

21. $(y + y^3)\, dx + 4(xy^2 - 1)\, dy = 0$; $y = 1$ when $x = 0$

22. $(2y - xy - 3)\, dx + x\, dy = 0$; $y = 1$ when $x = 1$

23. $y\, dx + 2(x - 2y^2)\, dy = 0$; $y = -1$ when $x = 2$

24. $dr = (1 + 2r \cot \theta)\, d\theta$; $r = 3$ when $\theta = \dfrac{\pi}{2}$

25. $(x^2 - 1)y' + (x^2 - 1)^2 + 4y = 0$; $y = -6$ when $x = 0$

**17. Equations linear in a function of y; Bernoulli equations.** By considering the dependent variable to be $f(y)$ the equation

$$f'(y) + P(x)f(y) = Q(x)$$

becomes a linear differential equation, and the method of Article 16 applies.

EXAMPLE 1. Find the general solution of the equation

$$xyy' + y^2 = \sin x.$$

SOLUTION. This equation is seen to be linear if the dependent variable is taken to be $y^2$. Its standard form is obtained by multiplication by $\dfrac{2}{x}$:

$$\frac{d}{dx}(y^2) + \frac{2}{x}y^2 = \frac{2\sin x}{x}.$$

From this point the steps of the solution are parallel to those outlined in the preceding article. The function $P(x)$ is $\dfrac{2}{x}$, so that $e^{\int P\,dx} = e^{2\ln x} = x^2$ is an integrating factor, and the process continues as follows:

$$x^2\frac{d}{dx}(y^2) + 2xy^2 = 2x\sin x$$

$$x^2 y^2 = \int 2x\sin x\,dx$$

$$x^2 y^2 = 2\sin x - 2x\cos x + C$$

EXAMPLE 2. Solve the equation $y' + xy\ln y = xye^{-x^2}$, subject to the condition that $y = 1$ when $x = 0$.

SOLUTION. Inspection shows that division by $y$ not only removes this variable from the right member, but converts the first term into the derivative of $\ln y$. Hence the steps of the solution can be set down as follows.

$$\frac{y'}{y} + x\ln y = xe^{-x^2}$$

$$\frac{d}{dx}(\ln y) + x\ln y = xe^{-x^2}$$

$$e^{\frac{x^2}{2}}\frac{d}{dx}(\ln y) + xe^{\frac{x^2}{2}}\ln y = xe^{-\frac{x^2}{2}}$$

$$e^{\frac{x^2}{2}}\ln y = -e^{-\frac{x^2}{2}} + C$$

The condition $y = 1$ when $x = 0$ can be satisfied only if $C$ has the value 1. Hence the particular solution sought is

$$e^{\frac{x^2}{2}}\ln y = -e^{-\frac{x^2}{2}} + 1.$$

**43**

EXAMPLE 3. Find the general solution of the equation

$$\tan y \, \frac{dy}{dx} + \cot x \ln \cos y = \sin 2x.$$

SOLUTION. Since $\dfrac{d}{dx} (\ln \cos y) = - \tan y \, \dfrac{dy}{dx}$, we may substitute

$v = \ln \cos y, \dfrac{dv}{dx} = - \tan y \, \dfrac{dy}{dx}.$ The equation takes the form

$$\frac{dv}{dx} - v \cot x = - 2 \sin x \cos x.$$

The integrating factor $e^{-\int \cot x \, dx} = \csc x$ transforms the given equation into

$$\csc x \, \frac{dv}{dx} - v \cot x \csc x = - 2 \cos x,$$

the solution of which is:

$$v \csc x = - 2 \sin x + C$$
$$v + 2 \sin^2 x = C \sin x$$

The general solution in terms of the original variables is

$$\ln \cos y + 2 \sin^2 x = C \sin x.$$

The examples just discussed have depended on the ability to discern functions of $y$ in terms of which the given equations are, or can be made, linear. There is a class of differential equations, called *Bernoulli* equations,* in which the selection of an appropriate function of $y$ is routine. A Bernoulli equation is one whose left member is that of a linear equation, but whose right member is the product of a function of $x$ by $y^n$, $n \neq 1$. It has the form

$$\frac{dy}{dx} + P(x)y = Q(x)y^n.$$

To solve such an equation, we multiply both members by $y^{-n}$:

$$y^{-n}y' + Py^{1-n} = Q.$$

---

* Named for James Bernoulli (1654–1705), Swiss mathematician and member of a family of whom eight were distinguished mathematicians, including James's younger brother John (1667–1748) and the latter's son Daniel (1700–1782).

After multiplication by the constant $1 - n$ the left member becomes

$$(1 - n)y^{-n}y' + (1 - n)Py^{1-n} = \frac{d}{dx}(y^{1-n}) + (1 - n)Py^{1-n},$$

so that the equation is linear in the dependent variable

$$f(y) = y^{1-n}.$$

The integrating factor can then be found and the solution carried out in the usual manner.

EXAMPLE 4. For the differential equation

$$y' + y = y^2 e^{2x},$$

find the particular solution $y(x)$ which satisfies the condition $y(0) = 1$.

SOLUTION. Since the equation is of the Bernoulli type, we begin by multiplying by $- y^{-2}$ and carry out the steps of the solution as follows:  $(1-n) \, y^{-n} \text{ or } -1 \cdot y^{-2}$

$$- y^{-2}y' - y^{-1} = - e^{2x}$$

$$\frac{d}{dx}(y^{-1}) - y^{-1} = - e^{2x}$$

$$e^{-x}\frac{d}{dx}(y^{-1}) - e^{-x}y^{-1} = - e^{x}$$

$$y^{-1}e^{-x} = - e^{x} + C$$

$$y^{-1} + e^{2x} = Ce^{x}$$

The initial condition $y(0) = 1$ determines the particular solution

$$y^{-1} + e^{2x} = 2e^{x}.$$

odd 1-21

In Problems 1–17 find the general solutions.

1. $3y^2y' - xy^3 = e^{\frac{1}{2}x^2}\cos x$
2. $y^3y' + xy^4 = xe^{-x^2}$
3. $\cosh y \, dy + \sinh y \, dx = e^{-x} \, dx$
4. $\sin \theta \, d\theta + \cos \theta \, dt = te^t \, dt$

5. $xy \, dy = (x^2 - y^2) \, dx$

6. $y' - xy = \sqrt{y} \, xe^{x^2}$

7. $t \, dx + x(1 - x^2 t^4) \, dt = 0$

8. $x^2 y' + y^2 = xy$

9. $\csc y \cot y \, dy = (\csc y + e^x) \, dx$

10. $y' - xy = xy^{-1}$

11. $xy' + y = y^2 x^2 \cos x$

12. $\dfrac{dr}{d\theta} + \left( r - \dfrac{1}{r} \right) \theta = 0$

13. $xy' + 2y = 3x^3 y^{\frac{4}{3}}$

14. $3y' + \dfrac{2y}{x+1} = \dfrac{x}{y^2}$

15. $\cos y \, dy + (\sin y - 1) \cos x \, dx = 0$

16. $x \tan^2 y \, dy + x \, dy = (2x^2 + \tan y) \, dx$

17. $y' + y \cos x = y^3 \sin 2x$

In each of the following problems, find the particular solution consistent with the given condition.

18. $\dfrac{dy}{dt} + y = y^2 e^{-t}$; $y = 2$ when $t = 0$

19. $y' = x(1 - e^{2y - x^2})$; $y = 0$ when $x = 0$

20. $2y \, dx = (x^2 y^4 + x) \, dy$; $y = 1$ when $x = 1$

21. $dx + xy(1 + xy^2) \, dy = 0$; $y = 0$ when $x = 1$

22. $(1 - x^2)y' + xy = x(1 - x^2)\sqrt{y}$; $y = 1$ when $x = 0$

## Miscellaneous problems — EXERCISE 12

Find the general solutions of the equations in Problems 1–38.

1. $(1 - x) \, dy - (1 + y) \, dx = 0$

2. $y^2 \, dx + (xy + x^2) \, dy = 0$

3. $(2x + y) \, dx - (x - 2y) \, dy = 0$

4. $x \ln x \, dy + (y - x) \, dx = 0$

5. $(x - 2y + 1) \, dx + (y - 2) \, dy = 0$

6. $(2xy - 2xy^3 + x^3) \, dx + (x^2 + y^2 - 3x^2 y^2) \, dy = 0$

7. $te^x \, dx + 2e^x \, dt = t^2 \, dt$

8. $2(y + 3) \, dx = xy \, dy$

9. $(x - 3y) \, dx = (3y - x + 2) \, dy$

10. $(y \sin x - 2 \cos y + \tan x) \, dx - (\cos x - 2x \sin y + \sin y) \, dy = 0$

11. $x^2 y \, dx - (x^3 + y^3) \, dy = 0$

12. $y - xy' = 2(y^2 + y')$

13. $\tan y \, dx = (3x + 4) \, dy$

14. $y' + y \ln y \cdot \tan x = 2y$

15. $(2xy + y^4) \, dx + (xy^3 - 2x^2) \, dy = 0$

16. $y \, dx + (3x - 2y) \, dy = 0$

17. $\dfrac{dr}{d\theta} = r \cot \theta$

18. $(3x + 4y) \, dy + (y + 2x) \, dx = 0$

19. $(2x^3 - y^3 - 3x) \, dx + 3xy^2 \, dy = 0$

20. $x \, dy - y \, dx = \sqrt{x^2 + y^2} \, dx$

21. $\dfrac{dr}{d\theta} + r + 3r^2 e^{-2\theta} = 0$

22. $\dfrac{dy}{dx} = \cos y \cos^2 x$

23. $(x + y) \, dx + (2x + 3y - 1) \, dy = 0$

24. $(1 + e^{\frac{x}{y}}) \, dx + e^{\frac{x}{y}} \left(1 - \dfrac{x}{y}\right) dy = 0$

25. $y' + x + y \cot x = 0$

26. $3(x - 2) \, dx = xy \, dy$

27. $(x - 2xy + e^y) \, dx + (y - x^2 + xe^y) \, dy = 0$

28. $2xy' - y + \dfrac{x^2}{y^2} = 0$

29. $x \, dy + y(y^2 + 1) \, dx = 0$

30. $y\sqrt{x^2 + y^2} \, dx = x(x \, dy - y \, dx)$

31. $3e^x \tan y \, dx = (1 - e^x) \sec^2 y \, dy$

32. $\sec^2 y \, dy = (\tan y + 2xe^x) \, dx$

33. $(2x \tan y + 3y^2 + x^2) \, dx + (x^2 \sec^2 y + 6xy - y^2) \, dy = 0$

34. $dr + (2 + r \tan \theta) \, d\theta = 0$

35. $y \cos \dfrac{x}{y} \, dx - \left(y + x \cos \dfrac{x}{y}\right) dy = 0$

36. $y(3x^2 + y) \, dx + x(x^2 - y) \, dy = 0$

37. $x \, dx + (2x + 3y + 2) \, dy = 0$

38. $x \, dy - 5y \, dx = x\sqrt{y} \, dx$

In each of the following problems, find the particular solution which corresponds to the given condition.

39. $x\sqrt{1-y}\, dx - \sqrt{1-x^2}\, dy = 0$; $y = 0$ when $x = 0$

40. $(xy - y^2)\, dx - x^2\, dy = 0$; $y = 1$ when $x = 1$

41. $xe^{-y^2}\, dx + y\, dy = 0$; $y = 0$ when $x = 0$

42. $\dfrac{2y^3 - 2x^2y^3 - x + xy^2 \ln y}{xy^2}\, dx + \dfrac{2y^3 \ln x - x^2y^3 + 2x + xy^2}{y^3}\, dy = 0$;

$y = 1$ when $x = 1$

43. $x\, dy - 2y\, dx = 2x^4y^3\, dx$; $y = 1$ when $x = 1$

44. $y^2\, dx - 2x^2\, dy = 3xy\, dy$; $y = 1$ when $x = 1$

45. $x\, dy = (x^4 + 4y)\, dx$; $y = 0$ when $x = 1$

46. $xy' + y = x^3y^6$; $y = 1$ when $x = 1$

47. $(1 - \tan^2 \theta)\, dr + 2r \tan \theta\, d\theta = 0$; $r = 1$ when $\theta = 0$

48. $\dfrac{dx}{d\theta} = x + x^2e^\theta$; $x = 2$ when $\theta = 0$

49. $(x^2 + y^2)\, dx = 2xy\, dy$; $y = 0$ when $x = 2$

50. $3xy\, dx + (3x^2 + y^2)\, dy = 0$; $y = 1$ when $x = 0$

51. $y' + 2y = 3e^{2x}$; $y = 1$ when $x = 0$

52. $4xy^2\, dx + (x^2 + 1)\, dy = 0$; $y = 1$ when $x = 0$

53. $(x - 2y + 3)\, dx = (x - 2y + 1)\, dy$; $y = 2$ when $x = 0$

54. $y^2\, dx + (x^3 - 2xy)\, dy = 0$; $y = 1$ when $x = 2$

55. $(2xy - 2y + 1)\, dx + x(x - 1)\, dy = 0$; $y = 2$ when $x = 2$

56. $y^3\, dx - 3x^3\, dy = 2xy(y\, dy - x\, dx)$; $y = 1$ when $x = 1$

57. $2(1 + x^2)\, dy = (2y^2 - 1)xy\, dx$; $y = 1$ when $x = 0$

# CHAPTER THREE

# Applications

**10. Geometrical applications.** The slope of a curve $y = f(x)$ at a point $P:(x, y)$ of the curve is equal to the derivative $\dfrac{dy}{dx}$ evaluated at $P$. Therefore if a curve is described by expressing its slope at any point as a function of the coordinates of that point, this description must be a first-order differential equation whose independent variable is $x$ and whose dependent variable is $y = f(x)$. The examples which follow illustrate the process of writing and solving such differential equations.

Before proceeding to the examples, however, it will be useful to recall that the equation of the tangent to the curve $y = f(x)$ at the point $P:(x, y)$ is

$$Y - y = f'(x)(X - x).$$

Here the distinction between $(x, y)$ and $(X, Y)$ must be clearly understood. The notation $(x, y)$ is used for the coordinates of a point free to move *on the curve*. The point $(X, Y)$ on the other hand is a variable point *on the tangent to the curve at* $P:(x, y)$.

A few other formulas will be mentioned. The area bounded by the segment of the $x$-axis from $x = a$ to $x = x$, the curve $y = f(x)$ lying above this segment, and the ordinates at the

49

extremities of this segment is a function $A(x)$ given by the formula

$$A(x) = \int_a^x f(x)\, dx.$$

The formula for the length of the arc of the curve $y = f(x)$ from $x = a$ to $x = x$ is

$$s(x) = \int_a^x \sqrt{1 + [f'(x)]^2}\, dx.$$

If polar coordinates $(r, \theta)$ are used, the positive angle $\psi$ made by the tangent line at $P:(r, \theta)$ with the radius vector of $P$ is given by the formula

$$\tan \psi = r\frac{d\theta}{dr}.$$

The area whose boundaries are the arc of the curve $r = f(\theta)$ between the fixed point $(r_1, \theta_1)$ on the curve and the variable point $(r, \theta)$, also on the curve, and the radius vectors of these points is

$$A(\theta) = \tfrac{1}{2}\int_{\theta_1}^{\theta} r^2\, d\theta.$$

EXAMPLE 1. Determine the curves characterized by the property that the segment of the tangent between the point of contact and the $y$-axis is bisected by the $x$-axis.

SOLUTION. If $P:(x, y)$ is the point of contact of a curve with its tangent, it follows (Fig. 2) from the defining property of the

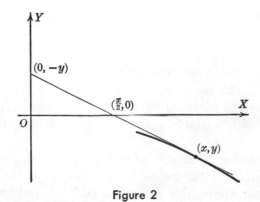

Figure 2

50

curve that the tangent cuts $OY$ in $(0, -y)$ and $OX$ in $(\frac{1}{2}x, 0)$. Hence $y'$, the slope of the tangent, can be found from the co-ordinates of these points:

$$y' = \frac{y}{\frac{1}{2}x} = \frac{2y}{x}$$

This differential equation has the general solution $y = Cx^2$, which represents the family of parabolas whose common vertex is the origin and which have $OY$ as common axis.

EXAMPLE 2. Find the curve through $(2, -4)$ for which the distance from the origin to the tangent is numerically equal to the abscissa of the point of contact.

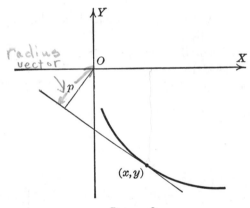

Figure 3

SOLUTION. (See Fig. 3.) When the equation

$$Y - y = y'(X - x)$$

of the tangent to the curve $y = f(x)$ at $(x, y)$ is written in the normal form

$$\frac{y'X - Y - (y'x - y)}{\pm \sqrt{(y')^2 + 1}} = 0,$$

the distance $p$ from the origin to the tangent is seen to be

$$p = \frac{|\,y'x - y\,|}{\sqrt{(y')^2 + 1}}.$$

51

Equating this to $|x|$, one is led to the differential equation

$$2xy\ dy - y^2\ dx + x^2\ dx = 0.$$

An integrating factor is $x^{-2}$ and the integral of the differential equation is found to be $x^2 + y^2 = Cx$.

From the family of circles we select the circle which passes through $(2, -4)$. For this circle $C = 10$, so that the particular solution required is

$$x^2 + y^2 = 10x.$$

EXAMPLE 3. If the normal to a curve at $P$ intersects the $x$-axis in the point $Q$, the projection of the segment $PQ$ on the $x$-axis has constant length. Find the curve if it makes the angle $\frac{1}{4}\pi$ with the $y$-axis at $(0, 3)$.

SOLUTION. If $k$ is the constant length of the projection $MQ$ (Fig. 4), it is seen that the required differential equation is formed by equating the slope of the line $PQ$ to $\dfrac{y}{-k}$:

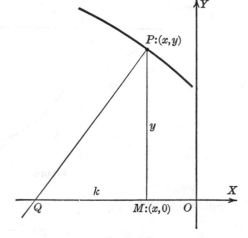

$$-\frac{1}{y'} = -\frac{y}{k}.$$

The simplified form of this equation is

(a)     $yy' = k$,

whose general solution,

(b)   $y^2 = 2kx + C$,

represents the family

Figure 4

of parabolas which have $OX$ as their common axis.

In this problem the values of two constants, $k$ and $C$, must be found in order to arrive at the particular solution required. We substitute $y = 3$, $y' = -1$ in (a) and find $k = -3$; then substitute $x = 0$, $y = 3$ in (b) and find $C = 9$. The particular parabola is therefore

$$y^2 = -6x + 9.$$

*the first ten*

In each of Problems 1–21, write in rectangular coordinates the differential equation of the family of curves described. Find the general solution of this equation. If initial conditions are given, find the particular solution thus determined.

1. The $x$-intercept of the tangent is equal to twice the abscissa of the point of contact.
2. The $x$-intercept of the tangent is equal to three times the abscissa of the point of contact.
3. The $x$-intercept of the tangent is equal to the ordinate of the point of contact.
4. The $y$-intercept of the tangent is equal to twice the abscissa of the point of contact.
5. The $x$-intercept of the normal is equal to three times the abscissa of the point of contact.
6. The segment of the tangent between the $x$-axis and the point of contact has a constant projection on $OX$.
7. The projection upon the normal at $P$ of the ordinate of $P$ is numerically equal to the abscissa of $P$.
8. The slope at every point equals the ratio of the ordinate of the point to the sum of the coordinates; $y$-intercept 2.
9. The ordinate of the point of contact is numerically equal to the distance of the tangent from the origin.
10. The slope at every point $P$ is proportional to the area of the triangle bounded by the ordinate of $P$, the $x$-axis, and the line which joins $P$ to $(5, 0)$; passes through $(2, 1)$ and $(3, e)$.
11. The tangent at every point $P$, the radius vector of $P$, and $OX$ form an isosceles triangle with base in $OX$; contains $(1, 2)$.
12. Solve Problem 11 if the isosceles triangle has the radius vector of $P$ as base.
13. The $x$-intercept of the normal is equal to the length of the radius vector of the point of contact.
14. The lines $x = a$, $x = x$, $y = 0$ and the curve $y = f(x)$ bound an area proportional to the difference of the bounding ordinates.
15. The lines $x = a$, $x = x$, $y = 0$ and the curve $y = f(x)$ bound an area proportional to the length of the bounding arc.

16. The rectangle bounded by the lines $x = 0$, $x = x$, $y = 0$, $y = y$ is divided by the curve $y = f(x)$ into two parts one of whose areas is double that of the other.

17. The triangle bounded by the $x$-axis, the normal to the curve $y = f(x)$ at $P : (x, y)$, and the ordinate of $P$ has area 5; $y = 3$ when $x = 1$.

18. The triangle bounded by the $x$-axis, the tangent to the curve at $P : (x, y)$, and the ordinate at $P$ has area 8.

19. The $x$-intercept of the normal and the $y$-intercept of the tangent are equal.

20. The segment of the tangent between the $x$-axis and the point of contact is bisected by the $y$-axis.

21. The segment of the tangent between the $x$-axis and the point of contact $P$ is equal in length to the radius vector of $P$; the curve passes through $(-2, 1)$.

In each of the following problems, use polar coordinates to find the family of curves which satisfy the given condition.

22. The tangent at $P : (r, \theta)$ makes the angle $\frac{1}{4}\pi$ with the radius vector of $P$.

23. The polar angle of $P : (r, \theta)$ equals the angle at $P$ from the radius vector to the tangent.

24. The tangent of the angle between the radius vector of $P : (r, \theta)$ and the tangent line at $P$ equals the radian measure of the vectorial angle of $P$.

25. The length of the perpendicular from the pole to the tangent is constant.

26. The area bounded by the curve $r = f(\theta)$, the polar axis, and the radius vector of $P : (r, \theta)$ is proportional to the length of the radius vector.

**19. Trajectories.** If a curve cuts each member of a one-parameter family of curves at the same angle, it is called an *isogonal trajectory* of the family. For any particular angle of intersection, a one-parameter family of curves ordinarily has a one-parameter family of isogonal trajectories.

At the point $P:(x, y)$ consider the curve $C_1$ which belongs to a given family and which passes through $P$. (See Fig. 5.)

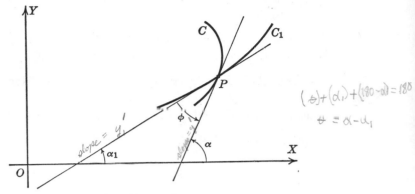

**Figure 5**

Consider also another curve $C$ which contains the point $P$. Let $\alpha_1$ and $y_1'$ be the inclination and slope respectively of $C_1$ at $P$, and let $\alpha$ and $y'$ be the corresponding quantities of $C$ at $P$. Then if $\phi$ is any angle which $C$ makes with $C_1$, it can be shown that $\tan \phi = \tan (\alpha - \alpha_1)$, so that

(1)
$$\frac{y' - y_1'}{1 + y'y_1'} = \tan \phi.$$

When the angle $\phi$ and the function $y_1'(x, y)$ are given, the equation (1) is the differential equation of the isogonal trajectories which make the angle $\phi$ with the given family. If the slope of either $C$ or $C_1$ is infinite at $P$ or if $\phi = \frac{\pi}{2}$, a modification of (1) can readily be made.

We recall that the equation of a one-parameter family of curves can be considered to be the primitive of a differential equation of the first order. If this differential equation is written in the form $y' = f(x, y)$, it may be represented geometrically as a slope-field as in Chapter One. If at each point $P:(x, y)$ of the slope-field the associated slope is replaced by that of the isogonal trajectory at that point, there results the slope-field (and consequently the differential equation) of the family of isogonal trajectories.

55

EXAMPLE 1. Write the differential equation of the isogonal trajectories of the family of parabolas $y = ax^2$ if the given angle is $\frac{\pi}{6}$.

SOLUTION. The differential equation of the family of parabolas is found by eliminating $a$ between the equations $y = ax^2$ and $y' = 2ax$. This differential equation is $y' = \frac{2y}{x}$. Hence if $\frac{2y}{x}$ is substituted for $y_1'$ and $\frac{\pi}{6}$ for $\phi$ in (1), the required differential equation of the trajectories results. It is:

$$\frac{y' - \frac{2y}{x}}{1 + \frac{2yy'}{x}} = \frac{1}{\sqrt{3}}$$

$$\sqrt{3}(xy' - 2y) = x + 2yy'$$
$$(x + 2\sqrt{3}y)\,dx + (2y - \sqrt{3}x)\,dy = 0$$

On account of important applications in various fields, the special case $\phi = \frac{1}{2}\pi$ is of particular interest. In this case the trajectories are called *orthogonal* trajectories and (1) is then replaced by the condition

(2) $$y_1'y' = -1.$$

When the original family of curves is represented by the differential equation $M\,dx + N\,dy = 0$ ($M \neq 0$, $N \neq 0$), $y_1'$ becomes $-\frac{M}{N}$. From the equation (2) $y'$ is found to be $\frac{N}{M}$, so that the differential equation of the family of orthogonal trajectories becomes

$$N\,dx - M\,dy = 0.$$

EXAMPLE 2. Find the orthogonal trajectories of the family of parabolas with vertices at the origin and axes along $OY$.

SOLUTION. The equation of the family of parabolas is $x^2 = 4ay$ and the differential equation of this family is

$$x\,dy - 2y\,dx = 0.$$

Hence the differential equation of the orthogonal trajectories is

$$x \, dx + 2y \, dy = 0,$$

whose general solution is

$$x^2 + 2y^2 = C.$$

Therefore each trajectory is an ellipse with center at the origin and whose major axis is on $OX$ with length $\sqrt{2}$ times that of the minor axis. (See Fig. 6.)

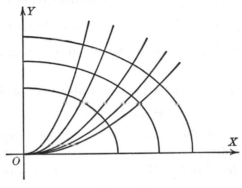

**Figure 6**

When polar coordinates are used, the differential equation of the orthogonal trajectories is derived from that of the original family as follows. Denote by $C_1$ (Fig. 7) that curve which belongs to the original family and which passes through $P:(r, \theta)$, and by $C$ the orthogonal trajectory through the same point. Denote by $\psi_1$ the positive angle less than $\pi$ which the tangent to $C_1$ at $P$ makes with the radius vector of $P$, and by $\psi$ the corresponding angle

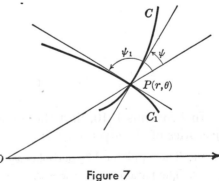

**Figure 7**

57

for $C$. Then if $C$ is orthogonal to $C_1$,

$$\psi_1 = \psi \pm \tfrac{1}{2}\pi$$

so that $\tan \psi_1 = - \cot \psi = - \dfrac{1}{\tan \psi}.$  Conversely, if

$$\tan \psi_1 = - \frac{1}{\tan \psi},$$

we may conclude that $\psi_1 = \psi \pm \tfrac{1}{2}\pi$.  As was recalled in Article 18, $\tan \psi_1 = r \dfrac{d\theta}{dr}$, so that the differential equation of the orthogonal trajectories is obtained from that of the original family by replacing $r \dfrac{d\theta}{dr}$ by its negative reciprocal.

EXAMPLE 3.  Find the orthogonal trajectories of the hyperbolas

$$r^2 \sin 2\theta = C.$$

SOLUTION.  The differential equation of these hyperbolas is obtained by differentiating the equation $r^2 \sin 2\theta = C$.  The result is easily reduced to $\tan 2\theta\, dr + r\, d\theta = 0$, from which

$$r \frac{d\theta}{dr} = - \tan 2\theta.$$

Hence the differential equation of the trajectories is

$$- \frac{1}{r} \frac{dr}{d\theta} = - \tan 2\theta,$$

whose integral is $r^2 \cos 2\theta = C$.

**EXERCISE 14**

In Problems 1–10, find the equations of the orthogonal trajectories of the given curves.

1. The equilateral hyperbolas $xy = k$.
2. The parabolas $y^2 = k - x$.

58

3. The parabolas $y = ax^2$.      4. The hyperbolas $x^2 - ky^2 = 6$.

5. The hyperbolas $y^2 - 3x^2 = k$.

6. The concentric circles whose common center is the origin.

7. The circles $x^2 + y^2 - 2ky = 25$.

8. The circles tangent to $OX$ at $(5, 0)$.

9. The equilateral hyperbolas with one vertex at the origin and with transverse axis along $OY$.

10. The similar ollipses $\dfrac{x^2}{a^2} + \dfrac{y^2}{b^2} = k$.

11. Show that the family of parabolas having common focus and axis is self-orthogonal.

12. The equation $\dfrac{x^2}{a^2} + \dfrac{y^2}{a^2 - c^2} = 1$ represents a family of central conics with foci $(\pm c, 0)$. Show that this family of confocal central conics is self-orthogonal.

13. Find the isogonal trajectories which cut at $\dfrac{\pi}{4}$ the equilateral hyperbolas of Problem 1.

14. Find the trajectories which cut at $\dfrac{\pi}{4}$ the concentric circles $x^2 + y^2 = a^2$.

In Problems 15–23 find the polar equations of the orthogonal trajectories of the given families.

15. The straight lines $r = k \sec \theta$.

16. The cardioids $r = a(1 - \cos \theta)$.

17. The logarithmic spirals $r = a^\theta$.

18. The lemniscates $r^2 = k \cos 2\theta$.

19. The curves $\left(r + \dfrac{5}{r}\right) \cos \theta = a$.

20. The curves $r^2(1 - \cos \theta) \sin \theta = k$.

21. The circles $r = 2k \sin \theta$.      22. The curves $r = k \sin \dfrac{\theta}{2}$.

23. The curves $r = a(\sec \theta + \tan \theta)$.

24. Show that if the curves $r^2 = k^2 \sin 2\theta$ are rotated about the pole through the angle $\dfrac{\pi}{4}$, the new curves are the orthogonal trajectories of the original system.

**20. Decomposition and growth.** When a natural substance decreases or increases in magnitude as a result of some action which affects all parts equally, the rate of decrease or increase is frequently a function of the amount of the substance present. One might surmise that the rate at which the change occurs is proportional to the quantity of the substance present. This law is indeed valid in many instances, at least as a useful approximation.

EXAMPLE. In a certain chemical reaction a given substance is being converted into another at a rate proportional to the amount of the substance unconverted. If one fifth of the original amount has been transformed in four minutes, how much time will be required to transform one half?

SOLUTION. Let $s$ be the number of grams of the substance which remains after $t$ minutes. The differential equation of the reaction is

$$\frac{ds}{dt} = ks,$$

whose general integral is easily found to be

$$\ln \frac{s}{C} = kt.$$

If $s_0$ is the original amount of the substance, then $\ln \frac{s_0}{C} = 0$ and $C = s_0$, which gives the particular solution

$(a)$ $$\ln \frac{s}{s_0} = kt.$$

Since $s = \frac{4}{5}s_0$ when $t = 4$, it is seen from $(a)$ that $\ln (0.8) = 4k$. Thus the particular solution $(a)$ assumes the form

$(b)$ $$\ln \frac{s}{s_0} = \tfrac{1}{4}t \ln (0.8).$$

If $t = t_1$ when $s = \frac{1}{2}s_0$, we have

$$t_1 = \frac{\ln (0.5)}{\tfrac{1}{4} \ln (0.8)} = 12.4,$$

which is the number of minutes required to transform one half the substance.

**21. Use of the definite integral.** When a particular solution of a differential equation is determined by initial conditions, it can sometimes be advantageously written by use of an appropriate definite integral. The same device can also be employed in solving for one variable when a particular value of the other variable is specified. As an illustration of this technique we use the example of the preceding article.

We first note the following pairs of corresponding values of $s$ and $t$:

$$(a)\ \ s_0,\ 0,\qquad (b)\ \ s,\ t,\qquad (c)\ \ \tfrac{4}{5}s_0,\ 4,\qquad (d\tfrac{1}{2})\ \ s_0,\ t_1$$

Then, after separating variables in the differential equation, we write:

$$\int_{s_0}^{s}\frac{ds}{s}=\int_0^t k\,dt,\qquad \int_{s_0}^{\frac{4}{5}s_0}\frac{ds}{s}=\int_0^4 k\,dt,\qquad \int_{s_0}^{\frac{1}{2}s_0}\frac{ds}{s}=\int_0^{t_1} k\,dt$$

The first of these equations becomes the particular solution, provided $k$ is evaluated by using the second equation. The third equation gives the value of $t$ for which $s$ becomes one half its original value.

**22. Use of the differential.** It is occasionally desirable to formulate the differential equation describing a particular application from the standpoint of the differentials involved. This device will be illustrated by the following example.

EXAMPLE 1. The sum of $1000 is compounded continuously, the nominal rate being four per cent per annum. In how many years will the amount be twice the original principal?

SOLUTION. In compound interest computations, when the accrued interest is added to the principal at the end of each period, the resulting amount serves as a new principal for the next period. The interest earned during the $(j+1)$th period $\Delta t$ is $p_j r\,\Delta t$, where $p_j$ is the amount at the beginning of the period, $r$ is the nominal rate per annum, and $\Delta t$ is the period in years. The amount at the end of the period is $p_{j+1}=p_j+p_j r\,\Delta t$. This formula is valid for any finite period $\Delta t$, however small. As the period $\Delta t$ decreases, approaching zero, it will be assumed that the corresponding increase $\Delta p=p_{j+1}-p_j$ also approaches zero and that

61

the ratio $\dfrac{\Delta p}{\Delta t}$ approaches a limit. Hence the equation $\Delta p = p_i r\ \Delta t$ leads to the differential equation

$$dp = pr\ dt.$$

Separating variables and writing the appropriate definite integrals, we have:

$$\int_{1000}^{2000} \frac{dp}{p} = \int_0^{t_1} 0.04\ dt$$

$$t_1 = \frac{\ln 2}{0.04} = \frac{0.6931}{0.04} = 17.3$$

EXAMPLE 2. Brine, whose salt concentration is two pounds per gallon, flows at the rate of three gallons per minute into a tank holding 100 gallons of fresh water. The mixture, kept uniform by stirring, flows out at the same rate. How many pounds of salt are in the tank at the end of one hour?

SOLUTION. Let $x$ be the number of pounds of salt in the tank after $t$ minutes. Then the salt concentration at this instant is $\dfrac{x}{100}$ pounds per gallon. In the time interval $dt$, $3\ dt$ gallons, carrying $(3\ dt)\left(\dfrac{x}{100}\right)$ pounds of salt, flow from the tank, being replaced by $3\ dt$ gallons carrying $(3\ dt)(2)$ pounds of salt. Hence in this interval the salt content of the tank increases by the amount

$$dx = (6 - 0.03x)\ dt.$$

After the variables are separated, this differential equation becomes

$$\frac{dx}{6 - 0.03x} = dt.$$

Since $x = 0$ when $t = 0$, the number $x_1$ of pounds of salt in the tank after one hour is given by the equation

$$\int_0^{x_1} \frac{dx}{6 - 0.03x} = \int_0^{60} dt.$$

The value of $x_1$ is found by the following steps:

$$-\frac{1}{0.03} \ln (6 - 0.03x) \Big]_0^{x_1} = 60$$

$$-\frac{1}{0.03}\ln\frac{6-0.03x_1}{6}=60$$

$$\frac{6-0.03x_1}{6}=e^{-1.8}=0.1653$$

$$6-0.03x_1=0.9918$$

$$0.03x_1=5.0082$$

$$x_1=167$$

## EXERCISE 15

1. Assuming that radium decomposes at a rate proportional to the amount present, in how many years will half the original amount be lost if ten per cent disappears in 243 years?
2. Five per cent of a radioactive substance is lost in 100 years. How much of the original amount will be present after 250 years?
3. After 25 years a quantity of radium has decreased to 52.4 grams. At the end of the next 25 years 51.8 grams remain. How many grams were there initially?
4. A chemical process transforms one substance into another at a rate proportional to the amount of the first substance untransformed. At the end of one hour 60 grams remain, at the end of four hours, 21 grams. How many grams of the first substance were there initially?
5. A certain chemical reaction converts one substance into another, the rate of conversion being proportional to the amount of the first substance unconverted. If in five minutes one third of this substance has been transformed, how much will be transformed in twelve minutes? In how many minutes will half the original amount have been converted?
6. The rate at which the population of a city increases at any time is proportional to the population at that time. If there were 125,000 people in the city in 1920 and 140,000 in 1950, what population may be predicted in 1970?

7. Bacteria grown in a nutrient solution increase at a rate proportional to the number present. In a particular culture the number triples in 3 hours and there were $10^7$ at the end of 12 hours. How many were there initially?

8. If the pressure of air at any height is equal to the weight of the vertical column of air above it, and if the density of air is proportional to the pressure, find the law connecting the pressure with the height.

9. A cylindrical tank 2 feet high, with a cross section of 9 square feet, is initially full of water. If there is a leak in the bottom and the leakage is proportional to the depth, find the volume of water in the tank at the end of 3 days if the tank is half full at the end of the first day.

10. If the interest on $500 is compounded continuously at the nominal rate of 6%, find the amount at the end of 5 years.

11. Find the rate of interest, compounded continuously, which would produce in 100 years one million dollars from an investment of $1,000.

12. A sum of money is to be compounded continuously at the nominal rate of 6% so as to provide an income of $200 per month for 4 years, at which time the principal is to be used up. How large a sum is necessary?

13. The rate at which a body loses heat to the surrounding air is proportional to the difference of its temperature from that of the air. If the temperature of the air is 35° and the temperature of the body drops from 120° to 60° in forty minutes, what will the temperature be after 100 minutes? When will the temperature be 45°?

14. A body, initially at the temperature 150°, is allowed to cool in air at the temperature 30°. Assuming the rate of cooling to vary as the difference between the temperature of the body and that of the air, how long will it take the body to cool to 80° if its temperature is 100° after 40 minutes? What will be its temperature after one hour?

15. Suppose that the population of a city would grow at a rate proportional to the current population and that in forty years the population would have doubled. If the natural increase of this population is offset by a roughly constant annual

64

loss of 500 persons due to unsatisfactory employment conditions, and if the population in 1950 was 20,000, estimate the population in the year 2000.

16. By natural increase the population of a city would double in 50 years. In how many years will the population, initially 100,000, double if the city attracts 1500 additional persons each year from without?

17. The natural tendency of an insect colony to grow at a rate proportional to the size of the colony and to increase by 50 per cent in one month, is offset by adverse conditions which destroy 200 per thousand per day. In how many days will the colony decrease to one tenth its original size?

18. A cake was removed from a 400° F. oven and placed in a room whose temperature is 72° F. In 15 minutes the cake cools to 200° F. Find how soon its temperature will fall to 100° F.

19. A tank contains 300 gallons of fresh water. A solution containing 1 pound of salt per gallon is added at the rate of 4 gallons per minute, and the resulting mixture, kept uniform by stirring, flows out at the same rate. Find the amount of salt in the tank at the end of 10 hours.

20. A tank contains 200 gallons of brine whose salt concentration is 2 pounds per gallon. Fresh water runs into the tank at the rate of 4 gallons per minute and the mixture, kept uniform, flows out at the rate of 5 gallons per minute. How long will it take to decrease the salt content of the tank to 150 pounds?

21. Fresh water flows into a tank at the rate of 2 gallons per minute. If the tank initially holds 200 gallons of brine containing 300 pounds of salt, and if the mixture flows out at the rate of 3 gallons per minute, how much time will be required to lower the salt content to 175 pounds if the mixture is kept uniform at all times?

22. The air in a room whose volume is 7200 cubic feet tests 0.1 per cent carbon dioxide. In order to reduce the carbon dioxide to 0.075 per cent in 20 minutes, how many cubic feet of outside air testing 0.045 per cent carbon dioxide must be admitted per minute?

**23. Steady-state flow of heat.** If a constant temperature is maintained at each point of the bounding surface of a body, after a time the so-called steady-state condition will have been reached, in which the temperature throughout the body does not vary with time, although different points of the body will not necessarily have the same temperature.

Suppose that the temperature $T$ is a function of a single space coordinate $x$. If the constant $C$ is so chosen that the locus of the equation $x = C$ contains points of the body, the temperature is the same at all points of the locus which lie in the body. Such a locus is called an *isothermal surface*. The rate at which heat flows across any portion (of area $A$) of an isothermal surface is proportional to

$$A \frac{dT}{dx}.$$

Thus we may write

(3) $$-kA \frac{dT}{dx} = Q,$$

where $k$ is the *thermal conductivity* of the material composing the body and where $Q$ is assumed to be constant and is measured in calories per second when c.g.s. units are employed.

> EXAMPLE. An iron pipe has inner and outer diameters of four centimeters and seven centimeters respectively. Constant temperatures of 180° C. and 40° C. are maintained on the inner and outer surfaces respectively. If $k = 0.14$, find the heat loss per hour of a section of the pipe one meter long. Express the temperature as a function of the distance from the axis. Find the temperature at a point two and one half centimeters from the axis of the pipe. At what points is the temperature 100° C.?
>
> SOLUTION. The isothermal surfaces are circular cylinders whose common axis is that of the pipe. Since the area of such a cylinder one meter long and of radius $r$ centimeters is $200\pi r$ square centimeters, equation (3) may be written
>
> $$-28\pi r \frac{dT}{dr} = Q.$$

Separating variables and using corresponding values of the variables, we write:

(a)
$$- 28\pi \int_{180}^{40} dT = Q \int_{2}^{3.5} \frac{dr}{r}$$
$$3920\pi = Q \ln 1.75$$
$$Q = 22{,}000$$

Hence the loss of heat in calories per hour is

$$22{,}000 \times 3600 = 79{,}200{,}000.$$

The expression for $T$ as a function of $r$ is found by replacing the upper limits in $(a)$ by $T$ and $r$:

$$- 28\pi \int_{180}^{T} dT = 22{,}000 \int_{2}^{r} \frac{dr}{r}$$
$$28\pi(180 - T) = 22{,}000 \ (\ln r - \ln 2)$$
$$T = 180 + 173 - 250 \ln r$$
$$T = 353 - 250 \ln r$$

When $r = 2.5$, we have
$$T = 353 - 250 \ln 2.5$$
$$= 124.$$

Putting $T = 100$, we find:
$$\ln r = \tfrac{253}{250} = 1.012$$
$$r = 2.75$$

**24. Flow of water through an orifice.** If water escapes from a tank through a small hole in the bottom, it can be shown that the rate of escape is proportional to the product of the area of the hole and the square root of the depth of the water. Under suitable conditions the factor of proportionality may be taken as − 4.8 if the units of time and length are the second and the foot respectively.

EXAMPLE. A cylindrical tank ten feet long and ten feet in diameter is placed with its axis in a horizontal position. Water, initially filling the tank, flows through a circular orifice of diameter one inch located in the bottom of the tank. How much time will be required for all the water to escape?

67

SOLUTION. According to the principle just stated for such problems, if $V$ is the number of cubic feet of water in the tank after $t$ seconds and $h$ is the depth in feet, then

$$\frac{dV}{dt} = -4.8\left(\frac{\pi}{24^2}\right)\sqrt{h} = -\frac{\pi\sqrt{h}}{120}.$$

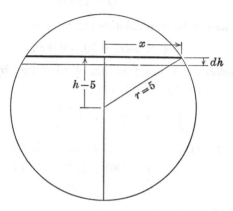

Figure 8

From Fig. 8 it follows that $dV = 10(2x)\,dh$, where

$$x = \sqrt{25 - (h-5)^2} = \sqrt{10h - h^2}.$$

Hence the differential equation is

$$20\sqrt{10h - h^2}\,\frac{dh}{dt} = -\frac{\pi\sqrt{h}}{120}.$$

After the variables have been separated, this takes the form

$$2400\sqrt{10 - h}\,dh = -\pi\,dt.$$

Integration between the limits 10 and 0 for $h$ produces the solution of the example as follows.

$$2400\int_{10}^{0}\sqrt{10-h}\,dh = -\pi\int_{0}^{t_1}dt$$

$$-1600(10-h)^{\frac{3}{2}}\Big]_{10}^{0} = -\pi t_1$$

$$t_1 = \frac{16{,}000\sqrt{10}}{\pi}\ \text{sec.} = 4.5\ \text{hr.}$$

**25. Second-order processes.** In a variety of applications it is assumed that the rate at which the amount $x$ of a substance increases or decreases is jointly proportional to two factors, each factor being a linear function of $x$. Processes whose rates of change are functions of this type are called second-order processes.

EXAMPLE 1. Two substances, $S_1$ and $S_2$, combine chemically to form a third substance $S_3$, each molecule of $S_3$ being formed from one molecule of each of the parent substances. The rate at which $S_3$ is formed varies jointly as the amounts of $S_1$ and $S_2$ present. Then if $s_1$ and $s_2$ are the initial amounts of $S_1$ and $S_2$ respectively, and $x$ is the amount of $S_3$ at $t$ minutes, the differential equation for the reaction is

$$\frac{dx}{dt} = k(s_1 - x)(s_2 - x).$$

EXAMPLE 2. The rate at which a substance dissolves is jointly proportional to the amount of the substance present and to the difference between the concentration of the substance in solution at any instant $t$ and its concentration in a saturated solution. That is, if $x$ is the amount of the substance undissolved at the instant $t$, $x_0$ the initial amount, $c$ the concentration at saturation, and $V$ the amount of solvent, then

$$\frac{dx}{dt} = kx\left(c - \frac{x_0 - x}{V}\right).$$

*Gordon Staff*

**EXERCISE 16**

1. If a temperature of 40° C. is maintained over the inner surface of a wall 25 centimeters thick and the outer surface has the constant temperature of 0° C., express the temperature of the wall as a function of the distance from the inner surface. If the thermal conductivity is $k = 0.0015$, find the heat loss per day through a square meter of the wall.

2. A steam pipe 20 centimeters in diameter is covered with an insulating sheath 5 centimeters thick, the conductivity of which is 0.00018. If the pipe has the constant temperature

69

100° C. and the outer surface of the sheath is kept at 30° C., express the temperature of the sheath as a function of the distance from the axis of the pipe. How much heat is lost per hour through a section one meter long?

3. A spherical iron shell has inner and outer diameters of 16 centimeters and 20 centimeters respectively. The inner temperature is kept at 100° C. and the outer temperature at 30° C. Find the temperature of the shell as a function of the distance from the center. Take $k = 0.14$.

4. A cylindrical tank whose axis is vertical has diameter 4 feet. If water flows out through a one-inch hole in the bottom, how long will it take to lower the level from 5 feet to $4\frac{1}{2}$ feet?

5. A vertical tank whose horizontal section is a square of side 2 feet has a $1\frac{1}{2}$-inch hole in the bottom. If there are 50 gallons of water in the tank initially, how much water will there be one minute later?

6. The conical portion of a funnel 10 inches across the top and 8 inches deep has a $\frac{3}{4}$-inch hole at the bottom. If it is initially full of water, in how many seconds will it empty?

7. A hemispherical bowl of depth $1\frac{1}{2}$ feet is initially full of water. If the water escapes through an inch hole in the bottom, in how many seconds will the level drop to 6 inches?

8. A bowl which has the form of a paraboloid of revolution measures 4 feet across at the top and is 2 feet deep. If an orifice at the bottom has diameter 1.5 inches, how long will it take to empty the bowl if it is initially full of water? How deep will the water be 80 seconds later?

9. If in Example 1 the initial amounts of the two parent substances are 8 and 6, and 2 units of the resulting substance are formed in 10 minutes, find the amount formed in 15 minutes.

10. Suppose that the initial amounts of $S_1$ and $S_2$ in Example 1 are 8 and 8, and that 3 units of $S_3$ are formed in 10 minutes, how much time will be required to produce 5 units?

11. The salt in the pores of an inert substance dissolves in 20 gallons of water. If the substance contains 10 pounds of salt initially, and half of this dissolves in 10 minutes, how much will dissolve in 20 minutes? Assume that a saturated brine will have 3 pounds of salt per gallon.

12. A quantity of insoluble material contains 20 pounds of salt which is allowed to dissolve in a tank of 25 gallons of water. If 12 pounds of salt have dissolved in 60 minutes, how long will it take 18 pounds to dissolve? Assume the concentration of salt in a saturated solution to be three pounds per gallon.

13. A certain substance loses moisture at a rate proportional to its moisture content and to the difference between the moisture content of the air and that of saturated air. A quantity of the substance containing 15 pounds of moisture is allowed to dry in a closed room whose dimensions are 20 feet, 15 feet, and 10 feet, the air of which has an initial relative humidity of 30 per cent. If the substance loses half its moisture in an hour and a half, how much will it have lost in one hour? Assume that at saturation, air will hold 0.015 pound of moisture per cubic foot.

14. Assume that if air expands adiabatically, that is, without gaining or losing heat, the pressure in pounds per square foot is proportional to $\delta^{1.4}$, where $\delta$ is the density in pounds per cubic foot. Consider that in a vertical column of air of unit cross section an increase $dh$ in height results in a decrease $-dp$ in pressure numerically equal to the weight of the volume of air in the column between the levels $h$ and $h + dh$. Write the differential equation in the variables $h$ and $\delta$. If at sea level $p = 2116$ pounds per square foot and $\delta = 0.08$ pound per cubic foot, what is the density at the height of one mile? At what height will the density be zero?

15. Suppose that at a depth of $h$ feet the pressure $p$ in a body of water is related to the density $\delta$ by the formula

$$p = 5 \cdot 10^7 \cdot \frac{\delta - \delta_0}{\delta_0},$$

where pressure is measured in pounds per square foot, density in pounds per cubic foot, and $\delta_0$, the sea-level density, is taken as 64 pounds per cubic foot. Using the fact that in a vertical column whose cross section has the area one square foot, the increase in pressure from the depth $h$ feet to the depth $h + dh$ feet is equal to the weight of water in the unit column between the corresponding levels, write the differential equation in the variables $h$ and $\delta$. Find the density at the depth of five miles.

71

# CHAPTER FOUR

# Linear differential equations
# of higher order

**26. Introduction.** A differential equation which is of the first degree in the unknown function and its derivatives is called a *linear differential equation*. Such an equation of the $n$th order may be written in the form

$$(1) \quad P_0(x)y^{(n)} + P_1(x)y^{(n-1)} + \cdots + P_{n-1}(x)y' + P_n(x)y = Q(x),$$

where $P_0(x)$, $P_1(x)$, . . ., $P_n(x)$, and $Q(x)$ are functions of $x$ defined and continuous on an interval $a \leq x \leq b$, and where $P_0(x)$ is not identically zero on this interval. The *homogeneous* linear differential equation

$$(2) \quad P_0(x)y^{(n)} + P_1(x)y^{(n-1)} + \cdots + P_{n-1}(x)y' + P_n(x)y = 0$$

is the special case of equation (1) in which the function $Q(x)$ is identically zero on the interval $a \leq x \leq b$. In this chapter it will be assumed that $P_0(x)$ is nowhere zero for $a \leq x \leq b$.

The solution of equation (2) in the general case is quite difficult. However, even in this case certain general properties can be obtained. Some of these properties will be established in Article 27.

72

The solution of (1) is particularly simple if the coefficients $P_i(x)$ are constants, and the general integral can be found by methods to be explained in Articles 29–38. The method described in Article 34 applies even when the coefficients are not constants. A special case of (1) in which the coefficients are not constants will be treated in Article 39.

**27. Properties of the homogeneous equation.** The homogeneous linear equation (2) has the following important property. If $y_1(x)$ and $y_2(x)$ are solutions of (2) and $c_1$, $c_2$ are constants, then the linear combination $c_1 y_1(x) + c_2 y_2(x)$ is also a solution. This may be shown as follows.

Since $y_1$ and $y_2$ are solutions of (2),

$$P_0 y_1^{(n)} + P_1 y_1^{(n-1)} + \cdots + P_n y_1 = 0$$
$$P_0 y_2^{(n)} + P_1 y_2^{(n-1)} + \cdots + P_n y_2 = 0$$

identically on $a \leqq x \leqq b$. When these equations are multiplied by $c_1$ and $c_2$ respectively and the resulting equations added, then since

$$(c_1 y_1 + c_2 y_2)^{(i)} = c_1 y_1^{(i)} + c_2 y_2^{(i)}$$

one has

$$P_0(c_1 y_1 + c_2 y_2)^{(n)} + P_1(c_1 y_1 + c_2 y_2)^{(n-1)} + \cdots + P_n(c_1 y_1 + c_2 y_2) = 0.$$

It is readily verified that if $y_1, y_2, \ldots, y_k$ are any $k$ solutions of (2) and $c_1, c_2, \ldots, c_k$ are constants, the linear combination $c_1 y_1 + c_2 y_2 + \cdots + c_k y_k$ is also a solution.

A second important property of equation (2) is concerned with the concept of linear independence. The functions $f_1(x), f_2(x), \ldots, f_k(x)$, defined on the interval $a \leqq x \leqq b$, are said to be *linearly independent* if the identity

(3) $$c_1 f_1(x) + c_2 f_2(x) + \cdots + c_k f_k(x) = 0$$

cannot be satisfied unless all the constants $c_i$ are zero; the functions are *linearly dependent* in case there exist constants $c_1$, $c_2, \ldots, c_k$ not all zero such that the identity (3) holds.

Suppose that the functions $f_1(x), f_2(x), \ldots, f_k(x)$ are linearly dependent so that an identity of the form (3) holds with con-

73

stants not all zero. After $k - 1$ differentiations of (3) one obtains the system of equations:

$$c_1f_1(x) + c_2f_2(x) + \cdots + c_kf_k(x) = 0$$
$$c_1f_1'(x) + c_2f_2'(x) + \cdots + c_kf_k'(x) = 0$$
$$\cdots \cdots \cdots \cdots \cdots \cdots \cdots$$
$$c_1f_1^{(k-1)}(x) + c_2f_2^{(k-1)}(x) + \cdots + c_kf_k^{(k-1)}(x) = 0$$

Since this system has a solution $c_1, c_2, \ldots, c_k$, not all zero, the determinant

$$\begin{vmatrix} f_1(x) & f_2(x) & \cdots & f_k(x) \\ f_1'(x) & f_2'(x) & \cdots & f_k'(x) \\ \cdots & \cdots & \cdots & \cdots \\ f_1^{(k-1)}(x) & f_2^{(k-1)}(x) & \cdots & f_k^{(k-1)}(x) \end{vmatrix}$$

must vanish identically on $a \leqq x \leqq b$. This determinant is called the *Wronskian** of the functions $f_1(x), f_2(x), \ldots, f_k(x)$. Thus if $f_1(x), f_2(x), \ldots, f_k(x)$ are linearly dependent, their Wronskian vanishes identically.

The interval on which the functions

$$f_1(x), f_2(x), \ldots, f_k(x)$$

are defined may have one or more subintervals on which the Wronskian of the functions is different from zero. It follows from the preceding paragraph that on such subintervals the functions are linearly independent.

In the following pages we shall be concerned with sets of functions which are known to be particular solutions of linear differential equations of the type (2). For such sets of functions the following theorem, here stated without proof, is valid.

*Theorem.* If the functions $f_1(x), f_2(x), \ldots, f_n(x)$ are solutions of an $n$th-order homogeneous linear differential equation on the interval $a \leqq x \leqq b$, their Wronskian either vanishes identically or vanishes at no point of the interval. Further, the solutions are linearly independent if and only if their Wronskian vanishes nowhere on the interval.

* Named for Hoëné Wronski (1778–1853), Polish mathematician, investigator in the theory of determinants.

If $f_1(x)$, $f_2(x)$, $\ldots$, $f_n(x)$ are linearly independent solutions of (2), the general solution of (2) can be expressed in the form

$$(4) \qquad y = c_1 f_1(x) + c_2 f_2(x) + \cdots + c_n f_n(x),$$

where $c_1$, $c_2$, $\ldots$, $c_n$ are arbitrary constants. To prove this, we show that if $y(x)$ is a particular solution of (2), then $y(x)$ can be expressed in the form (4) for a suitable choice of the constants $c_1$, $c_2$, $\ldots$, $c_n$. Consider the equations:

$$c_1 f_1(a) + c_2 f_2(a) + \cdots + c_n f_n(a) = y(a)$$
$$c_1 f_1'(a) + c_2 f_2'(a) + \cdots + c_n f_n'(a) = y'(a)$$
$$\cdots \cdots \cdots \cdots \cdots \cdots \cdots \cdots \cdots \cdots \cdots$$
$$c_1 f_1^{(n-1)}(a) + c_2 f_2^{(n-1)}(a) + \cdots + c_n f_n^{(n-1)}(a) = y^{(n-1)}(a)$$

This system of equations has a unique solution $c_1$, $c_2$, $\ldots$, $c_n$, since the determinant of the coefficients in the left members is the value at $a$ of the Wronskian of $f_1(x)$, $f_2(x)$, $\ldots$, $f_n(x)$ and therefore is not zero. Form the function

$$Y(x) = c_1 f_1(x) + c_2 f_2(x) + \cdots + c_n f_n(x) - y(x)$$

with these values $c_1$, $c_2$, $\ldots$, $c_n$. Then $Y(x)$ is a solution of (2), since it is a linear combination of such solutions with constant coefficients. Further, $Y(x)$ and its first $n - 1$ derivatives vanish at $x = a$. But, according to Theorem 2 of Article 6, the zero function is the unique solution of (2) which vanishes with its first $n - 1$ derivatives at $x = a$. Hence $Y(x)$ must be identical with the zero function, which is equivalent to saying that $y(x)$ has been expressed in the form (4).

EXAMPLE 1. Show that if $m_1 \neq m_2$, the functions $e^{m_1 x}$ and $e^{m_2 x}$ are linearly independent.

SOLUTION. The Wronskian of the two functions is:

$$\begin{vmatrix} e^{m_1 x} & e^{m_2 x} \\ m_1 e^{m_1 x} & m_2 e^{m_2 x} \end{vmatrix}$$

It equals

$$(m_2 - m_1) e^{(m_1 + m_2) x}$$

and is therefore different from zero. Hence the functions are linearly independent.

EXAMPLE 2. Evaluate the Wronskian of the functions $x^2$, $e^x$, $e^{-x}$, and thus test these functions for linear independence.

SOLUTION. The Wronskian of the functions to be tested is:

$$W = \begin{vmatrix} x^2 & e^x & e^{-x} \\ 2x & e^x & -e^{-x} \\ 2 & e^x & e^{-x} \end{vmatrix} = e^x \cdot e^{-x} \begin{vmatrix} x^2 & 1 & 1 \\ 2x & 1 & -1 \\ 2 & 1 & 1 \end{vmatrix}$$

The expansion of this determinant according to the minors of the elements of the first column is:

$$x^2 \begin{vmatrix} 1 & -1 \\ 1 & 1 \end{vmatrix} - 2x \begin{vmatrix} 1 & 1 \\ 1 & 1 \end{vmatrix} + 2 \begin{vmatrix} 1 & 1 \\ 1 & -1 \end{vmatrix} = 2(x^2 - 2)$$

Since $W$ becomes zero for $x = \sqrt{2}$ and $-\sqrt{2}$, and only for these values, we conclude from the test for independence stated on page 74 that the functions are linearly independent on the intervals $x < -\sqrt{2}$, $-\sqrt{2} < x < \sqrt{2}$, $x > \sqrt{2}$.

One can show that the 3rd-order equation (2) whose solutions are $x^2$, $e^x$, $e^{-x}$ has coefficients which fail to exist at $x = \pm \sqrt{2}$.

**28. The nonhomogeneous equation; complementary function.** In the search for the general solution of the nonhomogeneous equation (1), the general solution (4) of the associated homogeneous equation (2) plays an important role. The solution (4) is called the *complementary function* of the equation (1). Its usefulness is shown as follows.

Let $y_c$ denote the complementary function and let $y_p$ be a particular integral of (1). The result of substituting

$$y = y_c + y_p$$

into the left member of (1) is

$$P_0(y_c + y_p)^{(n)} + P_1(y_c + y_p)^{(n-1)} + \cdots + P_n(y_c + y_p)$$
$$= (P_0 y_c^{(n)} + P_1 y_c^{(n-1)} + \cdots + P_n y_c)$$
$$+ (P_0 y_p^{(n)} + P_1 y_p^{(n-1)} + \cdots + P_n y_p).$$

Since $y_c$ is an integral of (2), the first expression in the right member vanishes. Since $y_p$ is an integral of (1), the second expression reduces to $Q(x)$. We see, therefore, that $y = y_c + y_p$ is a solution of (1); it is the general solution because it contains $n$ independent arbitrary constants.

**29. The homogeneous equation with constant coefficients.** The properties derived in Articles 27 and 28 are valid when the coefficients in equations (1) and (2) are functions of $x$. Except for Articles 34 and 39 the remainder of the current chapter will be concerned with linear differential equations whose coefficients are constants. The homogeneous equation of this type can be written in the form

$$(5) \quad A_0 y^{(n)} + A_1 y^{(n-1)} + \cdots + A_{n-1} y' + A_n y = 0, \quad A_0 \neq 0.$$

The solution of equation (5) will be discussed in this and the three following articles.

In the special case $n = 1$ equation (5) becomes $A_0 y' + A_1 y = 0$, which has the solution $y = e^{-\frac{A_1}{A_0} x}$. This suggests the possibility that an integral of equation (5) may have the form

$$(6) \quad y = e^{mx}.$$

The condition for this, found by substituting (6) into (5), is

$$e^{mx}(A_0 m^n + A_1 m^{n-1} + \cdots + A_{n-1} m + A_n) = 0.$$

Hence $e^{mx}$ will be a solution of (5) if and only if $m$ is chosen to be a root of the *auxiliary equation*

$$(7) \quad A_0 m^n + A_1 m^{n-1} + \cdots + A_{n-1} m + A_n = 0.$$

The general solution of equation (5) for each of three special cases of the auxiliary equation will be examined in the next three articles.

**30. Auxiliary equation with distinct roots.** The simplest situation presented by the $n$ roots of the auxiliary equation (7) is that in which no two of them are equal. In this case the functions $e^{m_1 x}, e^{m_2 x}, \ldots, e^{m_n x}$ are evidently distinct integrals of the differential equation (5). It has been shown in Example 1 of Article 27 that the functions $e^{m_1 x}, e^{m_2 x}$ are linearly independent if $m_1 \neq m_2$. With somewhat greater difficulty the same method can be used to show the linear independence of the integrals $e^{m_1 x}, e^{m_2 x}, \ldots, e^{m_n x}$ if $m_1, m_2, \ldots, m_n$ are all distinct. The general solution of (5) may then be written

$$y = c_1 e^{m_1 x} + c_2 e^{m_2 x} + \cdots + c_n e^{m_n x},$$

where $c_1, c_2, \ldots, c_n$ are arbitrary constants.

EXAMPLE 1. Find the general solution of the equation

$$y''' - 2y'' - y' + 2y = 0.$$

SOLUTION. The auxiliary equation is $m^3 - 2m^2 - m + 2 = 0$. Since the roots of this equation are $2, -1$, and $1$, the general solution of the differential equation is

$$y = c_1 e^{2x} + c_2 e^{-x} + c_3 e^{x}.$$

EXAMPLE 2. Find the general solution of the equation

$$\frac{d^2x}{dt^2} + a^2x = 0.$$

SOLUTION. The auxiliary equation is $m^2 + a^2 = 0$; its roots are $\pm ai$. Hence $e^{ait}$ and $e^{-ait}$ are particular integrals, so that the general solution may be written in the form

$$x = c_1 e^{ait} + c_2 e^{-ait}.$$

*Note:* It will be shown in Article 32 how a more desirable form of the general solution can be obtained.

EXAMPLE 3. Find the general solution of the equation

$$y^{(5)} - 2y^{(4)} - 10y''' + 20y'' + 9y' - 18y = 0.$$

SOLUTION. It is known from algebra that any rational root of the auxiliary equation

$$m^5 - 2m^4 - 10m^3 + 20m^2 + 9m - 18 = 0$$

must be an integer which is a divisor of 18. Of the twelve possible rational roots, we find that $-3, -1, 1, 2, 3$ actually satisfy the auxiliary equation. The general solution is therefore

$$y = c_1 e^{-3x} + c_2 e^{-x} + c_3 e^{x} + c_4 e^{2x} + c_5 e^{3x}.$$

*first fifteen*

**EXERCISE 17**

Show that the functions in each of Problems 1–8 are linearly independent.

1. $1, x, x^2$
2. $e^x, e^{-x}$
3. $e^{6x}, e^{7x}, e^{8x}$
4. $e^{3x}, e^{-3x}, e^x$
5. $\sin 6x, \cos 6x$
6. $e^x, \cos x, \sin x$
7. $e^{-x}, xe^{-x}$
8. $e^x \sin 2x, e^x \cos 2x$

In each of Problems 9–14, determine intervals on which the functions are linearly independent.

9. $x, x^2, x^3$

10. $x^2, x^3, x^4$

11. $x, e^x, xe^x$

12. $x^3, e^{2x}, e^{-2x}$

13. $x, e^{-x}\sin x, e^{-x}\cos x$

14. $x^2, \sinh 2x, \cosh 2x$

Find the general solution of each of the following equations.

15. $y' - y = 0$     $16 \quad 4$

16. $y'' - 4y = 0$

17. $y'' + 7y' + 12y = 0$

18. $y'' - 3y' + 2y = 0$

19. $y'' - 7y' + 6y = 0$

20. $2y'' + 3y' - 2y = 0$

21. $y'' - 2y' - y = 0$

22. $y'' - 2y' - 2y = 0$

23. $y'' - 3y' + y = 0$

24. $2y'' + 2y' - y = 0$

25. $2y''' - y'' - 2y' + y = 0$

26. $y''' - 3y'' - 4y' + 12y = 0$

27. $y''' - 4y'' + y' + 6y = 0$

28. $y^{(4)} - 6y'' + 8y = 0$

29. $y''' - 7y' + 6y = 0$

30. $y''' - 6y'' + 11y' - 6y = 0$

31. $y''' - 4y'' - 17y' + 60y = 0$

32. $y''' - 9y'' + 23y' - 15y = 0$

33. $y^{(4)} + y''' - 7y'' - y' + 6y = 0$

34. $2y^{(4)} - 3y''' - 20y'' + 27y' + 18y = 0$

35. $12y^{(4)} - 4y''' - 3y'' + y' = 0$

36. $y''' - 4y'' + 3y' = 0$

37. $4y''' + 2y'' - 4y' + y = 0$

38. $y''' - 5y'' - 2y' + 24y = 0$

39. $y^{(4)} + 2y''' - 7y'' - 8y' + 12y = 0$

40. $y^{(5)} - 3y^{(4)} - 5y''' + 15y'' + 4y' - 12y = 0$

41. $y^{(5)} + y^{(4)} - 13y''' - 13y'' + 36y' + 36y = 0$

42. $y^{(5)} + 3y^{(4)} - 15y''' - 19y'' + 30y' = 0$

43. $y^{(4)} + 3y'' - 4y = 0$

44. $y^{(5)} + 3y''' + 2y' = 0$

**31. Auxiliary equation with multiple roots.** Suppose that two of the roots, say $m_1$, $m_2$, of the auxiliary equation (7) are equal. By the reasoning of the preceding article a solution of (5) is given by

$$y = (c_1 + c_2)e^{m_1 x} + c_3 e^{m_3 x} + \cdots + c_n e^{m_n x}.$$

However, since this solution has fewer than $n$ independent arbitrary constants, it is not the general solution.

If $m_1$ is a double root of (7), then $m_1$ is also a root of the equation obtained by differentiating (7) with respect to $m$. That is, $m_1$ satisfies each of the following conditions:

$$\phi_1(m_1) \equiv A_0 m_1^n + A_1 m_1^{n-1} + \cdots + A_{n-2} m_1^2 + A_{n-1} m_1 + A_n = 0$$
$$\phi_2(m_1) \equiv n A_0 m_1^{n-1} + (n-1)A_1 m_1^{n-1} + \cdots + 2A_{n-2} m_1 + A_{n-1} = 0$$

It is known that $y_1 = e^{m_1 x}$ is an integral of (5). That $y_2 = xe^{m_1 x}$ is also an integral is shown by calculating the derivatives of $y_2$ and substituting into the left member of (5). We find

$$y_2 = xe^{m_1 x}, \quad y_2' = m_1 xe^{m_1 x} + e^{m_1 x}, \quad \ldots, \quad y_2^{(n)} = (m_1^n x + n m_1^{n-1})e^{m_1 x}.$$

When these expressions are substituted, we have

$$[\phi_1(m_1)x + \phi_2(m_1)]e^{m_1 x}.$$

Since $\phi_1(m_1) = \phi_2(m_1) = 0$, $y_2 = xe^{m_1 x}$ is a solution of (5).

Let the remaining roots, $m_3$, $m_4$, $\ldots$, $m_n$, of (7) be distinct, each different from $m_1$. Then the solutions $e^{m_1 x}$, $xe^{m_1 x}$, $e^{m_3 x}$, $\ldots$, $e^{m_n x}$ are linearly independent, since their Wronskian is different from zero, as can be shown by a rather complicated calculation. The general solution of (5) may therefore be written

$$y = (c_1 + c_2 x)e^{m_1 x} + c_3 e^{m_3 x} + \cdots + c_n e^{m_n x}.$$

More generally it can be proved that if $m_1$ is a $p$-fold root of the auxiliary equation and the remaining roots are simple roots, the general solution of the differential equation (5) may be written

$$y = (c_1 + c_2 x + \cdots + c_p x^{p-1})e^{m_1 x} + c_{p+1} e^{m_{p+1} x} + \cdots + c_n e^{m_n x}.$$

EXAMPLE. Solve the equation $y^{(4)} - 2y''' - 3y'' = 0$.

SOLUTION. The roots of the auxiliary equation are 0, 0, 3, $-1$. Therefore the general solution is

$$y = c_1 + c_2 x + c_3 e^{3x} + c_4 e^{-x}.$$

## 32. Auxiliary equation with complex roots.

If the coefficients of the auxiliary equation are real numbers, the complex roots of this equation occur in conjugate pairs. Thus if $\alpha + i\beta$, where $\alpha$, $\beta$ are real numbers, is one of the roots, then $\alpha - i\beta$ is also a root. The general solution of the differential equation (5) will contain the expression

$$c_1 e^{(\alpha + i\beta)x} + c_2 e^{(\alpha - i\beta)x}.$$

We may transform the expression as follows:

$$\begin{aligned}
c_1 e^{(\alpha + i\beta)x} + c_2 e^{(\alpha - i\beta)x} &= e^{\alpha x}(c_1 e^{i\beta x} + c_2 e^{-i\beta x}) \\
&= e^{\alpha x}[c_1 (\cos \beta x + i \sin \beta x) + c_2 (\cos \beta x - i \sin \beta x)] \\
&= e^{\alpha x}[(c_1 + c_2) \cos \beta x + i(c_1 - c_2) \sin \beta x] \\
&= e^{\alpha x}(c_1' \cos \beta x + c_2' \sin \beta x),
\end{aligned}$$

where $c_1' = c_1 + c_2$ and $c_2' = i(c_1 - c_2)$ are new independent arbitrary constants.

If $\alpha + i\beta$ and $\alpha - i\beta$ are $p$-fold roots of the auxiliary equation, the general solution contains the expression

$$(c_1 + c_2 x + \cdots + c_p x^{p-1})e^{(\alpha + i\beta)x} + (d_1 + d_2 x + \cdots + d_p x^{p-1})e^{(\alpha - i\beta)x},$$

which can be reduced to the form

$$e^{\alpha x}[(c_1' + c_2' x + \cdots + c_p' x^{p-1}) \cos \beta x \\
+ (d_1' + d_2' x + \cdots + d_p' x^{p-1}) \sin \beta x].$$

EXAMPLE 1. Find the general solution of the equation

$$y'' - 3y' + 5y = 0.$$

SOLUTION. The auxiliary equation $m^2 - 3m + 5 = 0$ has the roots $m = \frac{1}{2}(3 \pm i\sqrt{11})$, so that the general solution is:

$$\begin{aligned}
y &= c_1 e^{\frac{1}{2}(3+i\sqrt{11})x} + c_2 e^{\frac{1}{2}(3-i\sqrt{11})x} \\
&= e^{\frac{3}{2}x}\left(c_1' \cos \frac{\sqrt{11}}{2} x + c_2' \sin \frac{\sqrt{11}}{2} x\right)
\end{aligned}$$

81

EXAMPLE 2. Solve the equation

$$y^{(4)} + 2y''' + 2y'' - 2y' - 3y = 0.$$

SOLUTION. The auxiliary equation $m^4 + 2m^3 + 2m^2 - 2m - 3 = 0$ has the roots $m = -1, 1, -1 \pm i\sqrt{2}$, so that the general solution is:

$$y = c_1 e^{-x} + c_2 e^x + c_3 e^{(-1+i\sqrt{2})x} + c_4 e^{(-1-i\sqrt{2})x}$$
$$= c_1 e^{-x} + c_2 e^x + e^{-x}(c_3' \cos \sqrt{2}x + c_4' \sin \sqrt{2}x)$$

**EXERCISE 18**

Find the general solution for each of the equations in Problems 1–26.

1. $y'' - 2y' + y = 0$
2. $y'' = 0$
3. $2y''' + y'' - 4y' - 3y = 0$
4. $y''' - 3y'' + 3y' - y = 0$
5. $y^{(4)} = 0$
6. $y''' + y'' - y' - y = 0$
7. $4y''' - 3y' + y = 0$
8. $4y^{(5)} - 3y''' - y'' = 0$
9. $y''' - 7y'' + 16y' - 12y = 0$
10. $4y''' - 8y'' + 5y' - y = 0$
11. $y^{(4)} - y = 0$
12. $y''' - 8y = 0$
13. $y'' - 2y' + 3y = 0$
14. $y^{(4)} + y'' - 20y = 0$
15. $y^{(4)} + 5y'' + 6y = 0$
16. $y^{(4)} - 4y''' + 6y'' - 8y' + 8y = 0$
17. $y^{(4)} - 2y''' - y' + 2y = 0$
18. $y^{(4)} + y''' - 3y'' - 4y' - 4y = 0$
19. $2y''' - 3y'' + 10y' - 15y = 0$
20. $2y''' - 3y'' + 11y' - 40y = 0$
21. $y^{(4)} - 3y''' + 4y'' - 12y' + 16y = 0$
22. $4y''' + 12y'' - 3y' + 14y = 0$
23. $y^{(5)} - y^{(4)} + 6y''' - 6y'' + 8y' - 8y = 0$

24. $y^{(6)} + k^2 y^{(4)} - k^4 y'' - k^6 y = 0$

25. $y^{(5)} - y^{(4)} + 2y''' - 2y'' + y' - y = 0$

26. $y^{(5)} + y^{(4)} + 8y''' + 8y'' + 16y' + 16y = 0$

27. Show that $c_1 e^{(\alpha + i\beta)x} + c_2 e^{(\alpha - i\beta)x}$ can be reduced to the form $d_1 e^{\alpha x} \sin(\beta x + d_2)$.

28. Show that $c_1 e^{(\alpha + i\beta)x} + c_2 e^{(\alpha - i\beta)x}$ can be reduced to the form $d_1 e^{\alpha x} \cos(\beta x + d_2)$.

**33. The nonhomogeneous equation; method of undetermined coefficients.** We turn now to the first of several methods to be considered for finding a particular integral of the nonhomogeneous equation. The application of this method, as well as that which will be described in Articles 37 and 38, is restricted to the case in which the coefficients in the left member of equation (1) are constants. Such an equation may be written in the form

(8) $\quad A_0 y^{(n)} + A_1 y^{(n-1)} + \cdots + A_{n-1} y' + A_n y = Q(x), \quad A_0 \neq 0.$

Suppose $Q(x)$ is a sum of terms from each of which only a finite number of linearly independent derivatives can be obtained. This amounts to restricting $Q(x)$ to contain terms such as $x^k$, $e^{ax}$, $\sin ax$, $\cos ax$ (where $k$ is a nonnegative integer and $a$ is a constant), and products of such functions. While thus limited in scope, the method is comparatively simple when applicable.

Consider first the case in which neither $Q(x)$ nor any of its derivatives contains a term which is a constant multiple of a term in the complementary function. To find a particular solution of (8) in this case, assume that such a solution may be written as a linear combination of the set of functions consisting of the terms of $Q(x)$ and their derivatives, with undetermined constant coefficients. It can be shown that these coefficients can be determined in such a way as to make the linear combination a particular integral of the equation.

EXAMPLE 1. Find the general solution of the equation

$$y'' - 3y' + 2y = x^2 + x.$$

SOLUTION. To find $y_c$ we solve the homogeneous equation $y'' - 3y' + 2y = 0$. The auxiliary equation $m^2 - 3m + 2 = 0$ has the roots 1, 2. Hence

$$y_c = c_1 e^x + c_2 e^{2x}.$$

To find a particular solution of the nonhomogeneous equation, substitute

$$y_p = k_1 x^2 + k_2 x + k_3$$

into the left member. The result,

$$2k_1 x^2 + (2k_2 - 6k_1)x + (2k_1 - 3k_2 + 2k_3),$$

must be identically equal to $x^2 + x$, so that $2k_1 = 1$, $2k_2 - 6k_1 = 1$, $2k_1 - 3k_2 + 2k_3 = 0$. Hence $k_1 = \frac{1}{2}$, $k_2 = 2$, $k_3 = \frac{5}{2}$. The general solution is

$$y = c_1 e^x + c_2 e^{2x} + \tfrac{1}{2}x^2 + 2x + \tfrac{5}{2}.$$

EXAMPLE 2. Find the general solution of the equation

$$y'' + 4y = xe^x + \sin 3x.$$

SOLUTION. The auxiliary equation $m^2 + 4 = 0$ has roots $\pm 2i$, so that $y_c = c_1 \cos 2x + c_2 \sin 2x$. To find a particular solution, let $y_p = k_1 xe^x + k_2 e^x + k_3 \sin 3x + k_4 \cos 3x$. Then:

$$y_p' = k_1 xe^x + (k_1 + k_2)e^x + 3k_3 \cos 3x - 3k_4 \sin 3x$$
$$y_p'' = k_1 xe^x + (2k_1 + k_2)e^x - 9k_3 \sin 3x - 9k_4 \cos 3x$$
$$y_p'' + 4y_p = 5k_1 xe^x + (2k_1 + 5k_2)e^x - 5k_3 \sin 3x - 5k_4 \cos 3x$$

The right member of the third equation must be identically equal to $xe^x + \sin 3x$, so that $k_1 = \frac{1}{5}$, $k_2 = -\frac{2}{25}$, $k_3 = -\frac{1}{5}$, $k_4 = 0$. Hence $y_p = \frac{1}{5}xe^x - \frac{2}{25}e^x - \frac{1}{5}\sin 3x$. The general solution is

$$y = c_1 \cos 2x + c_2 \sin 2x + \tfrac{1}{5}xe^x - \tfrac{2}{25}e^x - \tfrac{1}{5}\sin 3x.$$

Now if $Q(x)$ contains as one of its terms a constant multiple of a term $u$ of the complementary function, or a constant multiple of $x^k u$, where $k$ is a positive integer, the procedure outlined in the preceding paragraph will fail. However, if a simple root of the auxiliary equation corresponds to the term

$u$ of the complementary function, and $Q(x)$ contains a constant multiple of $u$, it can be shown that a satisfactory form of $y_p$ will be one which contains a linear combination of $xu$ and all independent terms arising from this product by differentiation. Of course, $y_p$ must also contain a linear combination corresponding to the other terms of $Q(x)$. If $Q(x)$ contains a constant multiple of $x^k u$, where $k$ is a positive integer, the trial form of $y_p$ must contain a linear combination of $x^{k+1} u$ and all terms obtained from this product by differentiation.

It is easy to modify the above procedure for the case in which an $r$-fold root ($r > 1$) of the auxiliary equation corresponds to $u$. The complementary function then contains, besides $u$, constant multiples of $xu$, $x^2 u$, ..., $x^{r-1} u$. If $x^k u$ occurs as a term of $Q(x)$, where $k$ is a nonnegative integer, the trial integral $y_p$ must contain a linear combination of $x^{k+r} u$ and all terms arising from this product by differentiation.

It should be noted that in the cases described in the two preceding paragraphs, it is possible to delete from the trial integral all terms which occur in the complementary function. This simplification results from the fact that the substitution of such terms into the left member of (8) reduces it to zero.

EXAMPLE 3. Solve the equation $y'' + 4y = \sin 2x$.

SOLUTION. In this case the right member is a constant multiple of a term of the complementary function $y_c = c_1 \cos 2x + c_2 \sin 2x$. Hence we consider a linear combination of $x \sin 2x$ and all terms obtained from it by differentiation. When the terms in $\sin 2x$ and $\cos 2x$ have been omitted because of their occurrence in the complementary function, we have

$$y_p = x(k_1 \sin 2x + k_2 \cos 2x).$$

Then:

$$y_p' = x(2k_1 \cos 2x - 2k_2 \sin 2x) + k_1 \sin 2x + k_2 \cos 2x$$

$$y_p'' = x(-4k_1 \sin 2x - 4k_2 \cos 2x) + 4k_1 \cos 2x - 4k_2 \sin 2x$$

$$y_p'' + 4y_p = 4k_1 \cos 2x - 4k_2 \sin 2x = \sin 2x$$

It follows that $k_1 = 0$, $k_2 = -\frac{1}{4}$, so that the general solution is

$$y = c_1 \cos 2x + c_2 \sin 2x - \tfrac{1}{4}x \cos 2x.$$

**85**

EXAMPLE 4. Find the general solution of $y''' - y'' = 5x^3$.

SOLUTION. The auxiliary equation $m^3 - m^2 = 0$ has roots $0, 0, 1$, so that $y_c = c_1 + c_2x + c_3e^x$. Here $u = 1$, $r = 2$, and $k = 3$. Hence we form a linear combination of $x^5$ and all its derivatives. Omitting terms that occur in the complementary function, we have

$$y_p = k_1x^5 + k_2x^4 + k_3x^3 + k_4x^2.$$

It follows that:

$$y_p' = 5k_1x^4 + 4k_2x^3 + 3k_3x^2 + 2k_4x$$
$$y_p'' = 20k_1x^3 + 12k_2x^2 + 6k_3x + 2k_4$$
$$y_p''' = 60k_1x^2 + 24k_2x + 6k_3$$
$$y_p''' - y_p'' = -20k_1x^3 + (60k_1 - 12k_2)x^2 + (24k_2 - 6k_3)x$$
$$+ (6k_3 - 2k_4)$$

Since this polynomial must equal $5x^3$ identically, the coefficients $k_1$, $k_2$, $k_3$, $k_4$ must satisfy the conditions $-20k_1 = 5$, $60k_1 - 12k_2 = 0$, $24k_2 - 6k_3 = 0$, $6k_3 - 2k_4 = 0$, so that $k_1 = -\frac{1}{4}$, $k_2 = -\frac{5}{4}$, $k_3 = -5$, $k_4 = -15$. The general solution of the differential equation is

$$y = c_1 + c_2x + c_3e^x - x^2(\tfrac{1}{4}x^3 + \tfrac{5}{4}x^2 + 5x + 15).$$

## EXERCISE 19

Find the general solution of each of the equations given in Problems 1–26.

1. $y'' - 4y = 3\cos x$
2. $y'' + y = \sin 2x$
3. $y'' + y' - 2y = e^x$
4. $y'' + 3y' + 2y = e^{-2x}$
5. $y'' + y' + y = \sin x$
6. $y'' + y' + y = x^2$
7. $y'' + 3y' + 2y = xe^{-x}$
8. $y^{(4)} - y = e^x$
9. $y'' - 4y = x + e^{2x}$
10. $y'' - 9y = e^{3x} + \sin 3x$
11. $y'' - y' - 6y = x^3$
12. $y'' - 3y' + 3y = xe^x$
13. $y'' + 4y = x\sin x$

14. $y''' - 4y'' = x^2 + 8$

15. $y'' + y' + y = e^x \sin 3x$

16. $y''' - 3y'' + 4y' - 12y = x + e^{2x}$

17. $y''' - 4y'' + y' - 4y = e^{4x} \sin x$

18. $y'' + 4y' + 4y = x^3 e^{2x}$

19. $y''' - 2y'' + y' - 2y = xe^{2x}$

20. $y^{(4)} + 2n^2 y'' + n^4 y = \sin kx \quad (n \neq k)$

21. $y'' + 2ny' + n^2 y = 5 \cos 6x$

22. $y'' + 9y = (1 + \sin 3x) \cos 2x$

23. $y'' + 4y' + 5y = 2x - e^{-4x} + \sin 2x$

24. $y''' + 2y'' = (2x^2 + x)e^{-2x} + 5 \cos 3x$

25. $y'' + 4y = 8 \sin^2 x$

26. $y^{(4)} + 4y = 5e^{2x} \sin 3x$

For each of the following equations find the particular solution satisfying the given initial condition.

27. $y'' - 5y' - 6y = e^{3x}$; $x_0 = 0$, $y_0 = 2$, $y_0' = 1$

28. $y'' + 4y = 12 \cos^2 x$; $x_0 = \dfrac{\pi}{2}$, $y_0 - 0$, $y_0' = \dfrac{\pi}{2}$

29. $y'' - 3y' + 2y = xe^{-x}$; $x_0 = 0$, $y_0 = \frac{1}{9}$, $y_0' = 0$

30. $y'' + y = e^x \sin x$; $x_0 = 0$, $y_0 = 3$, $y_0' = 2$

31. $2y'' + y' = 8 \sin 2x + e^{-x}$; $x_0 = 0$, $y_0 = 1$, $y_0' = 0$

32. $y'' + y = 3x \sin x$; $x_0 = 0$, $y_0 = 2$, $y_0' = 1$

33. $2y'' + 5y' - 3y = \sin x - 8x$; $x_0 = 0$, $y_0 = \frac{1}{2}$, $y_0' = \frac{1}{2}$

34. $8y'' - y = xe^{-\frac{x}{2}}$; $x_0 = 0$, $y_0 = 3$, $y_0' = 5$

**34. Variation of parameters.** The method to be described in this article is due to Lagrange.* It furnishes a technique for finding a particular integral of the general nonhomogeneous equation (1), provided the complementary function of that equation is known. The coefficients in (1) need not be constants.

Let $y_c = c_1 u_1 + c_2 u_2 + \cdots + c_n u_n$ be the complementary func-

---

* Joseph Louis Lagrange (1736–1813). One of the greatest mathematicians of modern times, Lagrange contributed much to the development of the theory of both ordinary and partial differential equations.

tion of equation (1). We replace the constants $c_i$ by functions $v_i(x)$ which will be determined so as to make

$$(9) \qquad y = v_1 u_1 + v_2 u_2 + \cdots + v_n u_n$$

a particular integral of (1). The first derivative of (9) is

$$(10) \qquad y' = (v_1 u_1' + v_2 u_2' + \cdots + v_n u_n')$$
$$+ (v_1' u_1 + v_2' u_2 + \cdots + v_n' u_n).$$

It is clear that (10) and its successive derivatives can be simplified by imposing the condition that

$$v_1' u_1 + v_2' u_2 + \cdots + v_n' u_n = 0.$$

Then $\qquad y'' = (v_1 u_1'' + v_2 u_2'' + \cdots + v_n u_n'')$
$$+ (v_1' u_1' + v_2' u_2' + \cdots + v_n' u_n').$$

Further simplification is obtained by requiring that

$$v_1' u_1' + v_2' u_2' + \cdots + v_n' u_n' = 0.$$

If the first $n - 1$ derivatives of (9) are treated similarly, the derivative of order $n - 1$ will be

$$y^{(n-1)} = v_1 u_1^{(n-1)} + v_2 u_2^{(n-1)} + \cdots + v_n u_n^{(n-1)}.$$

A final differentiation gives

$$y^{(n)} = (v_1 u_1^{(n)} + v_2 u_2^{(n)} + \cdots + v_n u_n^{(n)})$$
$$+ (v_1' u_1^{(n-1)} + v_2' u_2^{(n-1)} + \cdots + v_n' u_n^{(n-1)}).$$

Upon substitution of $y$, $y'$, $y''$, $\ldots$, $y^{(n)}$ into the equation (1), one obtains

$$P_0(x)(v_1' u_1^{(n-1)} + v_2' u_2^{(n-1)} + \cdots + v_n' u_n^{(n-1)}) = Q(x),$$

since the functions $u_i(x)$ are solutions of the homogeneous equation (2).

The conditions thus imposed upon the functions $v_i'(x)$ are:

$$(11) \qquad \begin{aligned} v_1' u_1 \quad &+ v_2' u_2 \quad + \cdots + v_n' u_n \quad = 0 \\ v_1' u_1' \quad &+ v_2' u_2' \quad + \cdots + v_n' u_n' \quad = 0 \\ &\cdots \cdots \cdots \cdots \cdots \cdots \\ v_1' u_1^{(n-2)} &+ v_2' u_2^{(n-2)} + \cdots + v_n' u_n^{(n-2)} = 0 \\ v_1' u_1^{(n-1)} &+ v_2' u_2^{(n-1)} + \cdots + v_n' u_n^{(n-1)} = \frac{Q(x)}{P_0(x)} \end{aligned}$$

These are $n$ linear equations for the determination of the functions $v_i'(x)$. They determine these functions uniquely, since the determinant of the coefficients, which is the Wronskian of the functions $u_i(x)$, is different from zero. When the system (11) has been solved for the functions $v_i'(x)$, the functions $v_i(x)$ are then found by indefinite integration.

EXAMPLE 1. Find the general solution of the equation

$$y'' + y = \cos 2x.$$

SOLUTION. Since the complementary function is

$$y_c = c_1 \cos x + c_2 \sin x,$$

we set $y = v_1 \cos x + v_2 \sin x$. Then

$$y' = (- v_1 \sin x + v_2 \cos x) + (v_1' \cos x + v_2' \sin x),$$

and the first condition to be imposed is

(a) $$v_1' \cos x + v_2' \sin x = 0.$$

The second derivative of $y$ is then

$$y'' = (- v_1 \cos x - v_2 \sin x) + (- v_1' \sin x + v_2' \cos x),$$

which leads to the second condition,

(b) $$- v_1' \sin x + v_2' \cos x = \cos 2x.$$

Equations (a) and (b) have the solution

$$v_1' = - \cos 2x \sin x, \qquad v_2' = \cos 2x \cos x,$$

so that:

$$v_1 = - \tfrac{1}{2} \cos x + \tfrac{1}{6} \cos 3x, \qquad v_2 = \tfrac{1}{2} \sin x + \tfrac{1}{6} \sin 3x$$

Here the constants of integration have been taken to be zero, since we do not seek the most general expressions for $v_1$ and $v_2$. The general solution of the differential equation is:

$$y = c_1 \cos x + c_2 \sin x + \cos x(- \tfrac{1}{2} \cos x + \tfrac{1}{6} \cos 3x)$$
$$+ \sin x(\tfrac{1}{2} \sin x + \tfrac{1}{6} \sin 3x)$$
$$y = c_1 \cos x + c_2 \sin x - \tfrac{1}{3} \cos 2x$$

Example 1 could also have been solved by the method of undetermined coefficients. Now we consider one which could not have been so solved.

EXAMPLE 2. Find the general solution of $y'' + y = \sec^3 x$.

SOLUTION. As in Example 1 the complementary function is $y_c = c_1 \cos x + c_2 \sin x$, so again we set $y = v_1 \cos x + v_2 \sin x$. If we differentiate twice and at each step impose the customary condition on the terms which involve $v_1'$ and $v_2'$, we have:

$$v_1' \cos x + v_2' \sin x = 0$$
$$- v_1' \sin x + v_2' \cos x = \sec^3 x$$

This system of equations has the solution

$$v_1' = - \tan x \sec^2 x, \qquad v_2' = \sec^2 x,$$

so that $\qquad v_1 = - \tfrac{1}{2} \tan^2 x, \qquad v_2 = \tan x,$

and the general solution of the original differential equation is

$$y = c_1 \cos x + c_2 \sin x + \tfrac{1}{2} \tan x \sin x.$$

## EXERCISE 20

Find the general solution of each of the following equations. Use the method of variation of parameters to find a particular solution in Problems 1–24.

1. $y'' + y = \sec x$
2. $y'' + 4y' + 4y = e^x$
3. $y'' + y = x^2$
4. $y'' - 2y' + y = e^{2x}$
5. $y'' + y = 4 \sin 2x$
6. $y'' + 4y = 2(x - \sin 2x)$
7. $y'' - y = 3x + 5e^x$
8. $y'' + 9y = e^x + \sin 4x$
9. $y''' + 3y'' - 4y' = \cos 2x$
10. $y''' + 4y'' - 5y' = e^{3x}$
11. $y'' + y = \tan x$
12. $y'' + a^2 y = \sec ax$
13. $y''' - 2y'' + y' = e^{2x}$
14. $y^{(4)} - 2y''' + y'' = x^2$
15. $y''' - 3y'' - 4y' = e^{2x} + \sin x$
16. $y'' - 2y' + y = \dfrac{e^x}{(1 - x)^2}$

17. $y'' - 3y' + 2y = \sin e^{-x}$
18. $y'' + 4y = \sec x \tan x$
19. $y'' - 2y = e^{-x} \sin 2x$
20. $y'' + 9y = \sec x \csc x$
21. $y'' + 9y = \csc 2x$

22. $9y'' + y = \tan^2 \dfrac{x}{3}$

23. $y''' + y' = \tan x$

24. $4y'' - 4y' + y = e^{\frac{x}{2}} \ln x$

25. Use the method of variation of parameters to obtain the solution of the equation $\dfrac{dy}{dx} + Py = Q$ in the form

$$y = e^{-\int P\, dx} \left[ \int Q e^{\int P\, dx}\, dx + C \right],$$

where $P$ and $Q$ are functions of $x$.

**35. Operators.** The process of taking the derivative $\dfrac{du}{dx}$ of a function $u(x)$ may be regarded as applying an *operator* $D = \dfrac{d}{dx}$ to the function $u$. Similarly, $D^2$, $D^3$, ..., $D^n$ may be defined as the operators which, when applied to $u$, produce $\dfrac{d^2u}{dx^2}$, $\dfrac{d^3u}{dx^3}$, ..., $\dfrac{d^nu}{dx^n}$. Such operators have many simple properties which follow from the familiar theorems of calculus concerning differentiation, by virtue of which these operators obey laws much like the ordinary laws of algebra.

We shall understand that for any positive integers $m$, $n$ and for any function $u$ and any constant $a$:

$$(D^m + D^n)u = D^m u + D^n u$$
$$(D^m \cdot D^n)u = D^m(D^n u)$$
$$(aD^m)u = a(D^m u)$$
$$D^0 u = u$$
$$(D^m + a)u = (D^m + aD^0)u$$
$$= D^m u + au$$

As a consequence of these definitions the operators $aD^m$, $D^m + D^n$, and $D^m \cdot D^n$ (which will for convenience be written $D^m D^n$) are seen to have the following properties.

(12) $\qquad D^m + D^n = D^n + D^m$

(13) $\qquad (D^m + D^n) + D^p = D^m + (D^n + D^p)$

(14) $\qquad D^m D^n = D^n D^m = D^{m+n}$

(15) $\qquad D^m(D^n D^p) = (D^m D^n)D^p = D^{m+n+p}$

(16) $\qquad D^m(D^n + D^p) = D^m D^n + D^m D^p$

The formulas (12)–(16) are valid for all nonnegative integers $m$, $n$, $p$. The extension to negative integers can be made if we define $D^{-1}u$ to be an expression $v$ such that $Dv = u$, so that $D^{-1}u = \int u \, dx$. Further, we define $D^{-2}u$ to be $D^{-1}(D^{-1}u)$, $D^{-3}u$ to be $D^{-1}(D^{-2}u)$, etc. It follows that $D^{-m}u$ is equivalent to a succession of $m$ integrations. An alternative notation for $D^{-m}u$ is $\dfrac{1}{D^m} u$.

More generally, if in any polynomial

$$f(z) = a_0 z^n + a_1 z^{n-1} + \cdots + a_n$$

we replace each power $z^k$ by the operator $D^k$, the corresponding operator $f(D)$ will be called a *polynomial operator* in $D$. From the laws (12)–(16), it follows that if $f(D) = g(D)h(D)$, then $f(D)u = g(D)[h(D)u]$.

The *inverse operator* $f^{-1}(D)$, or $\dfrac{1}{f(D)}$, is defined as an operator such that:

$$f(D) \left[ f^{-1}(D)u \right] = u$$

EXAMPLE 1. Apply the operator $D^2 - 3D + 2$ to the function $e^{3x}$.

SOLUTION. 
$$\begin{aligned}
(D^2 - 3D + 2)e^{3x} &= (D - 2)(D - 1)e^{3x} \\
&= (D - 2)(3e^{3x} - e^{3x}) \\
&= (D - 2)(2e^{3x}) \\
&= 6e^{3x} - 4e^{3x} \\
&= 2e^{3x}
\end{aligned}$$

Alternatively it can be verified that:

$$\begin{aligned}
(D^2 - 3D + 2)e^{3x} &= D^2 e^{3x} - 3De^{3x} + 2e^{3x} \\
&= 2e^{3x}
\end{aligned}$$

EXAMPLE 2. Find $y = D^{-3}(x^2)$

SOLUTION. $y = D^{-3}(x^2)$

$$= D^{-2}[D^{-1}(x^2)] = D^{-2}\left(\frac{x^3}{3} + c_1\right)$$

$$= D^{-1}\left[D^{-1}\left(\frac{x^3}{3} + c_1\right)\right] = D^{-1}\left(\frac{x^4}{12} + c_1 x + c_2\right)$$

$$= \frac{x^5}{60} + c_1 \frac{x^2}{2} + c_2 x + c_3$$

EXAMPLE 3. If $a$ is a constant, find $y = (D - a)^{-1}x^2$.
SOLUTION. $(D - a)y = (D - a)[(D - a)^{-1}x^2] = x^2$, or

$$\frac{dy}{dx} - ay = x^2.$$

The solution of this equation is

$$y = -\frac{x^2}{a} - \frac{2x}{a^2} - \frac{2}{a^3} + ce^{ax}.$$

The following theorem greatly facilitates the manipulation of operators in some cases. Its application is known as the *exponential shift*.

*Theorem.* If $f(D)$ is a polynomial operator, then for any constant $a$ and any function $u(x)$

(17) $$f(D)(ue^{-ax}) = e^{-ax}f(D - a)u.$$

In order to prove the theorem it is sufficient to show that $D^n(ue^{-ax}) = e^{-ax}(D - a)^n u$. It is first verified that the theorem is valid for $n = 0$ and $n = 1$:

$$D^0(ue^{-ax}) = ue^{-ax} = e^{-ax}(D - a)^0 u$$
$$D(ue^{-ax}) = -aue^{-ax} + u'e^{-ax}$$
$$= e^{-ax}(u' - au)$$
$$= e^{-ax}(D - a)u$$

Next suppose that (17) holds for a positive integer $n = k$. That is, assume that

$$D^k(ue^{-ax}) = e^{-ax}(D - a)^k u.$$

93

Then by differentiation it follows that:

$$\begin{aligned}
D^{k+1}(ue^{-ax}) &= D[D^k(ue^{-ax})] \\
&= D[e^{-ax}(D-a)^k u] \\
&= e^{-ax}D(D-a)^k u - ae^{-ax}(D-a)^k u \\
&= e^{-ax}(D-a)^{k+1}u
\end{aligned}$$

This means that the formula also holds for $n = k+1$, and hence the theorem has been proved.

When the exponential shift is applied to the case

$$f(D) = (D-a)^n,$$

the following corollary results.

*Corollary 1.* $(D-a)^n(ue^{ax}) = e^{ax}D^n u$.

For any constant $a$ and any nonnegative integer $k$ the operator $(D+a)^k$ when applied to the function $u(x) = 1$ yields $a^k$. This is readily verified by expanding $(D+a)^k$ by means of the binomial theorem. Hence:

$$\begin{aligned}
f(D+a)(1) &= [a_0(D+a)^n + a_1(D+a)^{n-1} + \cdots + a_n](1) \\
&= a_0 a^n + a_1 a^{n-1} + \cdots + a_n \\
&= f(a)
\end{aligned}$$

More generally, an application of (17) to the constant function $u = A$ establishes the following corollary.

*Corollary 2.* If $f(D)$ is a polynomial operator and $A$, $a$ are any constants, then

$$f(D)(Ae^{ax}) = Ae^{ax}f(a).$$

*Corollary 3.* If $a$ is any constant and $v$ is any function,

$$(18) \qquad \frac{1}{f(D)}\, ve^{ax} = e^{ax}\,\frac{1}{f(D+a)}\, v.$$

This corollary can be verified by operating on both members with $f(D)$:

$$f(D)\left[\frac{1}{f(D)}\, ve^{ax}\right] = ve^{ax} = f(D)\left[e^{ax}\,\frac{1}{f(D+a)}\, v\right]$$

94

The exponential shift (17) is now applied to the right member:

$$f(D) \left[ e^{ax} \frac{1}{f(D+a)} v \right] = e^{ax} f(D+a) \left[ \frac{1}{f(D+a)} v \right] = v e^{ax}$$

Hence formula (18) is valid.

EXAMPLE 4. Evaluate $(D^2 + 3D + 2)(x^3 e^{-x})$.
SOLUTION. Using the exponential shift, we have:

$$\begin{aligned}
(D^2 + 3D + 2)(x^3 e^{-x}) &= e^{-x}[(D-1)^2 + 3(D-1) + 2]x^3 \\
&= e^{-x}(D^2 + D)x^3 \\
&= e^{-x}(6x + 3x^2) \\
&= 3x(x+2)e^{-x}
\end{aligned}$$

EXAMPLE 5. Find $(D-2)^3(e^{2x} \sin 2x)$.
SOLUTION. Applying Corollary 1, we have:

$$\begin{aligned}
(D-2)^3(e^{2x} \sin 2x) &= e^{2x} D^3 (\sin 2x) \\
&= -8e^{2x} \cos 2x
\end{aligned}$$

EXAMPLE 6. Find $(D^3 - 5D + 9)e^{7x}$.
SOLUTION. From Corollary 2:

$$\begin{aligned}
(D^3 - 5D + 9)e^{-7x} &= e^{-7x}[(-7)^3 - 5(-7, +9] \\
&= -299e^{-7x}
\end{aligned}$$

## EXERCISE 21

Evaluate each of the expressions in Problems 1–16.

1. $(D^2 - 6D + 5) \cos 5x$
2. $(D^3 - 3D^2 + 3D - 1)e^{4x}$
3. $(D^2 - 6D + 9)(e^{3x} \sec x)$
4. $(4D^4 - 3D^2) \sin 5x$
5. $(D - a)(x^2 e^{-ax})$
6. $(D - 1)^3(x \sin 3x)$
7. $(D + 1)^3(x^5 + x)$
8. $(D^2 - a^2) \cos kx$
9. $D^{-1}(x^3)$
10. $D^{-2}(3x^4)$

11. $D^{-3}(7x)$

12. $D^{-2}(x^6)$

13. $(aD + b)^{-1}(e^{2x})$

14. $(D - 2)^{-2}(e^{3x})$

15. $(2D - 1)^{-1} \cos 2x$

16. $(D - b)^{-3}(5)$

Use the theorem of Article 35 to perform each of the operations in Problems 17–22.

17. $(D^2 + 5D + 6)(e^{-3x} \cos x)$

18. $(9D^2 + 8D - 17)(e^{2x} \sin x)$

19. $(D^3 + 1)(x^5 e^{-x})$

20. $(D - 3)^2(e^{3x} \tan 4x)$

21. $(D^2 + D)(e^{5x} \sec x)$

22. $(D^2 - 5D + 10)(e^{5x} \ln 2x)$

Use Corollary 1 of Article 35 to perform each of the operations in Problems 23–28.

23. $(D - 1)^3(e^x \cos x)$

24. $(D + 1)(e^{-x} \cos x)$

25. $(D + 2)^2(e^{-2x} \tan x)$

26. $(D - 2)^3(e^{2x} \ln 3x)$

27. $(D - 3)^4(e^{3x} \sin 2x)$

28. $(D - 1)^2(e^x \text{ Arc } \sin x)$

Use Corollary 2 of Article 35 to perform each of the following operations.

29. $(D^4 + 5D + 6)e^{5x}$

30. $(D - a)^2 e^{ax}$

31. $(D + a)^2 e^{-ax}$

32. $(D - 1)(D - 2)(D + 1)e^{-4x}$

33. $(D^2 + 7D + 11)e^{12x}$

34. $\dfrac{(D^2 - D + 1)e^{11x}}{(D^2 + D - 2)e^{-5x}}$

35. $[(D + a)e^{bx}][(D + b)e^{ax}]$

36. $\dfrac{[(D + a)e^{ax}][(D + b)e^{bx}]}{(D + c)e^{cx}}$

**36. Solution of the nonhomogeneous equation by operators.** Let the equation (8) be written in the form

(19) $$(D - a_1)(D - a_2) \ldots (D - a_n)y = Q(x)$$

where $a_1, a_2, \ldots, a_n$ are the roots, not necessarily distinct, of the auxiliary equation (7). Put

$$u_1 = (D - a_2)(D - a_3) \ldots (D - a_n)y,$$

so that the equation (19) becomes

$$(D - a_1)u_1 = Q(x).$$

This is a first-order linear equation in the unknown function $u_1$, for which a particular integral is readily found. Next we put

$$u_2 = (D - a_3)(D - a_4) \ldots (D - a_n)y$$

and write

$$(D - a_2)u_2 = u_1$$

where $u_1$ is now a known function of $x$, and solve this first-order equation for $u_2$.

Continuing in this way, we have a sequence of linear first-order equations

(20) $$(D - a_i)u_i = u_{i-1} \qquad (i = 1, 2, \ldots, n),$$

where

$$u_0 = Q(x), \ u_n = y, \ u_i = (D - a_{i+1})(D - a_{i+2}) \ldots (D - a_n)y$$

$$(i = 1, 2, \ldots, n - 1)$$

and where, for each value of $i$, $u_{i-1}$ is a known function of $x$. After $n - 1$ such steps we obtain the final first-order differential equation of the sequence (20), namely

$$(D - a_n)y = u_{n-1},$$

a solution of which is a particular integral of (19).

The sequential integration of the equations (20) is obviously a routine process. Each such equation has the integrating factor $e^{a_i x}$ and the solution

$$u_i = e^{a_i x} \int e^{-a_i x} u_{i-1}(x) \ dx \qquad (i = 1, 2, \ldots, n).$$

EXAMPLE 1. Find a particular solution of the differential equation $y'' - 2y' = \cos x$.

SOLUTION. The equation may be written as $D(D - 2)y = \cos x$. If we set $u_1 = (D - 2)y$, we are able to rewrite the original differential equation in the form $Du_1 = \cos x$, for which a particular solution is $u_1 = \int \cos x \, dx = \sin x$. Substituting $u_1 = \sin x$ into the equation $u_1 = (D - 2)y$, we next solve this equation, noting that an integrating factor is $e^{-2x}$. A particular solution is thus found to be:

$$y = e^{2x} \int e^{-2x} \sin x \, dx = e^{2x}[- \tfrac{1}{5}e^{-2x}(\cos x + 2 \sin x)]$$
$$= - \tfrac{1}{5}(\cos x + 2 \sin x)$$

EXAMPLE 2. Find the general solution of the differential equation $(D^3 + 2D^2 - D - 2)y = e^{-x}$.

SOLUTION. We write the differential equation in the form

$$(D - 1)(D + 1)(D + 2)y = e^{-x}.$$

We set $u_1 = (D + 1)(D + 2)y$ and have the first-order equation $(D - 1)u_1 = e^{-x}$, for which $e^{-x}$ is an integrating factor and a particular solution is

$$u_1 = e^x \int e^{-2x} \, dx = - \tfrac{1}{2}e^{-x}.$$

Next we set $u_2 = (D + 2)y$ and obtain the first-order equation $(D + 1)u_2 = u_1 = - \tfrac{1}{2}e^{-x}$. An integrating factor is $e^x$ and a particular solution is

$$u_2 = e^{-x} \int - \tfrac{1}{2} \, dx = - \tfrac{1}{2}xe^{-x}.$$

The final first-order equation of the sequence is therefore $(D + 2)y = - \tfrac{1}{2}xe^{-x}$, for which we have the integrating factor $e^{2x}$ and the particular solution:

$$y_p = e^{-2x} \int e^{2x}(- \tfrac{1}{2}xe^{-x}) \, dx$$
$$= - \tfrac{1}{2}e^{-2x} \int xe^x \, dx = - \tfrac{1}{2}(x - 1)e^{-x}$$

This is a particular integral of the original differential equation.

The general solution is

$$y = c_1 e^x + c_2 e^{-x} + c_3 e^{-2x} - \tfrac{1}{2}(x-1)e^{-x}.$$

We note that one of the terms of the particular integral may be absorbed into the second term of the complementary function, and therefore write the general solution as

$$y = c_1 e^x + c_2 e^{-x} + c_3 e^{-2x} - \tfrac{1}{2}xe^{-x}.$$

EXAMPLE 3.  Find a particular solution of the equation

$$(D+1)^3 y = xe^{-x}.$$

SOLUTION.  It will be noticed that at each stage of the solution the integrating factor is $e^x$, which reduces each integrand function to a power of $x$.

$$u_1 = (D+1)^2 y, \ (D+1)u_1 = xe^{-x}, \ u_1 = e^{-x}\int x\,dx = \tfrac{1}{2}x^2 e^{-x};$$

$$u_2 = (D+1)y, \ (D+1)u_2 = \tfrac{1}{2}x^2 e^{-x}, \ u_2 = e^{-x}\int \tfrac{1}{2}x^2\,dx = \tfrac{1}{6}x^3 e^{-x};$$

$$u_3 = y, \ (D+1)y = \tfrac{1}{6}x^3 e^{-x}, \ y = e^{-x}\int \tfrac{1}{6}x^3\,dx = \tfrac{1}{24}x^4 e^{-x}.$$

## EXERCISE 22

Find the general solution of each of the following equations.

1. $(D^2 - 6D + 9)y = e^{3x}$
2. $(D^2 + 4D + 4)y = e^{-2x}$
3. $(D^3 - 3D^2 + 3D - 1)y = e^x$
4. $(D - 2)^3 y = e^x$
5. $(D - 2)(D - 3)y = x^2$
6. $(D + 2)(D + 3)y = xe^{2x}$
7. $(D^3 + 6D^2 + 12D + 8)y = x$
8. $(D^2 + 3D + 2)y = \sin x$
9. $(D^2 - 1)y = \cos x$
10. $(D - 1)^2(D + 1)y = x^2 e^x$
11. $(D + 2)^2(D - 3)y = xe^{-2x}$
12. $(D + 1)D^3 y = \cos 2x$
13. $(D + 1)^2 y = \dfrac{e^{-x}}{x}$
14. $(D - 1)^2 y = e^x \ln x$
15. $(D + 1)^2(D - 1)^3 y = x$
16. $(D^2 - 4)y = e^{-2x}\sin^2 x$
17. $(D + 1)^2 y = x \sin x$
18. $(D - 1)^2 y = x \cos x$
19. $(D - a_1)(D - a_2)(D - a_3)y = Q(x)$
20. $(D - a_1)(D - a_2) \ldots (D - a_n)y = Q(x)$

## 37. Inverse operators applied to special types of Q(x).

*A*. $Q(x) = ke^{ax}$. Whenever $Q$ is written as a sum of terms of the type $ke^{ax}$, where $a$ is any real or complex number, the following formulas can be used to simplify the work of finding a particular integral.

$$(21) \qquad \frac{1}{f(D)} ke^{ax} = \frac{ke^{ax}}{f(a)}, \quad f(a) \neq 0$$

$$(22) \qquad \frac{1}{f(D)} k = \frac{k}{f(0)}, \quad f(0) \neq 0$$

$$(23) \qquad \frac{1}{(D-a)^r g(D)} ke^{ax} = \frac{kx^r e^{ax}}{r! g(a)}, \quad g(a) \neq 0$$

Formula (21) is a consequence of Corollary 2 of Article 35. To see this, operate on both members of (21) with $f(D)$:

$$f(D) \frac{1}{f(D)} ke^{ax} = ke^{ax} = f(D) \left[ \frac{ke^{ax}}{f(a)} \right]$$

Then by Corollary 2, with $A = \dfrac{k}{f(a)}$:

$$f(D) \left[ \frac{ke^{ax}}{f(a)} \right] = \frac{ke^{ax}}{f(a)} f(a) = ke^{ax}$$

Formula (22) is the special case of (21) with $a = 0$.

To verify (23) define $f(D) = (D - a)^r g(D)$. Then by (18), with $v = k$:

$$\frac{1}{(D-a)^r g(D)} ke^{ax} = \frac{1}{f(D)} ke^{ax} = e^{ax} \frac{1}{f(D+a)} k$$

But $f(D + a) = D^r g(D + a)$ and hence by (22):

$$\frac{1}{f(D+a)} k = \frac{1}{D^r g(D+a)} k = \frac{1}{D^r} \frac{k}{g(a)}$$

Since $D^{-r} \left[ \dfrac{k}{g(a)} \right] = \dfrac{kx^r}{r! g(a)}$, the validity of (23) is established.

EXAMPLE 1. Find a particular solution of the equation

$$y'' + 2y' - 8y = 7e^{4x}.$$

SOLUTION. The equation may be written

$$(D^2 + 2D - 8)y = 7e^{4x}.$$

Hence a particular integral must take the form

$$y_p = \frac{1}{D^2 + 2D - 8}\,(7e^{4x}).$$

Applying (21) with $a = 4$, $k = 7$, we obtain

$$y_p = \tfrac{7}{16}e^{4x}.$$

**B.** $Q(x) = \sin bx$; $Q(x) = \cos bx$. In the discussion of this portion of Article 37 it will be assumed that $b$ is real. From the exponential forms of $\sin bx$ and $\cos bx$ and from the formulas (21) and (23), it is evident that we shall be concerned with the possibility that $ib$ is a root of $f(D) = 0$. We suppose that $ib$ is an $r$-fold root of $f(D) = 0$. It follows that $-ib$ is also an $r$-fold root and we may write $f(D) = (D^2 + b^2)^r g(D)$, where $g(ib) \neq 0$. It will be helpful to separate those terms of the polynomial $g(D)$ which are of even degree from those of odd degree, expressing $g(D)$ in the form $g_1(D^2) + Dg_2(D^2)$. Thus the complex number $g(ib) = g_1(-b^2) + ibg_2(-b^2)$ has $g_1(-b^2)$ and $bg_2(-b^2)$ as its real and pure imaginary components, respectively. The square of the modulus of $g(ib)$ is:

$$
\begin{aligned}
\mid g(ib) \mid^2 &= g(ib) \cdot g(-ib) \\
&= [g_1(-b^2) + ibg_2(-b^2)][g_1(-b^2) - ibg_2(-b^2)] \\
&= [g_1(-b^2)]^2 + b^2[g_2(-b^2)]^2
\end{aligned}
$$

We also adopt the following abbreviations:

$$G_1(-b^2) = g_1(-b^2)/\mid g(ib) \mid^2, \quad G_2(-b^2) = g_2(-b^2)/\mid g(ib) \mid^2$$

From formula (23) we have

$$
\begin{aligned}
y_{p,r} &= \frac{1}{f(D)}\,\sin bx = \frac{1}{(D - ib)^r(D + ib)^r g(D)}\left(\frac{e^{ibx} - e^{-ibx}}{2i}\right) \\
&= \frac{x^r}{2i \cdot r!}\left[\frac{e^{ibx}}{(2ib)^r g(ib)} - \frac{e^{-ibx}}{(-2ib)^r g(-ib)}\right] \\
&= \frac{x^r}{2i \cdot r!(2b)^r \cdot i^r}\left[\frac{g(-ib)e^{ibx} - (-1)^r g(ib)e^{-ibx}}{\mid g(ib) \mid^2}\right] \\
&= \frac{x^r}{2i \cdot r!(2b)^r \cdot i^r}\left\{\frac{[g_1(-b^2) - ibg_2(-b^2)]e^{ibx}}{\mid g(ib) \mid^2}\right. \\
&\qquad\qquad \left. - (-1)^r\frac{[g_1(-b^2) + ibg_2(-b^2)]e^{-ibx}}{\mid g(ib) \mid^2}\right\}.
\end{aligned}
$$

**101**

In this formula for the particular solution $y_{p,r}$, the presence of the denominator factor $i^r$ and of the coefficient $-(-1)^r$ make it necessary to discuss separately the cases in which $r = 2s$ and $r = 2s + 1$, where $s$ is any positive integer or zero. If $r = 2s$, $y_{p,r}$ takes the form

$$y_{p,2s} = \frac{(-1)^s x^{2s}}{(2s)!(2b)^{2s}} \left[ G_1(-b^2) \left( \frac{e^{ibx} - e^{-ibx}}{2i} \right) \right.$$

$$\left. - bG_2(-b^2) \left( \frac{e^{ibx} + e^{-ibx}}{2} \right) \right]$$

(24a)    $$y_{p,2s} = \frac{(-1)^s x^{2s}}{(2s)!(2b)^{2s}} [G_1(-b^2) \sin bx - bG_2(-b^2) \cos bx].$$

In the case $r = 2s + 1$, we have

$$y_{p,2s+1} = \frac{(-1)^{s+1} x^{2s+1}}{(2s+1)!(2b)^{2s+1}} \left[ G_1(-b^2) \left( \frac{e^{ibx} + e^{-ibx}}{2} \right) \right.$$

$$\left. + bG_2(-b^2) \left( \frac{e^{ibx} - e^{-ibx}}{2i} \right) \right]$$

(24b)    $$y_{p,2s+1} = \frac{(-1)^{s+1} x^{2s+1}}{(2s+1)!(2b)^{2s+1}} [G_1(-b^2) \cos bx$$

$$+ bG_2(-b^2) \sin bx].$$

Corresponding formulas for $f^{-1}(D) \cos bx$ are derived similarly. They are

(24c)    $$y_{p,2s} = \frac{(-1)^s x^{2s}}{(2s)!(2b)^{2s}} [G_1(-b^2) \cos bx + bG_2(-b^2) \sin bx]$$

(24d)    $$y_{p,2s+1} = \frac{(-1)^s x^{2s+1}}{(2s+1)!(2b)^{2s+1}} [G_1(-b^2) \sin bx$$

$$- bG_2(-b^2) \cos bx].$$

The bracketed expressions of the four formulas (24a), (24b), (24c), and (24d) possess a noteworthy similarity. Recalling the derivative relations between the two trigonometric functions involved, we are led to define $G(D)$ to be the linear operator $G_1(-b^2) - G_2(-b^2)D$. We are thus able to put the formulas (24a)–(24d) into the following remarkably simple forms.

For $Q(x) = \sin bx$:

(25a) $$y_{p,2s} = \frac{(-1)^s x^{2s}}{(2s)!(2b)^{2s}} G(D) \sin bx$$

(25b) $$y_{p,2s+1} = \frac{(-1)^{s+1} x^{2s+1}}{(2s+1)!(2b)^{2s+1}} G(D) \cos bx$$

For $Q(x) = \cos bx$:

(25c) $$y_{p,2s} = \frac{(-1)^s x^{2s}}{(2s)!(2b)^{2s}} G(D) \cos bx$$

(25d) $$y_{p,2s+1} = \frac{(-1)^s x^{2s+1}}{(2s+1)!(2b)^{2s+1}} G(D) \sin bx$$

To show how the linear operator $G(D)$ may be derived formally from the inverse operator $1/g(D)$, we write the inverse operator as follows:

$$\frac{1}{g(D)} = \frac{1}{g_1(D^2) + Dg_2(D^2)}$$
$$= \frac{g_1(D^2) - Dg_2(D^2)}{[g_1(D^2)]^2 - D^2[g_2(D^2)]^2}$$

If now in each even power of $D$ we put $D = ib$ but leave the first power of $D$ as it is, the fractional operator takes the form

$$\frac{g_1(-b^2) - g_2(-b^2)D}{[g_1(-b^2)]^2 + b^2[g_2(-b^2)]^2} = G_1(-b^2) - G_2(-b^2)D = G(D).$$

The student will probably have more frequent contact with the simpler cases in which $ib$ is not a root of the equation $f(D) = 0$. It will be useful, therefore, to write separately the special formulas which are adapted to such contacts. These special formulas are obtained by setting $s = 0$ in formulas (25a) and (25c):

(26a) $$y_p = f^{-1}(D) \sin bx = F(D) \sin bx$$

(26c) $$y_p = f^{-1}(D) \cos bx = F(D) \cos bx,$$

where $F(D)$ bears the same relation to $f^{-1}(D)$ as $G(D)$ does to $g^{-1}(D)$.

EXAMPLE 2. Using one of the formulas (25), find the general solution of the equation

$$(D^2 + 9)^2(D^3 + 4D^2 + D - 6)y = \sin 3x.$$

SOLUTION. First we verify that $3i$ is a zero of multiplicity 2 of $(D^2 + 9)^2$, but is not a zero of $g(D) = D^3 + 4D^2 + D - 6$. Since $r = 2s = 2$ and $Q(x) = \sin 3x$, we select formula (25a) and note that the fractional coefficient reduces to $-\dfrac{x^2}{72}$.

In setting up the operator $G(D)$ we may substitute $D^2 = -b^2 = -9$ at the outset in

$$g^{-1}(D) = \frac{1}{D^3 + 4D^2 + D - 6} = \frac{1}{4D^2 - 6 + D(D^2 + 1)}$$

thus obtaining

$$G(D) = \frac{1}{-42 - 8D} = \frac{-1}{2(21 + 4D)} = \frac{-(21 - 4D)}{2(441 - 16D^2)} = \frac{4D - 21}{1170}.$$

The particular solution given by (25a) is then

$$y_{p,2} = -\frac{x^2}{72} \cdot \frac{(4D - 21)\sin 3x}{1170} = \frac{x^2(7 \sin 3x - 4 \cos 3x)}{28080}.$$

The roots of $f(D) = 0$ are $\pm 3i, 1, -2, -3$; the general solution is $y_{p,2} + (c_1 x + c_2)\cos 3x + (c_3 x + c_4)\sin 3x + c_5 e^x + c_6 e^{-2x} + c_7 e^{-3x}$.

EXAMPLE 3. Solve the equation

$$(D^2 + 4)(D^4 + D^3 - D^2 - D)y = \cos 2x.$$

SOLUTION. Here $r = 1$, $s = 0$, $b = 2$, so that the fractional coefficient of (25d) becomes $\dfrac{x}{4}$. To form the operator $G(D)$, we replace $D^2$ by $-4$ in

$$g^{-1}(D) = \frac{1}{D^4 + D^3 - D^2 - D} = \frac{1}{D^2(D^2 - 1) + D(D^2 - 1)}$$

and proceed as in Example 2:

$$G(D) = \frac{1}{20 - 5D} = \frac{4 + D}{5(16 - D^2)} = \frac{4 + D}{100}.$$

A particular solution is therefore

$$y_{p,1} = \frac{x}{4} \cdot \frac{4 + D}{100}\sin 2x = \frac{x}{200}(2 \sin 2x + \cos 2x).$$

EXAMPLE 4. Solve the equation

$$(D^4 + 3D^3 - 2D^2 - D)y = e^{-x} \sin 2x.$$

SOLUTION. First we employ formula (18) of Article 35.

$$y = \frac{1}{D^4+3D^3-2D^2-D} e^{-x} \sin 2x = e^{-x} \frac{1}{D^4-D^3-5D^2+8D-3} \sin 2x.$$

Next we turn to formula (26a), forming the operator $F(D)$ by substituting $D^2 = -4$ in

$$f^{-1}(D) = \frac{1}{D^4 - D^3 - 5D^2 + 8D - 3} = \frac{1}{D^4 - 5D^2 - 3 - D(D^2 - 8)}.$$

$$F(D) = \frac{1}{33 + 12D} = \frac{1}{3} \cdot \frac{1}{11 + 4D} = \frac{11 - 4D}{3(121 - 16D^2)} = \frac{11 - 4D}{555}.$$

Hence a particular integral is $e^{-x}(11 \sin 2x - 8 \cos 2x)/555$.

C. $Q(x) = x^r$. It can be proved that under certain conditions it is possible to expand the inverse operator $f^{-1}(D)$ as a power series of the form

$$a_0 + a_1D + a_2D^2 + \cdots + a_kD^k + \cdots$$

and so write a solution of the equation $f(D)y = Q(x)$ as

$$y_p = (a_0 + a_1D + a_2D^2 + \cdots + a_rD^r + a_{r+1}D^{r+1} + \cdots)Q(x),$$

where $DQ(x) = Q'(x)$, $D^2Q(x) = Q''(x)$, etc. When $Q(x) = x^r$, where $r$ is a positive integer, all terms of the power series beyond $a_rD^r$ produce zero when operating on $Q(x)$, so that the solution takes the form of a polynomial in $x$.

EXAMPLE 5. Solve the equation $(D^3 + 2D^2 + D)y = x^3$.
SOLUTION. The absence from $f(D)$ of the term independent of $D$ makes the power series for $f^{-1}(D)$ unobtainable. Hence we write

$$f^{-1}(D) = \frac{1}{D} \cdot \frac{1}{1 + 2D + D^2} = \frac{1}{D}(1 - 2D + 3D^2 - 4D^3 + \cdots),$$

where we have exhibited the cubic polynomial, which contains all the useful terms of the power series for $1/(1 + 2D + D^2)$. Hence

$$y_p = \frac{1}{D}(1 - 2D + 3D^2 - 4D^3)x^3 = \frac{1}{D}(x^3 - 6x^2 + 18x - 24)$$

$$= \int (x^3 - 6x^2 + 18x - 24)\, dx = \tfrac{1}{4}x^4 - 2x^3 + 9x^2 - 24x.$$

**105**

Find a particular integral for each of the following equations. Use the methods of Article 37.

1. $(D^2 + 4)y = 2e^x$
2. $(D^2 + 3)y = 3e^{-4x}$
3. $(D^2 + 4D + 4)y = \frac{1}{2}(e^x + e^{-x})$
4. $(D^2 + D - 2)y = e^{-2x}$
5. $(D^2 + 2)y = \sin x$
6. $(D^2 + 4D + 4)y = \frac{1}{2}(e^{3x} - e^{-3x})$
7. $(D^2 + 3D - 2)y = \sin 2x$
8. $(D^2 + 3D + 2)y = e^x \sin x$
9. $(D^3 - 1)y = e^x$
10. $(D^3 - 4D^2 + D - 4)y = \sin x - e^{4x}$
11. $(D^4 + 3D^2 - 4)y = 4e^x + 3 \cos 2x$
12. $(D^2 + 1)y = e^{3x}(1 + \sin 2x)$
13. $(D^2 + 2n^2D + n^4)y = \sin kx$
14. $(D^2 + 4D + 5)y = \frac{1}{2}(e^x + e^{-x})$
15. $(D^2 + D - 2)y = xe^{-x}$
16. $(D^2 + 4)y = xe^x$
17. $(D^2 + 2)y = x^2 e^{-x}$
18. $(D^2 - D - 2)y = x^2 - 8$
19. $(D^3 - 1)y = x^2$
20. $(D^3 + 4D^2 - 5D)y = x^2 e^{-x}$
21. $(D^4 - 2D^3 + D^2)y = x^2$
22. $(D^3 - D)y = e^x(\sin x - x^2)$
23. $(D^3 - 4D^2)y = e^{2x}(x - 3)$
24. $(D^4 + 6D^3 + 9D^2)y = \sin 3x + xe^x$
25. $(D^3 - 6D^2 + 11D - 6)y = x^2 e^{2x}$
26. $(D^3 + 2D)y = x^2 + \cos x$
27. $(D^4 + 3D^2 - D + 2)y = \sin 2x$
28. $(D^2 + 1)(D + 2)y = \cos x$
29. $(D - 1)(D^2 + 1)^2 y = \sin x$
30. $(D^4 + 2D^2 + D)y = x^3 - \frac{1}{2} \cos 2x$
31. $D(D^2 + 4D + 5)y = e^{-2x} \cos x$
32. $(D^3 + D^2 - 2D)y = e^{-2x} \cos 2x$      $D(D+2)(D-1)$
33. $D(D^2 + 2)y = x^2 \sin x$
34. $(D^4 - 1)y = x^2 \cos x$

**38. Inverse operators in terms of partial fractions.** A solution of equation (8) can be written in the symbolic form

$$y = \frac{1}{(D - a_1)(D - a_2) \cdots (D - a_n)} Q(x).$$

If the constants $a_1$, $a_2$, ..., $a_n$ are distinct, we can write the inverse operator as the sum of partial fractions

$$\frac{K_1}{D - a_1} + \frac{K_2}{D - a_2} + \cdots + \frac{K_n}{D - a_n}.$$

The validity of this form of the inverse operator can be verified directly. It can also be inferred from the fact that such operators obey the laws enunciated in Article 35 and hence have a decomposition into partial fractions exactly like that for rational algebraic functions. A particular integral of equation (8) can therefore be written in the form

$$y_p = \frac{K_1}{D - a_1} Q(x) + \frac{K_2}{D - a_2} Q(x) + \cdots + \frac{K_n}{D - a_n} Q(x).$$

The usual modification is required if some of the constants $a_1$, $a_2$, ..., $a_n$ are equal. For example if $a_1 = a_2 = a_3$ the corresponding partial fractions are

$$\frac{K_1}{D - a_1} + \frac{K_2}{(D - a_1)^2} + \frac{K_3}{(D - a_1)^3}.$$

The determination of a particular integral of equation (8) has thus been reduced to the application of operators of the type $\frac{1}{(D - a)^k}$ to the function $Q(x)$.

When $Q(x)$ is of one of the types treated in Article 37, the particular integral may be found as readily without resorting to partial fractions. When $Q(x)$ is not of these types, the method of the present article may offer some advantage.

EXAMPLE 1. Using partial fractions, find a particular integral of the equation $D(D - 1)^2 y = x$.

SOLUTION. The inverse operator involved is $\frac{1}{D(D - 1)^2}$, for which we assume the partial fraction expansion

$$\frac{1}{D(D - 1)^2} = \frac{a}{D} + \frac{b}{D - 1} + \frac{c}{(D - 1)^2}.$$

From the identity $1 = a(D - 1)^2 + bD(D - 1) + cD$ we find the values $a = 1$, $b = -1$, $c = 1$ by successively substituting $D = 0$, $1$, $-1$. Therefore

$$y_p = \frac{1}{D}x + \frac{1}{1 - D}x + \frac{1}{1 - 2D + D^2}x$$
$$= \tfrac{1}{2}x^2 + (1 + D)x + (1 + 2D)x = \tfrac{1}{2}x^2 + 2x + 3.$$

Since the complementary function is $c_1 + (c_2 + c_3x)e^x$, the general solution is

$$y = c_1 + (c_2 + c_3x)e^x + \tfrac{1}{2}x^2 + 2x,$$

the constant term of $y_p$ having been absorbed into $c_1$.

EXAMPLE 2. Solve the equation $D(D^2 + 1)y = x \cos x$.

SOLUTION. The operator $\dfrac{1}{D(D^2 + 1)}$ may be expressed in the form

$\dfrac{a}{D} + \dfrac{bD + c}{D^2 + 1}$. From the identity $a(D^2 + 1) + bD^2 + cD = 1$ we find $a = 1$, $b = -1$, $c = 0$. Therefore

$$y_p = \left(\frac{1}{D} - \frac{D}{D^2 + 1}\right)x \cos x = \int x \cos x\, dx - \frac{1}{D^2 + 1}(\cos x - x \sin x)$$

$$= \cos x + x \sin x - \frac{1}{D^2 + 1}\cos x + \frac{1}{D^2 + 1}\frac{xe^{ix} - xe^{-ix}}{2i}$$

$$= \cos x + x \sin x - \tfrac{1}{2}x \sin x$$

$$+ \frac{1}{2i}\left[e^{ix}\frac{1}{D^2 + 2iD}x - e^{-ix}\frac{1}{D^2 - 2iD}x\right],$$

where formulas (25) and (18) have been used. Partial fractions enable us to evaluate the bracketed terms as follows:

$$\frac{1}{2i}\left[e^{ix}\cdot\frac{i}{2}\left(-\frac{1}{D} + \frac{1}{D + 2i}\right)x - e^{-ix}\cdot\frac{i}{2}\left(\frac{1}{D} - \frac{1}{D - 2i}\right)x\right]$$

$$= \frac{e^{ix}}{4}\left(-\frac{1}{D} - \frac{i}{2} + \frac{D}{4}\right)x - \frac{e^{-ix}}{4}\left(\frac{1}{D} - \frac{i}{2} - \frac{D}{4}\right)x$$

$$= \frac{e^{ix}}{4}\left(-\frac{x^2}{2} - \frac{ix}{2} + \frac{1}{4}\right) - \frac{e^{-ix}}{4}\left(\frac{x^2}{2} - \frac{ix}{2} - \frac{1}{4}\right)$$

$$= \frac{1}{8}\cos x + \frac{x}{4}\sin x - \frac{x^2}{4}\cos x$$

In the general solution we absorb the term in $\cos x$ of $y_p$:

$$y = y_c + y_p = c_1 + c_2 \cos x + c_3 \sin x + \tfrac{1}{4}(x \sin x - x^2 \cos x).$$

## EXERCISE 24

Using the partial fraction form of the inverse operator, find a particular solution of each of the following problems.

1. $(D^2 + 4)y = x \sin x$
2. $(D^2 + 1)y = x^2 \cos x$
3. $(D^2 - 1)y = x^3 \cos x$
4. $(D^3 + 4D)y = e^x + \sin x$
5. $(D^5 + D^4)y = x^2$
6. $(2D^2 + 3D - 2)y = x^2 e^x$
7. $(D + 1)(D^2 + 1)y - x^3 e^{-x}$
8. $D(D^2 + 1)y = \sin x$
9. $(D^3 - D)y = x \sin x$
10. $(D^3 + 2D^2)y = x \cos 2x$
11. $(D^2 + 3D + 2)y = x^2 \cos x$
12. $(D^2 - 4D + 3)y = x^2 \sin x$
13. $(D^2 - 1)y = x \sin 2x$
14. $(D^2 + 2D)y = x^3 \sin 2x$
15. $D(D - 1)y = xe^x \sin x$
16. $(D^2 - 4)y = xe^{2x} \cos x$
17. $D(D + 2)y = x^2 e^{-x} \sin x$

**39. The Cauchy equation.** The linear equation

$$(27) \qquad a_0 x^n \frac{d^n y}{dx^n} + a_1 x^{n-1} \frac{d^{n-1}y}{dx^{n-1}} + \cdots + a_{n-1} x \frac{dy}{dx} + a_n y = G(x),$$

in which the coefficient of the $k$th derivative is the product of a constant and $x^k$, is called a *Cauchy equation.*\* An equation of this type is transformed into an equation with constant coefficients by means of the substitution $x = e^v$. To show this, it will be necessary to express the derivatives of $y$ with respect to $x$ in terms of derivatives with respect to $v$.

The substitution used is equivalent to $v = \ln x$, so that $\dfrac{dv}{dx} = \dfrac{1}{x}$, and the identity $\dfrac{dy}{dx} = \dfrac{dy}{dv} \cdot \dfrac{dv}{dx}$ reduces in this case to the relation

$$(a) \qquad x \frac{dy}{dx} = \frac{dy}{dv}.$$

This relation may be interpreted as a statement of the equiva-

---

\* First studied by Augustin Louis Cauchy (1789–1857), renowned for his work in algebra, number theory, and many branches of analysis.

lence of the operators $x \dfrac{d}{dx}$ and $\dfrac{d}{dv}$ as applied to any function $y$.

The relation between $\dfrac{d^2y}{dx^2}$ and $\dfrac{d^2y}{dv^2}$ is found by applying the

operator $x \dfrac{d}{dx}$ to the left member of $(a)$ and the equivalent

operator $\dfrac{d}{dv}$ to the right member:

$$x \frac{d}{dx}\left(x \frac{dy}{dx}\right) = \frac{d}{dv}\left(\frac{dy}{dv}\right)$$

$$x\left(x \frac{d^2y}{dx^2} + \frac{dy}{dx}\right) = \frac{d^2y}{dv^2}$$

By means of $(a)$ this equation can be put in the form

$(b)$ $$x^2 \frac{d^2y}{dx^2} = \frac{d^2y}{dv^2} - \frac{dy}{dv}.$$

The relation between $\dfrac{d^n y}{dx^n}$ and the derivatives of $y$ with respect to $v$ will be established by mathematical induction. If
we denote the operator $\dfrac{d^k}{dx^k}$ by $D^k$ and introduce the symbol $\theta^k$

for the operator $\dfrac{d^k}{dv^k}$, then equations $(a)$ and $(b)$ may be written:

$(a')$ $\qquad\qquad x\, Dy = \theta y$

$(b')$ $\qquad\qquad x^2\, D^2 y = \theta(\theta - 1)y$

The formula

$(c)$ $\qquad\qquad x^k\, D^k y = \theta(\theta - 1) \cdots (\theta - k + 1)y,$

which is suggested by $(a')$ and $(b')$, has thus been verified for
$k = 1$ and $k = 2$. It remains to prove that if $(c)$ is valid for $k$
it is also valid for $k + 1$. Applying the operator $x\, D$ to the left
member of $(c)$, we have

$$x\, D(x^k\, D^k y) = x(x^k\, D^{k+1}y + kx^{k-1}\, D^k y)$$
$$= x^{k+1}\, D^{k+1}y + kx^k\, D^k y$$
$$= x^{k+1}\, D^{k+1}y + k\theta(\theta - 1) \cdots (\theta - k + 1)y,$$

while the application of the equivalent operator $\theta$ to the right member produces

$$\theta^2(\theta - 1) \cdots (\theta - k + 1)y.$$

Hence:

$$x^{k+1} D^{k+1}y + k\theta(\theta - 1) \cdots (\theta - k + 1)y$$
$$= \theta^2(\theta - 1) \cdots (\theta - k + 1)y$$

$$x^{k+1} D^{k+1}y = \theta^2(\theta - 1) \cdots (\theta - k + 1)y$$
$$- k\theta(\theta - 1) \cdots (\theta - k + 1)y$$
$$= \theta(\theta - 1) \cdots (\theta - k + 1)(\theta - k)y$$

It follows that (c) holds for all positive integral values of $k$.

Each term of the left member of equation (27) can thus be expressed as a linear combination of derivatives of $y$ with respect to $v$, the coefficients being constants. To complete the transformation, the right member must be written $G(e^v)$.

EXAMPLE. Solve the equation $x^2y'' - xy' - 3y = x^2 \ln x$.

SOLUTION. The identity (c) shows that the substitution $x = e^v$ transforms the left member of the differential equation into

$$\theta(\theta - 1)y - \theta y - 3y = [\theta(\theta - 1) - \theta - 3]y = (\theta^2 - 2\theta - 3)y;$$

the right member becomes $ve^{2v}$. Therefore the problem reduces to solving the equation

$$(\theta^2 - 2\theta - 3)y = ve^{2v}.$$

The auxiliary equation, $m^2 - 2m - 3 = 0$, has roots 3 and $-1$, so that the complementary function is

$$y_c = c_1 e^{3v} + c_2 e^{-v}.$$

A particular integral is:

$$y_p = \frac{1}{(\theta - 3)(\theta + 1)} ve^{2v} = \left(\frac{\frac{1}{4}}{\theta - 3} - \frac{\frac{1}{4}}{\theta + 1}\right)ve^{2v}$$
$$= -\tfrac{1}{4}e^{2v}(v + 1) - \tfrac{1}{36}e^{2v}(3v - 1)$$
$$= -\tfrac{1}{9}e^{2v}(3v + 2)$$

The general solution is:

$$y = c_1 e^{3v} + c_2 e^{-v} - \tfrac{1}{9}e^{2v}(3v + 2)$$
$$= c_1 x^3 + \frac{c_2}{x} - \frac{1}{9}x^2(3 \ln x + 2)$$

111

### EXERCISE 25

Find the general solution of each of the following equations.

1. $x^2y'' - 4xy' + y = 0$
2. $x^2y'' + xy' + 16y = 0$
3. $4x^2y'' - 16xy' + 25y = 0$
4. $x^2y'' + 5xy' + 10y = 0$
5. $2x^2y'' - 3xy' - 18y = \ln x$
6. $2x^2y'' - 3xy' + 2y = \ln x^3$
7. $x^2y'' - 3xy' + 4y = x^3$
8. $x^2y'' + 3xy' + y = 1 - x$
9. $x^3y''' + 2x^2y'' - xy' + y = \dfrac{1}{x}$
10. $x^2y'' - 2xy' + 2y = 4x + \sin(\ln x)$
11. $x^2y'' - xy' + 2y = x^2\ln x$
12. $x^2y'' + 4xy' + 3y = (x - 1)\ln x$
13. $4x^3y''' + 8x^2y'' - xy' + y = x + \ln x$
14. $3x^3y''' + 4x^2y'' - 10xy' + 10y = 4x^{-2}$
15. $x^4y^{(4)} + 7x^3y''' + 9x^2y'' - 6xy' - 6y = \cos(\ln x)$
16. $x^3y''' - 2x^2y'' - xy' + 4y = \sin(\ln x)$

**40. Simultaneous linear equations.** Suppose $x(t)$ and $y(t)$ are functions which satisfy the simultaneous equations

$$(28) \qquad f_1(D)x + g_1(D)y = h_1(t)$$

$$(29) \qquad f_2(D)x + g_2(D)y = h_2(t)$$

where $D$ represents the operator $\dfrac{d}{dt}$ and $f_1(D)$, $g_1(D)$, $f_2(D)$, $g_2(D)$ are polynomial operators. It can be shown * that the number of arbitrary constants appearing in the general solution of this system of equations is equal to the degree of the expression

$$\begin{vmatrix} f_1(D) & g_1(D) \\ f_2(D) & g_2(D) \end{vmatrix}$$

considered as a polynomial in $D$.

* Forsyth, *A Treatise on Differential Equations* (6th ed.; London: Macmillan, 1929), p. 344.

To find a solution of the system (28), (29), we eliminate $x$ between the equations and solve the resulting equation for $y$. Similarly we eliminate $y$ and solve for $x$. The arbitrary constants in the two expressions thus obtained are ordinarily not independent. An independent set of these constants can be obtained by means of the relations which result from substituting the expressions into (28) and (29). The details of this method will be illustrated by the following example.

EXAMPLE 1. Find the general solution of the system:
$$Dx - (D - 2)y = \cos 2t$$
$$(D - 2)x + Dy = 20$$

SOLUTION. The determinant of the symbolic coefficients of $x$ and $y$ is

$$\begin{vmatrix} D & -(D-2) \\ D & 2 & D \end{vmatrix} = 2D^2 - 4D + 4,$$

so that the general solution must have two arbitrary constants. Operate on the first equation with $D$ and on the second with $D - 2$. Addition of the resulting equations leads to the equation

(a) $$(D^2 - 2D + 2)x = -\sin 2t - 20,$$

whose complementary function is

$$x_c = e^t(c_1 \cos t + c_2 \sin t).$$

A particular integral of (a) is

$$x_p = \frac{1}{D^2 - 2D + 2}(-\sin 2t - 20)$$
$$= \tfrac{1}{10}\sin 2t - \tfrac{1}{5}\cos 2t - 10,$$

so that the general solution of (a) is

(b) $$x = e^t(c_1 \cos t + c_2 \sin t) + \tfrac{1}{10}\sin 2t - \tfrac{1}{5}\cos 2t - 10.$$

The elimination of $x$ between the equations of the original system is accomplished by operating on the first equation by $-(D - 2)$ and on the second by $D$. Addition of the results gives

$$(D^2 - 2D + 2)y = \cos 2t + \sin 2t,$$

the general solution of which turns out to be

(c) $$y = e^t(c_1' \cos t + c_2' \sin t) - \tfrac{3}{10}\sin 2t + \tfrac{1}{10}\cos 2t.$$

113

To determine the necessary relations among the four parameters, we substitute (b) and (c) into the second equation of the original system. The following identity results:

$$(c_2 - c_1 + c_1' + c_2')e^t \cos t + (- c_1 - c_2 - c_1' + c_2')e^t \sin t \equiv 0.$$

Since the functions $e^t \cos t$ and $e^t \sin t$ are linearly independent, it follows that $c_1' = - c_2$, $c_2' = c_1$. Thus the general solution of the system may be written:

$$x = e^t(c_1 \cos t + c_2 \sin t) + \tfrac{1}{10} \sin 2t - \tfrac{1}{5} \cos 2t - 10$$
$$y = e^t(c_1 \sin t - c_2 \cos t) - \tfrac{3}{10} \sin 2t + \tfrac{1}{10} \cos 2t$$

Since the number of independent arbitrary constants has been reduced to the desired number, substitution of (b) and (c) into the first equation of the original system can yield no further reduction in their number.

A variation of the method described above is illustrated by the following example.

EXAMPLE 2. Solve the system:

$$Dx + (D + 3)y = t^2$$
$$(D - 2)x + (D - 1)y = 3t$$

SOLUTION. The determinant of the coefficients of $x$ and $y$ is

$$\begin{vmatrix} D & D + 3 \\ D - 2 & D - 1 \end{vmatrix} = - 2D + 6,$$

so that the general solution has one arbitrary constant. The result of eliminating $x$ is the equation $(D - 3)y = t - t^2 - \tfrac{3}{2}$, which has the solution

$$y = \tfrac{1}{3}t^2 - \tfrac{1}{9}t + \tfrac{25}{54} + c_1e^{3t}.$$

Substituting this expression into the first equation of the system and integrating, one has

$$x = - \tfrac{1}{6}t^2 - \tfrac{23}{18}t - 2c_1e^{3t} + c_2.$$

Finally, substitution of these expressions for $x$ and $y$ into the second equation of the system shows that $c_2 = - \tfrac{25}{27}$, so that the general solution of the system is:

$$x = - \tfrac{1}{6}t^2 - \tfrac{23}{18}t - 2c_1e^{3t} - \tfrac{25}{27}$$
$$y = \tfrac{1}{3}t^2 - \tfrac{1}{9}t + \tfrac{25}{54} + c_1e^{3t}$$

## EXERCISE 26

Solve the following systems of differential equations.

1. $Dx - x = \cos t, \quad Dy + y = 4t$
2. $Dx + 5x = 3t^2, \quad Dy + y = e^{3t}$
3. $Dx + 2x = 3t, \quad Dx + 2\,Dy + y = \cos 2t$
4. $Dx - x + y = 2 \sin t, \quad Dx + Dy = 3y - 3x$
5. $2\,Dx + 3x - y = e^t, \quad 5x - 3\,Dy = y + 2t$
6. $5\,Dy - 3\,Dx - 5y = 5t, \quad 3\,Dx - 5\,Dy - 2x = 0$
7. $D^2y - x - 4y = \cos t, \quad D^2x + x + 6y = \sin t$
8. $D^2y - D^2x - x + y = \cos 2t, \quad 2\,Dx - Dy - y = 0$
9. $D^2x + D^2y + Dx = \sin 2t, \quad 2\,D^2x - D^2y = t^2$
10. $D^2x + 5x + 5y = 0, \quad D^2y - 2x - 2y - 2t = 0$
11. $D^2x - y - 2x = 3e^{2t} + 1, \quad D^2y - 5x + 2y = 5e^{2t} + 1$
12. $Dx = 3x, \quad Dy = 2x + 3y, \quad Dz = 3y - 2z$

**41. Dynamical applications.** Differential equations of the second order are encountered in considering the motion of a mass particle constrained to move along a straight line under the influence of a force $F$. Let a coordinate system be set up on the line of motion by assigning a positive sense to the line and designating by $x$ the signed distance (measured in feet) of the particle from an origin $O$ on the line. If $t$ represents the number of seconds which have elapsed from a given instant which is taken as the origin on the time scale, then $x$ will be a function of $t$ and by Newton's second law of motion * (force equals time rate of change of momentum)

$$(30) \qquad\qquad m\frac{d^2x}{dt^2} = F.$$

In general, the force $F$ may depend upon the time $t$, the displacement $x$, and the velocity $v = \dfrac{dx}{dt}$ of the particle at the time $t$. We shall consider various special cases.

---

* The laws of dynamics were first stated in their modern form by Sir Isaac Newton (1642–1727), to whose genius we also owe the discovery of the law of gravitation and the invention of the infinitesimal calculus.

A. *Motion in a gravitational field.* Let the particle move in a vertical line subject to the gravitational attraction of the earth. If the $x$-axis is directed towards the earth's center, we may write the equation (30) in the form

$$(31) \qquad m\frac{d^2x}{dt^2} = mg,$$

since the force of gravitation exerted by the earth upon a particle near its surface is nearly proportional to the mass of the particle. Here $g$ is the constant acceleration due to gravity, which we shall take to be 32 ft./sec.². The simple linear second-order equation (31) is readily solved. Its solution is

$$x = x_0 + v_0t + \tfrac{1}{2}gt^2,$$

where the arbitrary constants $x_0$, $v_0$ are seen to have immediate physical interpretations, being respectively the values of the displacement $x$ and the velocity $v$ at the time $t = 0$.

EXAMPLE 1. A ball is thrown upward from the top of a tower 50 feet high with a speed of 30 m.p.h. Neglecting air resistance, describe the subsequent motion. With what speed will the ball strike the ground?

SOLUTION. If we take the positive direction of the $x$-axis downward, with the origin at ground level, then $x_0 = -50$, $v_0 = -44$ (in ft./sec.). Hence

$$x = -50 - 44t + 16t^2.$$

The velocity of the ball at any time $t$ is given by

$$v = \frac{dx}{dt} = -44 + 32t.$$

The ball rises with decreasing speed, reaching its highest point when $v = 0$, that is, $1\frac{3}{8}$ sec. after it leaves the top of the tower. It then begins to fall with increasing speed, striking the ground when $x = 0$, that is, when

$$16t^2 - 44t - 50 = 0.$$

The solutions of this equation are

$$t = 3.6, \ -0.9.$$

Thus the ball strikes the ground 3.6 seconds after being thrown. Its speed upon reaching the ground is

$$- 44 + 32(3.6) = 71.2 \text{ ft./sec.}$$

The value $t = -0.9$ has the following significance. A ball thrown upward from the ground with an initial speed of 71.2 ft./sec. would require 0.9 second to pass the top of the tower at a speed of 44 ft./sec.

*B. Motion under Hooke's Law.** In this case the particle moves in a straight line subject to a force which tends to restore it to a position of equilibrium, the magnitude of the force being proportional to the displacement of the particle from this position. If the position of equilibrium is taken to be the origin $O$, the equation (30) may be written

(32) $$m \frac{d^2x}{dt^2} = - m\kappa^2 x,$$

This is a homogeneous linear equation of the second order the general solution of which may be written in either of the forms:

$$x = A \cos \kappa t + B \sin \kappa t$$
$$x = C \cos (\kappa t + \alpha)$$

The second form of the solution is particularly useful since it reveals that the motion of the particle is a periodic oscillation about $O$ with period

$$T = \frac{2\pi}{\kappa}.$$

The *frequency* $\nu$ is defined as the reciprocal of the period, so that

$$\nu = \frac{\kappa}{2\pi}.$$

The constant $C$ is called the *amplitude* of the motion and represents the greatest displacement from $O$ that the particle attains. The angle $\alpha$ is known as the *phase angle*. The resulting motion is called *simple harmonic motion* and may be described in the

* Discovered by Robert Hooke (1635–1703), English physicist and Secretary of the Royal Society from 1677 to 1682.

following terms: the particle $P$ moves along the $x$-axis so that it is at all times the projection upon the $x$-axis of a particle $Q$ which moves with constant angular velocity $\omega_0 = 2\pi\nu = \kappa$

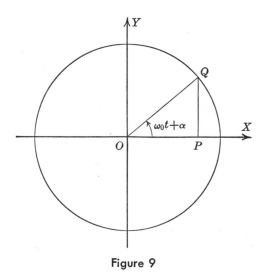

Figure 9

around a circle with center at $O$ and radius $C$. (See Fig. 9.) At any instant $t$, the radius vector $OQ$ makes an angle $\omega_0 t + \alpha$ with the $x$-axis. In particular, when $t = 0$, this angle is the phase angle $\alpha$.

EXAMPLE 2. An object weighing 10 lb., when hung on a helical spring, causes the spring to stretch 1 inch. The object is then pulled down 2 inches and released. Discuss its motion.

SOLUTION. If we assume that the elastic force in the spring is proportional to the elongation of the spring, then this force is 10 lb. per inch of elongation, or 120 lb. per foot. Let $O$ be the position of equilibrium of the object as it hangs on the spring. If the object is displaced $x$ feet from $O$, the total elongation of the spring is $(\frac{1}{12} + x)$ feet and the elastic force developed is $120(\frac{1}{12} + x)$ lb. The resultant force $F$ acting on the object is the algebraic sum of the weight $W$ and the elastic force, so that

$$F = 10 - 120(\tfrac{1}{12} + x) = -120x.$$

118

Hence the equation (32) becomes

(a) $$\frac{5}{16}\frac{d^2x}{dt^2} = -120x,$$

since the mass $m$ of the object is given by $m = \dfrac{W}{g} = \dfrac{10}{32} = \dfrac{5}{16}.$

Then we have $\dfrac{d^2x}{dt^2} = -384x$, where $\kappa = \omega_0 = \sqrt{384} = 8\sqrt{6}$, and the solution of the equation may be written

(b) $$x = C\cos{(8\sqrt{6}\,t + \alpha)}.$$

To determine the values of $C$ and $\alpha$, we have

$$\frac{dx}{dt} = -8\sqrt{6}C\sin{(8\sqrt{6}\,t + \alpha)}.$$

Since $x = \dfrac{1}{6}$ and $\dfrac{dx}{dt} = 0$ when $t = 0$:

(c) $$C\cos\alpha = \tfrac{1}{6}, \quad -8\sqrt{6}C\sin\alpha = 0$$

From the second equation (c) it follows that $\alpha = 0$, and the first equation gives $C = \tfrac{1}{6}$. Hence (b) may be written

$$x = \tfrac{1}{6}\cos{(8\sqrt{6}\,t)}.$$

The motion is simple harmonic about the point $O$, with amplitude $\tfrac{1}{6}$ ft. and period $T = \dfrac{2\pi}{8\sqrt{6}} = \dfrac{\pi\sqrt{6}}{24} = 0.32$ sec.

*C. Hooke's Law with a resisting force.* The particle moves in a straight line subject to a restoring force as in the preceding case, but in addition the motion is resisted by a force which is proportional to the velocity of the particle. This is approximately the case if the resistance to the motion of the particle is that offered by air when the speed is not too great. The equation (30) may then be written

(33) $$m\frac{d^2x}{dt^2} = -2mk\frac{dx}{dt} - m\omega_0^2 x,$$

where we have written $\omega_0^2$ in place of the "spring constant" $\kappa^2$ and have denoted the constant of proportionality for the resisting force by $2mk$ for reasons of convenience.

**119**

The equation (33) is linear, homogeneous, and of the second order. Its auxiliary equation $r^2 + 2kr + \omega_0^2 = 0$ has the roots

$$(34) \qquad r = -k \pm \sqrt{k^2 - \omega_0^2},$$

and the nature of these roots will characterize the motion.

If $k^2 < \omega_0^2$, the *damping* force $2mk \dfrac{dx}{dt}$ is small in comparison with the *restoring* force $m\omega_0^2 x$. The roots (34) are complex and the general solution of (33) may be written

$$x = Ce^{-kt} \cos(t\sqrt{\omega_0^2 - k^2} + \alpha).$$

The motion, illustrated by the following Example 3, is known as *damped simple harmonic motion*. The particle oscillates about $O$ with constant frequency

$$\nu_1 = \frac{1}{2\pi} \sqrt{\omega_0^2 - k^2}$$

but with an amplitude which decreases exponentially due to the factor $e^{-kt}$. If the particle has a (relative) maximum displacement at

$$t = t_1,$$

it will have another at the time

$$t = t_1 + \frac{1}{\nu_1}$$

and the corresponding amplitudes are

$$Ce^{-kt_1} \text{ and } Ce^{-k\left(t_1 + \frac{1}{\nu_1}\right)}.$$

The *logarithmic decrement* of the motion is the decrease in the logarithm of these amplitudes and has the value:

$$\delta = \ln Ce^{-kt_1} - \ln Ce^{-k\left(t_1 + \frac{1}{\nu_1}\right)}$$
$$= \ln \frac{Ce^{-kt_1}}{Ce^{-k\left(t_1 + \frac{1}{\nu_1}\right)}}$$
$$= \frac{k}{\nu_1}$$

If the frequency is expanded as a power series in $k$, one finds

$$\nu_1 = \frac{1}{2\pi}\sqrt{\omega_0{}^2 - k^2} = \frac{1}{2\pi}\left(\omega_0 - \frac{k^2}{2\omega_0} + \cdots\right),$$

so that for small damping the frequency is only slightly smaller than the frequency

$$\nu_0 = \frac{\omega_0}{2\pi}$$

of the undamped motion, and the logarithmic decrement has the approximate value

$$\delta = \frac{k}{\nu_0} = \frac{2\pi k}{\omega_0}.$$

If $k^2 > \omega_0{}^2$, the damping effect is great. The roots (34) are then real and the general solution of (33) is:

$$x = e^{-kt}(A e^{t\sqrt{k^2 - \omega_0{}^2}} + B e^{-t\sqrt{k^2 - \omega_0{}^2}})$$
$$= C e^{-kt}\cosh\,(t\sqrt{k^2 - \omega_0{}^2} + \alpha)$$

The motion is not oscillatory but dies down gradually. Figure 10 shows the graph of a particular case of this type of motion,

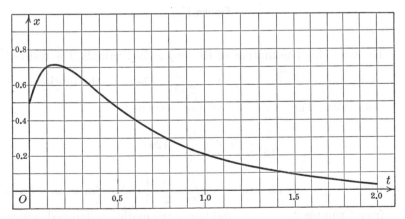

Figure 10

the case $k = 4\sqrt{2}$, $\omega_0 = 4$, for the initial conditions $x(0) = \frac{1}{2}$, $v(0) = 4$.

121

The case $k^2 = \omega_0^2$ is known as the critical case. The roots (34) are then real and equal and the general solution of (33) is

$$x = (At + B)e^{-kt}.$$

Here too the motion is not oscillatory. A graph which illustrates the critical case is shown in Fig. 11.

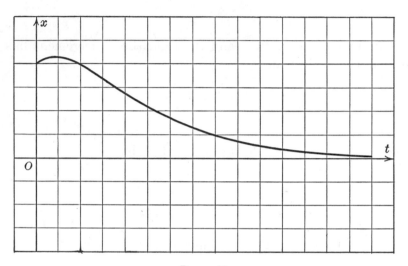

**Figure 11**

EXAMPLE 3. The motion of the object in Example 2 is resisted by the air with a force equal to $\dfrac{5}{2}\dfrac{dx}{dt}$. Describe the motion.

SOLUTION. The equation (33) now has the form

$$\frac{5}{16}\frac{d^2x}{dt^2} = -\frac{5}{2}\frac{dx}{dt} - 120x,$$

where $-\dfrac{5}{2} = -2mk$ and $k = \dfrac{\frac{5}{2}}{2m} = \dfrac{5}{2}\cdot\dfrac{8}{5} = 4$. Since $\omega_0 = 8\sqrt{6}$ from Example 2, $k^2 < \omega_0^2$ and hence the motion is damped simple harmonic and is given by

$$x = \frac{\sqrt{138}}{69}\,e^{-4t}\cos(4\sqrt{23}t + \alpha), \quad \alpha = -\text{Arc tan}\,\frac{1}{\sqrt{23}}.$$

The frequency is $\nu_1 = \dfrac{4\sqrt{23}}{2\pi} = 3.1$ cycles per second. The graph is shown in Fig. 12.

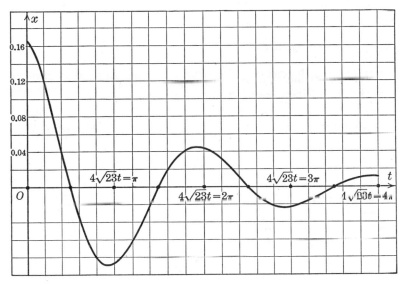

Figure 12

**42. Dynamical applications (continued).** In the preceding article the particle was considered to have been initially displaced from its position of equilibrium and then released to go through its motion under the influence of the restoring and the resisting forces. We wish now to consider the case that arises when the particle is set in motion by being linked dynamically with another oscillating system. We shall suppose that the particle is acted upon by an *impressed force* which will be assumed to have the value $F_0 \cos \omega t$, so that the impressed force varies sinusoidally with the time. The differential equation (33) is now replaced by

$$m\frac{d^2x}{dt^2} = -2mk\frac{dx}{dt} - m\omega_0^2 x + F_0 \cos \omega t,$$

123

which may be put into the form

$$(35) \qquad \frac{d^2x}{dt^2} + 2k \frac{dx}{dt} + \omega_0^2 x = \frac{F_0}{m} \cos \omega t.$$

In discussing this equation it will be assumed that $k^2 < \omega_0^2$. The complementary function is then

$$(36) \qquad x_c = Ce^{-kt} \cos (t\sqrt{\omega_0^2 - k^2} + \alpha).$$

A particular integral may be found by the method of undetermined coefficients. It may be written

$$x_p = \frac{F_0}{m[(\omega_0^2 - \omega^2)^2 + 4k^2\omega^2]} [(\omega_0^2 - \omega^2) \cos \omega t + 2k\omega \sin \omega t],$$

$$(37) \quad x_p = \frac{F_0}{m[(\omega_0^2 - \omega^2)^2 + 4k^2\omega^2]^{\frac{1}{2}}} \cos (\omega t + \theta),$$

where the angle $\theta$ is such that $0 \leqq \theta < 2\pi$ and

$$\cos \theta = \frac{\omega_0^2 - \omega^2}{[(\omega_0^2 - \omega^2)^2 + 4k^2\omega^2]^{\frac{1}{2}}}, \qquad \sin \theta = \frac{-2k\omega}{[(\omega_0^2 - \omega^2)^2 + 4k^2\omega^2]^{\frac{1}{2}}}.$$

Thus the general solution of (35) may be written

$$x = Ce^{-kt} \cos (t\sqrt{\omega_0^2 - k^2} + \alpha)$$

$$+ \frac{F_0}{m[(\omega_0^2 - \omega^2)^2 + 4k^2\omega^2]^{\frac{1}{2}}} \cos (\omega t + \theta).$$

When the impressed force is first applied, the motion is quite complicated, being a combination of the two harmonic motions (36) and (37), whose frequencies $\nu_1 = \dfrac{\sqrt{\omega_0^2 - k^2}}{2\pi}$ and $\nu = \dfrac{\omega}{2\pi}$ are in general different. In a relatively short time, however, the influence of the "free" motion (36) will practically have disappeared, even if $k$ is small, due to the presence of the damping factor $e^{-kt}$. For this reason, (36) is known as the *transient motion*. The motion will then be virtually that due to (37) and the particle will have achieved the so-called *steady state*.

The amplitude of the steady state is

$$A = \frac{F_0}{m[(\omega_0^2 - \omega^2)^2 + 4k^2\omega^2]^{\frac{1}{2}}}.$$

Considered as a function of $\omega$, $A$ has a maximum when

$$\omega^2 = \omega_0^2 - 2k^2.$$

If $k$ is small, it is approximately correct to say that $A$ attains its maximum when $\omega = \omega_0$, that is, when the frequency of the impressed force, $\nu = \dfrac{\omega}{2\pi}$, is the same as the natural frequency,

$\nu_0 = \dfrac{\omega_0}{2\pi}$, of the free motion. This condition is called *resonance;* the resisting force being small, the oscillating particle yields a maximum response to the impressed force when the frequency of the impressed force equals the natural frequency of the particle.

### EXERCISE 27

1. An object weighing 20 pounds, when hung on a helical spring, causes the spring to stretch 3 inches. The object is then pulled down 4 inches and released. Discuss its motion.

2. A particle in simple harmonic motion makes 40 complete oscillations per minute. If the amplitude is 1 foot, find the velocity and acceleration of the particle when $x = \frac{1}{4}$ foot.

3. Prove that if a particle undergoing simple harmonic motion is given a constant acceleration in addition, the particle will oscillate in simple harmonic motion about a new central position with the same period as before.

4. An object falls from rest in a medium whose resistance varies as the velocity of the object. When the velocity is 10 feet per second the resistance is $\frac{1}{15}$ the weight of the object. Find the speed and distance fallen 5 seconds after the start.

5. An object is projected with an initial velocity $v_0$ inclined at an angle $\alpha$ to the horizontal. If the object is acted upon by gravity alone, show that its motion is confined to a plane and that the equations of its path may be written $x = x_0 + v_0 t \cos \alpha$, $y = y_0 + v_0 t \sin \alpha - \frac{1}{2}gt^2$.

6. An object projected with a velocity of 120 feet per second passes horizontally over a wall in 2 seconds. Find the distance and height of the wall.

7. An object is projected from the top of a tower 100 feet high with a velocity of 55 feet per second inclined at an angle of 40° to the horizontal. Find where the object strikes the ground and the angle at which it strikes.

8. A chain 30 inches long, weighing 2 ounces per inch, is extended on a perfectly smooth table, with 4 inches of the chain hanging over the edge. If the chain is allowed to slip from rest on the table, find the velocity of the end of the chain at the instant that 20 inches are hanging over the edge.

9. If a hole were bored through the center of the earth, the pull of gravity upon an object in the hole would vary directly as the distance of the object from the earth's center. Show that the motion would be simple harmonic and find the time required for an object starting from rest at one end of the hole to reach the other end. Assume the radius of the earth to be 4000 miles.

10. An object attached to the end of an elastic string of natural length 5 feet hangs in equilibrium with the string stretched to a length of 6 feet. If the object is held with the string stretched 4 inches longer than its natural length and is then released, find (1) the position of the object when 4 seconds have elapsed, (2) the velocity of the object at that time, (3) the time required for the object to fall 9 inches, (4) the velocity of the object at the time when it has fallen 9 inches.

11. A particle executes damped simple harmonic motion of period 2.5 seconds. If the damping factor decreases by one half in 18 seconds, find the differential equation of the motion.

12. A weight of 5 lb. is hung on a spring and causes an elongation of 3 inches. It is set vibrating and has a period of $\frac{\pi}{3}$ seconds. Assuming that the motion is resisted by a force proportional to the velocity, find the time required for the damping factor to decrease 80 per cent.

13. A spring is stretched 6 inches by a weight of 2 lb. The spring is acted upon by an impressed force of $11 \sin 3t$ lb. If the weight is displaced 3 inches from its position of equilibrium, describe the motion. Find the first instant after $t = 0$ when the weight is momentarily at rest.

**43. Electrical applications.** We shall consider the case of an electrical circuit in which resistance, inductance, and capacitance are connected in series. The physical laws which govern the circuit can be stated as follows. If $q$ is the charge in coulombs on the condenser at the time $t$, then the drop in electromotive force across the condenser is $E_c = \dfrac{1}{C} q$, where $E_c$ is measured in volts and $C$ is a constant, known as the capacitance and measured in farads. If $i$ is the current in amperes flowing in the circuit, the drop in electromotive force across the resistance is $E_R = Ri$, where $E_R$ is measured in volts and the constant $R$ is the resistance in ohms. The drop in electromotive force in volts due to the inductance is $E_L = L \dfrac{di}{dt}$, where $L$ is the coefficient of inductance measured in henrys. The current $i$ and the charge $q$ are related by the formula $i = \dfrac{dq}{dt}$. Finally, Kirchhoff's second law * states that the algebraic sum of the electromotive forces around a closed circuit is zero. Hence if an electromotive force $E(t)$ is impressed upon the circuit the equation

$$L \frac{di}{dt} + Ri + \frac{1}{C} q = E(t)$$

must result. If we divide by $L$ and differentiate with respect to $t$, we obtain the equation

(38) $$\frac{d^2 i}{dt^2} + \frac{R}{L} \frac{di}{dt} + \frac{1}{LC} i = \frac{1}{L} \frac{d}{dt} E(t)$$

from which to determine the current $i(t)$.

Consider the case in which $E(t) = E_0 \sin \omega t$. Then (38) becomes

(39) $$\frac{d^2 i}{dt^2} + \frac{R}{L} \frac{di}{dt} + \frac{1}{LC} i = \frac{E_0 \omega}{L} \cos \omega t.$$

The parallelism between equations (39) and (35) is at once

* Formulated by Gustav Robert Kirchhoff (1824–1887), German physicist.

127

evident. The discussion of Article 42 can be translated to fit the present situation by substituting the constants $\frac{R}{L}$, $\frac{1}{LC}$, and $\frac{E_0\omega}{L}$ for $2k$, $\omega_0^2$, and $\frac{F_0}{m}$. Thus if the ratio $\frac{R}{2L}$ is small by comparison with $\frac{1}{LC}$, the current $i(t)$ in the circuit is given as a sum

$$i = i_T + i_S,$$

where $i_T$ is the *transient current* having the value

$$i_T = Ke^{-\frac{R}{2L}t}\cos\left(\frac{t}{2LC}\sqrt{4LC - R^2C^2} + \alpha\right)$$

and $i_S$ is the *steady-state current* given by

$$i_S = \frac{E_0}{\left[R^2 + \left(\omega L - \frac{1}{\omega C}\right)^2\right]^{\frac{1}{2}}}\cos(\omega t + \theta).$$

The quantity $z = \left[R^2 + \left(\omega L - \frac{1}{\omega C}\right)^2\right]^{\frac{1}{2}}$ is known as the *impedance* of the circuit. It has its minimum value when

$$\omega^2 = \frac{1}{LC},$$

and hence the amplitude of the steady-state current will be at a maximum, for a given resistance $R$, when the frequency of the impressed electromotive force has the value

$$\nu = \frac{\omega}{2\pi} = \frac{1}{2\pi\sqrt{LC}}.$$

This is the condition for resonance; the circuit is then said to be in resonance with the impressed electromotive force.

**44. Electrical applications (continued).** In the case of a network such as that illustrated in Fig. 13, it is necessary to apply Kirchhoff's first law, which states that the algebraic sum of the currents at any junction point is zero. It follows that

(40) $$i = i_1 + i_2.$$

By Kirchhoff's second law, applied to the circuit on the left,

$$(41) \qquad Ri + L_2 \frac{di_2}{dt} + \frac{1}{C} q = E.$$

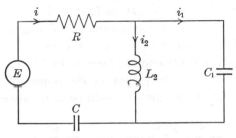

**Figure 13**

When applied to the circuit on the right, the same law yields

$$(42) \qquad - L_2 \frac{di_0}{dt} + \frac{1}{C_1} q_1 = 0.$$

Differentiating (41), (42), and using (40), we have:

$$(43) \qquad \begin{cases} L_2 \dfrac{d^2 i_2}{dt^2} + R \left( \dfrac{di_1}{dt} + \dfrac{di_2}{dt} \right) + \dfrac{1}{C} \left( i_1 + i_2 \right) = \dfrac{dE}{dt} \\[2mm] L_2 \dfrac{d^2 i_2}{dt^2} - \dfrac{1}{C_1} i_1 = 0 \end{cases}$$

The equations (43) are simultaneous linear equations which may be solved by the methods of Article 40.

### EXERCISE 28

1. An electrical circuit contains a constant source of electromotive force of 6 volts, a resistance of 12 ohms, an inductance of 0.01 henry, a capacitance of $2.5 \times 10^{-4}$ farad, and a switch, all connected in series. The charge $q$ on the condenser is zero at $t = 0$ and the switch is open so that $i = 0$ when $t = 0$. If the switch is closed, find the expression for the current which flows in the circuit.

2. Solve Problem 1 if the inductance is absent from the circuit and the charge on the condenser is initially 0.001 coulomb.

3. Solve Problem 1 if the constant electromotive force is replaced by 120 sin 120$\pi t$.

4. Solve Problem 1 if the resistance is 100 ohms, the inductance is 0.05 henry, the capacitance is $4 \times 10^{-5}$ farad, and the electromotive force at time $t$ is 120 sin 120$\pi t$ volts.

5. Solve Problem 1 if the capacitance is missing from the circuit, the switch is closed at $t = 0$, and $i = 0$ when $t = 0$.

6. If the constant electromotive force in Problem 1 is replaced by 120 sin $\omega t$, find the frequency of the impressed electromotive force with which the circuit would be in resonance.

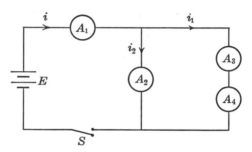

Figure 14

In the following problems derive the differential equations which determine the currents $i$, $i_1$, $i_2$ flowing in the network of Figure 14 when the switch is closed, if $E$, $A_1$, $A_2$, $A_3$, $A_4$ have the given values.

7. $E$ is an electromotive force of $E$ volts, $A_1$ is a resistance of $R$ ohms, $A_2$ is an inductance of $L_2$ henrys, $A_3$ is a resistance of $R_1$ ohms, and $A_4$ is a capacitance of $C_1$ farads. The currents $i$, $i_1$, $i_2$ are all zero when $t = 0$.

8. Solve Problem 6 if the capacitance $C_1$ is replaced by an inductance of $L_1$ henrys.

9. Solve Problem 6 if the inductance $L_2$ is replaced by a capacitance of $C_2$ farads, and the capacitance $C_1$ is replaced by an inductance of $L_1$ henrys.

# CHAPTER FIVE

# Numerical methods

**45. Introduction.** This chapter will be concerned with devices for obtaining approximate solutions of differential equations. Such approximations, which are necessary when no exact solution can be found, may also be of advantage in other cases. Attention will be restricted to equations of the first and second orders, and to systems of first-order equations. However, the methods which will be presented can be generalized to apply to equations of higher order.[*]

**46. Picard's [†] method.** While the practical utility of this method is limited, it will be presented because it has theoretical importance as well as historical interest. It illustrates a type of procedure frequently employed in other fields of application.

The other methods described in this chapter proceed from an approximate value of a solution at one point to the determination of an approximate value at a nearby point. Picard's method, on the other hand, furnishes a sequence of functions

---

[*] For a fuller account of the methods discussed in this chapter the reader may consult the following references:

A. A. Bennett, W. E. Milne, H. Bateman, *Numerical Integration of Differential Equations*. Report of the National Research Council Committee on Numerical Integration (Washington, D.C.: National Academy of Sciences, 1933).

W. E. Milne, *Numerical Calculus* (Princeton University Press, 1949).

[†] Charles Émile Picard (1856–1941) was an eminent French analyst.

defined over an interval, each function of the sequence approximating the desired solution over the entire interval. This sequence of functions ordinarily approaches the exact solution as a limit.

We shall consider the application of Picard's method to the problem of finding a solution $y = \phi(x)$ of the differential equation

(1) $$\frac{dy}{dx} = f(x, y)$$

subject to the initial condition $\phi(x_0) = y_0$. This problem is equivalent to finding a function $\phi(x)$ which satisfies the equation

(2) $$\phi(x) = y_0 + \int_{x_0}^{x} f[x, \phi(x)] \, dx,$$

since it follows from (2) that

(3) $$\frac{d\phi(x)}{dx} = f[x, \phi(x)],$$

and $\phi(x_0) = y_0$. Conversely, (2) is obtained from (3) by integrating over the interval $(x_0, x)$.

We determine a sequence of approximations to the solution (2) as follows. We assume an initial approximation $y = \phi_1(x)$. In the absence of information concerning the general nature of $y(x)$, $\phi_1(x)$ will be taken to be the constant $y_0$. When $\phi_1(x)$ is substituted for $y$ in $f(x, y)$, a function $f[x, \phi_1(x)]$ is obtained, from which a second approximation

(4) $$\phi_2(x) = y_0 + \int_{x_0}^{x} f[x, \phi_1(x)] \, dx$$

results. This in turn leads to a third approximation

(5) $$\phi_3(x) = y_0 + \int_{x_0}^{x} f[x, \phi_2(x)] \, dx.$$

In this way a sequence of successive approximations

(6) $$\phi_{n+1}(x) = y_0 + \int_{x_0}^{x} f[x, \phi_n(x)] \, dx, \quad n = 1, 2, \ldots$$

is obtained, and each of these approximating functions satisfies the initial condition $\phi_{n+1}(x_0) = y_0$.

132

If the function $f(x, y)$ has continuous partial derivatives of the first order in a neighborhood of the point $(x_0, y_0)$, the sequence of functions $\phi_1, \phi_2, \ldots, \phi_n, \ldots$ approaches a limiting function $\phi(x)$ over some interval about $x = x_0$. The function $\phi(x)$ is the unique solution of the differential equation (1) which satisfies the prescribed initial condition. The preceding discussion, when carried out in detail, furnishes a proof of Theorem 1 of Article 6. In practice the function $\phi(x)$ cannot usually be determined easily. Instead, a function $\phi_n(x)$ of the sequence is taken as an approximate solution, the accuracy of which can be judged roughly by comparing the values of $\phi_n(x)$ and $\phi_{n-1}(x)$ for a certain value of $x$.

EXAMPLE. By Picard's method find a fourth approximation to the solution of

$$y' = xy$$

for which $y = 1$ when $x = 0$. Does this suggest the solution of the equation?

SOLUTION. Take the constant function $\phi_1 = 1$ as a first approximation. In this case equation (6) becomes

$$\phi_{n+1}(x) = 1 + \int_0^x \left[ - x\phi_n(x) \right] dx, \quad n = 1, 2, \cdots$$

from which, successively, we find:

$$\phi_2(x) = 1 + \int_0^x (- x) \, dx = 1 - \frac{x^2}{2}$$

$$\phi_3(x) = 1 + \int_0^x \left( - x + \frac{x^3}{2} \right) dx = 1 - \frac{x^2}{2} + \frac{x^4}{2 \cdot 4}$$

$$\phi_4(x) = 1 + \int_0^x \left( - x + \frac{x^3}{2} - \frac{x^5}{2 \cdot 4} \right) dx = 1 - \frac{x^2}{2} + \frac{x^4}{2 \cdot 4} - \frac{x^6}{2 \cdot 4 \cdot 6}$$

These expressions suggest that the limit of the sequence of approximating functions is the function:

$$\phi(x) = 1 - \frac{x^2}{2} + \frac{x^4}{2 \cdot 4} - \frac{x^6}{2 \cdot 4 \cdot 6} + \cdots + (- 1)^n \frac{x^{2n}}{2^n \cdot n!} + \cdots$$

$$= e^{-\frac{1}{2}x^2}$$

This is actually true since $\phi(x) = e^{-\frac{1}{2}x^2}$ is the solution of the

133

differential equation for which $\phi(0) = 1$, as the reader can easily show. The graphs of the approximating functions $\phi_1(x)$, $\phi_2(x)$, $\phi_3(x)$, $\phi_4(x)$, and of the exact solution $\phi(x)$ are shown in Fig. 15.

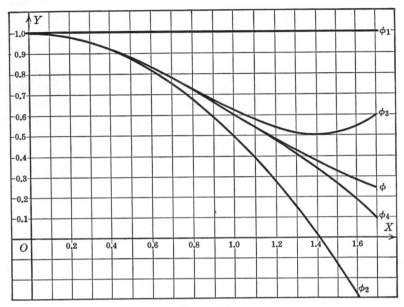

Figure 15

It should be noted that each of the graphs passes through $(0, 1)$ and that the sequence of approximating curves seems to approach the actual solution curve

$$y = e^{-\frac{1}{2}x^2}.$$

As an indication of the degree of the approximation achieved by stopping with $\phi_4(x)$, it may be noted that for $x = 0.5$,

$$\phi_3 = 0.8828,$$
$$\phi_4 = 0.8825.$$

The value, accurate to four digits, is in fact

$$e^{-0.125} = 0.8825.$$

In this example the sequence of approximating functions $\phi_n(x)$ converges to $e^{-\frac{1}{2}x^2}$ for all values of $x$.

134

## EXERCISE 29

In each of Problems 1–7 find the first five Picard approximations to the indicated particular solution of the differential equation. Compare the values of $\phi_4$ and $\phi_5$ for the given value $\xi$ of the independent variable. Find the exact solution $y(x)$ and its value at $x = \xi$.

1. $y' = x - y$; $y(0) = 1$; $\xi = 0.5$
2. $y' = r + y$; $y(0) = 1$, $\xi = 0.5$
3. $y' = x^2 + y$; $y(1) = 3$; $\xi = 2$
4. $y' = x^2 - y$; $y(1) = 2$; $\xi = 0.5$
5. $y' = ye^x$; $y(0) = 2$; $\xi = 1.5$
6. $y' = y + \sin x$; $y(0) = 0.5$; $\xi = 0.4$
7. $y' = \cos 2x - y$; $y(0) = 0.7$; $\xi = 0.3$

8. Find the first four Picard approximations to the particular solution of the equation $y' = 1 + y^2$ for which $y(0) = 1$. Evaluate for $x = 0.3$ and compare with the exact solution.
9. Obtain $\phi_1$, $\phi_2$, and $\phi_3$ for the particular solution of the equation $y' = x + y^2$ for which $y(0) = 0.4$. Evaluate for $x = 0.2$.
10. Obtain $\phi_1$, $\phi_2$, and $\phi_3$ for the particular solution of the equation $y' = x + y \cos x$ for which $y(0) = 1$. Evaluate for $x = 0.6$.

**47. Use of Taylor's series.*** This method is the first of the so-called "step-by-step" methods of approximation to the solution of a differential equation. It is particularly useful in providing preliminary estimates from which one may proceed to even closer approximations by means of the devices to be described later in this chapter.

We shall first explain the application of the technique to an equation

$$\frac{dy}{dx} = f(x, y)$$

of the first order. Let it be required to find a solution $y(x)$ of

---

* Brook Taylor (1685–1731) first used the series which bears his name in connection with the calculus of finite differences, which he invented.

this equation for which $y(x_0) = y_0$. If in a neighborhood of the point $(x_0, y_0)$ the function $f(x, y)$ has continuous partial derivatives of all orders up to and including the $k$th order, then for $x$ near $x_0$ the solution $y(x)$ will have continuous derivatives of all orders up to and including the $(k + 1)$th order. These derivatives may be calculated by differentiating the equation $y'(x) = f[x, y(x)]$ successively with respect to $x$:

$$
\begin{aligned}
y'(x) &= f[x, y(x)] \\
y''(x) &= f_x + f_y y'(x) \\
y'''(x) &= f_{xx} + 2f_{xy} y'(x) + f_{yy}[y'(x)]^2 + f_y y''(x)
\end{aligned}
$$

(7)

$$\cdot \quad \cdot \quad \cdot \quad \cdot \quad \cdot \quad \cdot \quad \cdot \quad \cdot \quad \cdot \quad \cdot \quad \cdot \quad \cdot$$

The values $y_0'$, $y_0''$, ..., $y_0^{(k)}$, of the first $k$ derivatives of $y(x)$ at $x_0$ can be found by substituting $x = x_0$ into the equations (7).

If now $x_1 > x_0$ is a value close to $x_0$, we can find the approximate value $y_1$ of $y(x_1)$ by using the first $k + 1$ terms in the Taylor expansion of $y(x)$ about $x = x_0$. Putting $h_1 = x_1 - x_0$ we have

$$(8) \qquad y_1 = y_0 + y_0' h_1 + \frac{y_0''}{2!} h_1^2 + \cdots + \frac{y_0^{(k)}}{k!} h_1^k.$$

The error $y(x_1) - y_1$, which has the value

$$\frac{y_0^{(k+1)}(x_0 + \theta h_1)}{(k+1)!} \cdot h_1^{k+1}$$

where $\theta$ is some number between 0 and 1, will be small if $h_1$ is sufficiently small.

For a value $x_2 > x_1$ but close to $x_1$ we may repeat the process. It is now necessary to use the Taylor expansion of $y(x)$ about the point $x = x_1$. The numbers $y(x_1)$, $y'(x_1)$, ..., $y^{(k)}(x_1)$ which are needed for this expansion may be approximated by the values $y_1$, $y_1'$, ..., $y_1^{(k)}$ which are obtained from (7) by substituting $x_1$, $y_1$ in the right members. One thus obtains

$$(9) \qquad y_2 = y_1 + y_1' h_2 + \frac{y_1''}{2!} h_2^2 + \cdots + \frac{y_1^{(k)}}{k!} h_2^k,$$

where $h_2 = x_2 - x_1$, as the approximate value of $y(x_2)$.

In general, if $\xi > x_0$ we may interpolate $n - 1$ equidistant values $x_1, x_2, \ldots, x_{n-1}$ between $\xi$ and $x_0$ so that

$$x_0 < x_1 < x_2 < \cdots < x_{n-1} < x_n = \xi.$$

At the $i$th stage the formula (8) is replaced by

$$(10) \qquad y_{i+1} = y_i + y_i'h + \frac{y_i''}{2!} h^2 + \cdots + \frac{y_i^{(k)}}{k!} h^k$$

with $h = \dfrac{\xi - x_0}{n}$, which serves to determine $y_{i+1}$ when $y_i$, $y_i'$, $\ldots$, $y_i^{(k)}$ have been previously determined. After $n$ repetitions the process will yield a value $y_n$ which is an approximation to $y(\xi)$.

We note again the difference between this method and that of Article 46. Picard's process provides a sequence of curves approximating the particular integral curve of the differential equation. The method of this article produces a set of points $(x_i, y_i)$ all lying near the integral curve.

As a first example we apply this method to the example of the preceding article for comparison.

EXAMPLE 1. Find the approximate value at $x = 0.5$ of that solution $y(x)$ of the equation $y' = -xy$ for which $y(0) = 1$. Take $h = 0.1$ and obtain a result correct to four decimal places.

SOLUTION. In this problem $x_0 = 0$, $x_1 = 0.1$, $x_2 = 0.2$, $x_3 = 0.3$, $x_4 = 0.4$, $x_5 = 0.5$; $y_0 = 1$. The Taylor's series to be employed are obtained from (10) by giving successively to $i$ the values 0, 1, 2, 3, 4. Since in each of the five cases $h$ has the same value 0.1, it will be advantageous to rewrite (10) with this value substituted for $h$. The revised series are

$$(a) \quad y_{i+1} = y_i + 0.1y_i' + 0.005y_i'' + 0.000167y_i''' + 0.000004y_i^{(4)},$$
$$i = 0, 1, 2, 3, 4,$$

where terms in derivatives of order five and higher are omitted, because they can be shown not to give results which affect the first five decimal places; that is, $k$ in (10) is taken as 4. The derivatives $y_i^{(k)}$ which are needed in $(a)$ are found from the differential equation as follows.

137

$$y' = - xy$$
$$y'' = - xy' - y = - x(- xy) - y = (x^2 - 1)y$$
$$y''' = (x^2 - 1)y' + 2xy = (x^2 - 1)(- xy) + 2xy = (- x^3 + 3x)y$$
$$y^{(4)} = (- x^3 + 3x)(- xy) + (- 3x^2 + 3)y = (x^4 - 6x^2 + 3)y$$

By setting $x = x_i$, we have

(b)
$$\begin{cases} y_i' = - x_i y_i \\ y_i'' = (x_i^2 - 1)y_i \\ y_i''' = (- x_i^3 + 3x_i)y_i \\ y_i^{(4)} = (x_i^4 - 6x_i^2 + 3)y_i \end{cases}$$

where $x_0 = 0$, $x_1 = 0.1$, $x_2 = 0.2$, $x_3 = 0.3$, $x_4 = 0.4$. The following table gives the values of the coefficients of $y_i$ in (b).

| $x_i$ | $x_i^2$ | $x_i^3$ | $x_i^4$ | $- x_i$ | $x_i^2 - 1$ | $- x_i^3 + 3x_i$ | $x_i^4 - 6x_i^2 + 3$ |
|---|---|---|---|---|---|---|---|
| 0 | 0 | 0 | 0 | 0 | $- 1$ | 0 | 3 |
| 0.1 | 0.01 | 0.001 | 0.0001 | $- 0.1$ | $- 0.99$ | 0.299 | 2.9401 |
| 0.2 | 0.04 | 0.008 | 0.0016 | $- 0.2$ | $- 0.96$ | 0.592 | 2.7616 |
| 0.3 | 0.09 | 0.027 | 0.0081 | $- 0.3$ | $- 0.91$ | 0.873 | 2.4681 |
| 0.4 | 0.16 | 0.064 | 0.0256 | $- 0.4$ | $- 0.84$ | 1.136 | 2.0656 |

The expressions (b) can now be written in the form:

(c)
$$\begin{cases} y_0' = 0 & y_0'' = - y_0 & y_0''' = 0 & y_0^{(4)} = 3 \\ y_1' = - 0.1y_1 & y_1'' = - 0.99y_1 & y_1''' = 0.299y_1 & y_1^{(4)} = 2.9401y_1 \\ y_2' = - 0.2y_2 & y_2'' = - 0.96y_2 & y_2''' = 0.592y_2 & y_2^{(4)} = 2.7616y_2 \\ y_3' = - 0.3y_3 & y_3'' = - 0.91y_3 & y_3''' = 0.873y_3 & y_3^{(4)} = 2.4681y_3 \\ y_4' = - 0.4y_4 & y_4'' = - 0.84y_4 & y_4''' = 1.136y_4 & y_4^{(4)} = 2.0656y_4 \end{cases}$$

When the values $y_i^{(k)}$ given by (c) are substituted into (a), we express each $y_{i+1}$ as a multiple of its predecessor:

(d)
$$\begin{cases} y_1 = y_0 + 0.1y_0' + 0.005y_0'' + 0.000167y_0''' + 0.000004y_0^{(4)} \\ \quad = (1 - 0.005 + 0.00001)y_0 = 0.99501 \\[4pt] y_2 = y_1 + 0.1y_1' + 0.005y_1'' + 0.000167y_1''' + 0.000004y_1^{(4)} \\ \quad = (1 - 0.01 - 0.00495 + 0.00005 + 0.00001)y_1 = 0.98511y_1 \\[4pt] y_3 = y_2 + 0.1y_2' + 0.005y_2'' + 0.000167y_2''' + 0.000004y_2^{(4)} \\ \quad = (1 - 0.02 - 0.0048 + 0.00010 + 0.00001)y_2 = 0.97531y_2 \\[4pt] y_4 = y_3 + 0.1y_3' + 0.005y_3'' + 0.000167y_3''' + 0.000004y_3^{(4)} \\ \quad = (1 - 0.03 - 0.00455 + 0.00015 + 0.00001)y_3 = 0.96561y_3 \\[4pt] y_5 = y_4 + 0.1y_4' + 0.005y_4'' + 0.000167y_4''' + 0.000004y_4^{(4)} \\ \quad = (1 - 0.04 - 0.0042 + 0.00019 + 0.00001)y_4 = 0.95600y_4 \end{cases}$$

The required solution $y_5 = y(\xi)$ is then found by assembling the results of the system $(d)$. That is

$$y_5 = (0.95600)(0.96561)(0.97531)(0.98511)(0.99501) = 0.8825.$$

Of course, the values of the intermediate solutions $y_2, y_3, y_4$ can also be obtained from $(d)$. In the example of Article 46 it was noted that the particular solution $y(x)$ of the differential equation now under discussion is actually $e^{-\frac{1}{2}x^2}$. The result $y_5$ obtained by means of Taylor's series agrees with the value of $e^{-\frac{1}{2}x^2}$ at $x = 0.5$ to four decimal places.

The above procedure is readily modified so as to apply to an equation

$$y'' = f(x, y, y')$$

of the second order. If one seeks the approximate value at $x = \xi$ of that solution $y(x)$ for which $y(x_0) = y_0$ and $y'(x_0) = y_0'$, one supplements the formula $(10)$ by the additional formula

$$(11) \quad y_{i+1}' = y_i' + y_i''h + \frac{y_i'''}{2!}h^2 + \cdots + \frac{y_i^{(k)}}{(k-1)!}h^{k-1}.$$

The necessary modifications will be made clear by the following example.

EXAMPLE 2. Find the approximate value at $x = 0.2$ of the solution $y$ of the equation $y'' - 2y^3 = 0$ for which $y = 1$ and $y' = -1$ at $x = 0$. Take $h = 0.1$ and obtain a result correct to four decimal places.

SOLUTION. From the differential equation we find by differentiation

$$(a) \quad \begin{cases} y''' = 6y^2y' \\ y^{(4)} = 6y^2y'' + 12yy'^2 \\ y^{(5)} = 6y^2y''' + 36yy'y'' + 12y'^3 \\ y^{(6)} = 6y^2y^{(4)} + 48yy'y''' + 36y(y'')^2 + 72(y')^2y'' \end{cases}$$

so that for $x_0 = 0$ we have $y_0 = 1$, $y_0' = -1$, $y_0'' = 2$, $y_0''' = -6$, $y_0^{(4)} = 24$, $y_0^{(5)} = -120$, $y_0^{(6)} = 720$. Then with $i = 0$, $k = 5$ in $(10)$ we find

$$y_1 = 1 - h + h^2 - h^3 + h^4 - h^5,$$

so that for $h = 0.1$

$$y_1 = 0.90909.$$

By means of (11) with $i = 0$, $k = 6$ we obtain

$$y_1' = -1 + 2h - 3h^2 + 4h^3 - 5h^4 + 6h^5,$$

which for $h = 0.1$ gives

$$y_1' = -0.82644.$$

By substitution into the original differential equation and into (a) we find:

$y_1'' = 2(0.90909)^3 = 1.50262$

$y_1''' = 6(0.90909)^2(-0.82644) = -4.09800$

$y_1^{(4)} = 6(0.90909)^2(1.50262) + 12(0.90909)(-0.82644)^2 = 14.902$

Now from (10) with $i = 1$, $k = 4$ we have

$$y_2 = 0.90909 - 0.82644h + 0.75131h^2 - 0.68300h^3 + 0.62092h^4.$$

Putting $h = 0.1$ gives

$$y_2 = 0.8333,$$

which is the approximate value of $y$ at $x_2 = 0.2$.

## EXERCISE 30

For each of the following differential equations use the method of this article to find the value $y(\xi)$ of the indicated particular solution at the point $x = \xi$. Take $h = 0.1$ and make the result correct to four significant digits.

1. $y' = x - y$; $y(0) = 2$, $\xi = 0.2$
2. $y' = y^2$; $y(0) = 1$, $\xi = 0.3$
3. $y' = \cos y$; $y(0) = 0.5$, $\xi = 0.2$
4. $y' = \sin xy$; $y(0) = 0.5$, $\xi = 0.2$
5. $y' = \sin x + \tan y$; $y(0) = 3$, $\xi = 0.2$
6. $y'' = xy$, $y(0) = 1$; $y'(0) = -1$, $\xi = 0.2$
7. $y'' - xy' + y = 0$; $y(0) = 1$, $y'(0) = -1$, $\xi = 0.3$
8. $2xy'' - y' + xy = 0$; $y(1) = 0$, $y'(1) = -1$, $\xi = 1.2$
9. $xy'' - y' - xy = 0$; $y(3) = 2$, $y'(3) = -1$, $\xi = 3.3$
10. $y'' = \ln y$; $y(0) = 1$, $y'(0) = 1$, $\xi = 0.2$

**48. The Runge-Kutta method.** The Runge-Kutta method differs from that of the preceding article in that one uses the values of the first derivatives of $f(x, y)$ at several points instead of the values of the successive derivatives at a single point. Let us designate by $y_n$ the exact or approximate value at $x = x_n$ of a solution $y(x)$ of the differential equation $y' = f(x, y)$. We seek an approximate value $y_{n+1}$ of this solution at $x = x_{n+1} = x_n + h$. The objective of the present method is to obtain an expression for $y_{n+1}$ which coincides through terms of a certain order $r$ with the Taylor development of $y(x_{n+1})$ in powers of $h$. For $r = 2, 3,$ and 4 the formulas are:

(12) $\quad y_{n+1} = y_n + \frac{1}{2}(k_1 + k_2)$, where $\begin{cases} k_1 = hf(x_n, y_n) \\ k_2 = hf(x_n + h, y_n + k_1) \end{cases}$

(13) $\quad y_{n+1} = y_n + \frac{1}{6}(l_1 + 4l_2 + l_3)$, where
$$\begin{cases} l_1 = hf(x_n, y_n) \\ l_2 = hf(x_n + \frac{1}{2}h, y_n + \frac{1}{2}l_1) \\ l_3 = hf(x_n + h, y_n + 2l_2 - l_1) \end{cases}$$

(14) $\quad y_{n+1} = y_n + \frac{1}{6}(m_1 + 2m_2 + 2m_3 + m_4)$, where
$$\begin{cases} m_1 = hf(x_n, y_n) = l_1 \\ m_2 = hf(x_n + \frac{1}{2}h, y_n + \frac{1}{2}m_1) = l_2 \\ m_3 = hf(x_n + \frac{1}{2}h, y_n + \frac{1}{2}m_2) \\ m_4 = hf(x_n + h, y_n + m_3) \end{cases}$$

These formulas will be referred to as the second-, third-, and fourth-order formulas respectively.

We give a proof for the second-order formula only; derivations of the remaining formulas can be made similarly. If the notations $f_n, f_{nx}, f_{ny}$ are used to represent

$$f(x_n, y_n), \quad \frac{\partial}{\partial x}f(x_n, y_n), \quad \frac{\partial}{\partial y}f(x_n, y_n),$$

the Taylor expansion of $y_{n+1}$ in powers of $h$ through terms of the second order may be written

(15) $$y_{n+1} = y_n + hf_n + \frac{h^2}{2}(f_{nx} + f_n f_{ny}).$$

141

We assume an approximation of the form

(16)     $y_{n+1} = y_n + \alpha h f_n + \beta h f(x_n + \gamma h, y_n + \delta h f_n)$

and proceed to determine values of the constants $\alpha$, $\beta$, $\gamma$, $\delta$ so that the right member of (16) agrees with that of (15) through terms of the second order in $h$.

The Taylor series for $f(x + H, y + K)$ is

$$f(x + H, y + K) = f(x, y) + H f_x + K f_y + \cdots,$$

so that we may write

$$f(x_n + \gamma h, y_n + \delta h f_n) = f_n + h(\gamma f_{nx} + \delta f_n f_{ny}) + \cdots.$$

Substitution into (16) gives

(17)     $y_{n+1} = y_n + (\alpha + \beta) f_n h + \beta(\gamma f_{nx} + \delta f_n f_{ny}) h^2.$

The right members of (15) and (17) can be made identical by putting $\alpha = \beta = \frac{1}{2}$, $\gamma = \delta = 1$. We are thus led to the Runge-Kutta formula of the second order by substituting these values into (16).

EXAMPLE 1.   Find the approximate value at $x = 0.2$ of that solution $y(x)$ of the equation $y' = x + y^2$ for which $y(0) = 1$. Use each of the formulas (12), (13), (14), with $h = 0.2$.

SOLUTION.

Using (12):  $k_1 = 0.2(1) = 0.2$
$k_2 = 0.2[0.2 + (1.2)^2] = 0.328$
$y_1 = 1 + \frac{1}{2}(0.528) = 1.264$

Using (13):  $l_1 = 0.2$
$l_2 = 0.2[0.1 + (1.1)^2] = 0.262$
$l_3 = 0.2[0.2 + (1.324)^2] = 0.391$
$y_1 = 1 + \frac{1}{6}(1.639) = 1.273$

Using (14):  $m_1 = 0.2$
$m_2 = 0.262$
$m_3 = 0.2[0.1 + (1.131)^2] = 0.276$
$m_4 = 0.2[0.2 + (1.276)^2] = 0.366$
$y_1 = 1 + \frac{1}{6}(1.642) = 1.274$

A second-order differential equation

$$y'' = f(x, y, y')$$

with the initial conditions $y = y_0$, $y' = y_0'$ at $x = x_0$ may be solved by use of formulas analogous to (12), (13), (14). For example, the pair of third-order formulas analogous to (13) is

(18)
$$y_{n+1} = y_n + \tfrac{1}{6}(l_1 + 4l_2 + l_3),$$
$$y_{n+1}' = y_n' + \tfrac{1}{6}(l_1' + 4l_2' + l_3'),$$

where $l_1, l_2, l_3, l_1', l_2', l_3'$ are given by the equations:

$$l_1 = hy_n'$$
$$l_1' = hf(x_n, y_n, y_n')$$
$$l_2 = h(y_n' + \tfrac{1}{2}l_1')$$
$$l_2' = hf(x_n + \tfrac{1}{2}h, y_n + \tfrac{1}{2}l_1, y_n' + \tfrac{1}{2}l_1')$$
$$l_3 = h(y_n' + 2l_2' - l_1')$$
$$l_3' = hf(x_n + h, y_n + 2l_2 - l_1, y_n' + 2l_2' - l_1')$$

EXAMPLE 2. For the equation $y'' - 2y^3 = 0$ find the approximate value at $x = 0.2$ of the solution $y(x)$ for which

$$y(0) = 1, \quad y'(0) = -1.$$

Find also the value of $y'(x)$ at the same point.

SOLUTION. From the equations following (18) the values of $l_1, l_1', l_2, l_2', l_3, l_3'$ are found as follows.

$$l_1 = 0.2(-1) = -0.2$$
$$l_1' = 0.2(2) = 0.4$$
$$l_2 = 0.2(-1 + 0.2) = -0.16$$
$$l_2' = 0.2(1.458) = 0.2916$$
$$l_3 = 0.2(-1 + 0.5832 - 0.4) = -0.1634$$
$$l_3' = 0.2(1.3629) = 0.2726$$

Substitution of these values into (18) gives the results:

$$y_1 = 1 + \tfrac{1}{6}(-1.0034) = 0.8328,$$
$$y_1' = -1 + \tfrac{1}{6}(1.8390) = -0.6935$$

143

## EXERCISE 31

Each of the first eight problems is concerned with the particular solution of the given differential equation determined by the indicated condition. Find the approximate values of this solution corresponding to the values $x_0 + 0.1$, $x_0 + 0.2$, $x_0 + 0.3$, $x_0 + 0.4$, $x_0 + 0.5$ of the independent variable. Use the Runge-Kutta formulas of the indicated order, and find the results correct to four digits.

1. $y' = \dfrac{x+y}{x-y}$; $x_0 = 0$, $y_0 = 3$. Second-order formulas.

2. $y' = x^2 - y$; $x_0 = 0$, $y_0 = 1$. Third-order formulas.

3. $y' = y + \tan x$; $x_0 = 0$, $y_0 = 0.5$. Fourth-order formulas.

4. $y' = e^{x-y}$; $x_0 = 0$, $y_0 = 0.2$. Third-order formulas.

5. $y' = e^x + \cos x + \sin y$; $x_0 = 0$, $y_0 = -0.5$. Third-order formulas.

6. $y' = \text{Arc tan } xy$; $x_0 = 0$, $y_0 = 1$. Second-order formulas.

7. $y' = x + \sin y$; $x_0 = 0$, $y_0 = 0.6$. Fourth-order formulas.

8. $y' = \ln xy$; $x_0 = 1$, $y_0 = 2$. Fourth-order formulas.

For each of the following differential equations a particular solution is defined by the given initial conditions. Using the third-order Runge-Kutta formulas for equations of the second order, find correct to four digits the approximate values of $y(x)$ and $y'(x)$ corresponding to the values $x = 0.1, 0.2, 0.3$.

9. $y'' + y' = xy$; $x_0 = 0$, $y_0 = 1$, $y_0' = -1$

10. $y'' + xy' - y = 0$; $x_0 = 0$, $y_0 = -2$, $y_0' = 3$

11. $y'' + \sin xy + y^2 = 0$; $x_0 = 0$, $y_0 = 1$, $y_0' = -2$

12. $(1 + x)y'' + y' + e^{-xy} = 0$; $x_0 = 0$, $y_0 = 2$, $y_0' = 2$

**49. Adams' method.** In this method the step from $y_n$ to $y_{n+1}$ is made by means of an integration formula expressed in terms of differences of $f(x, y)$. In order to form the table of differences, it is necessary to have several approximate values of $y(x)$ in addition to the given initial value $y_0$. Such values may be found by either of the preceding two methods.

Suppose that $y(x)$ is the desired solution of the differential equation $y' = f(x, y)$. Integration between the limits $x_n$ and $x_{n+1}$ gives

$$(19) \qquad y(x_{n+1}) = y(x_n) + \int_{x_n}^{x_{n+1}} f[x, y(x)] \, dx.$$

We obtain an approximation $y_{n+1}$ to $y(x_{n+1})$ by substituting for $y(x_n)$ an approximate value $y_n$ and replacing the integral in the right member of (19) by the expression

$$(20) \qquad h[f_n + \tfrac{1}{2}\Delta f_n + \tfrac{5}{12}\Delta^2 f_n + \tfrac{3}{8}\Delta^3 f_n + \tfrac{251}{720}\Delta^4 f_n + \cdots],$$

in which $h = x_{n+1} - x_n$, $f_n = f(x_n, y_n)$, and $\Delta f_n = f_n - f_{n-1}$, $\Delta^2 f_n = \Delta f_n - \Delta f_{n-1}$, etc. The expression (20) ends with the term in $\Delta^k f_n$ if one has approximated $y'(x)$ by means of a polynomial of degree $k$ which assumes prescribed values at

$$x_{n-k}, \; x_{n-k+1} = x_{n-k} + h, \; x_{n-k+2} = x_{n-k+1} + h, \; \ldots, \; x_n = x_{n-1} + h.$$

These prescribed values are taken to be $f_{n-k}, f_{n-k+1}, \ldots, f_n$.

The demonstration of the validity of the formula (20) for the case $k = 1$ is as follows. For $k = 1$, $y' = f(x, y)$ is assumed to be expressed as $a + bx$. Then

$$f_n = f(x_n, y_n) = a + bx_n$$
$$f_{n-1} = f(x_{n-1}, y_{n-1}) = a + bx_{n-1}$$
$$\Delta f_n = f_n - f_{n-1} = b(x_n - x_{n-1}) = bh$$

so that $b = \dfrac{\Delta f_n}{h}$, $a = f_n - \dfrac{x_n \Delta f_n}{h}$, and:

$$y' = f(x, y)$$

$$= f_n - \frac{x_n \Delta f_n}{h} + \frac{x \Delta f_n}{h}$$

$$= f_n + \frac{x - x_n}{h} \Delta f_n$$

$$y_{n+1} = y_n + \int_{x_n}^{x_{n+1}} \left( f_n + \frac{x - x_n}{h} \Delta f_n \right) dx$$

$$= y_n + f_n h + \frac{(x_{n+1} - x_n)^2}{2h} \Delta f_n$$

$$= y_n + f_n h + \frac{h}{2} \Delta f_n$$

**145**

EXAMPLE 1. If $y(x)$ is the solution of $y' = x + 2y$ for which $y(0) = 1$, find the approximate values of $y$ for $x = 0.1, 0.2, 0.3, 0.4$, 0.5 by the third-order Runge-Kutta formulas. Then determine the value of $y$ for $x = 0.6$ by Adams' method, correct to three decimal places.

SOLUTION. The first table presents the computation of $y_1$, $y_2$, $y_3$, $y_4$, $y_5$.

| $x_n$ | $y_n$ | $l_1$ | $l_2$ | $l_3$ | $y_{n+1}$ |
|-------|-------|-------|-------|-------|-----------|
| 0.0 | 1.0000 | 0.2000 | 0.2250 | 0.2600 | 1.2267 |
| 0.1 | 1.2267 | 0.2553 | 0.2859 | 0.3286 | 1.5146 |
| 0.2 | 1.5146 | 0.3229 | 0.3602 | 0.4124 | 1.8773 |
| 0.3 | 1.8773 | 0.4055 | 0.4510 | 0.5148 | 2.3313 |
| 0.4 | 2.3313 | 0.5063 | 0.5619 | 0.6398 | 2.8969 |

Using these results in Adams' formula we obtain

| $x_n$ | $y_n$ | $f_n = x_n + 2y_n$ | $\Delta f_n$ | $\Delta^2 f_n$ | $\Delta^3 f_n$ |
|-------|-------|---------------------|--------------|----------------|----------------|
| 0.0 | 1.0000 | 2.0000 | | | |
| 0.1 | 1.2267 | 2.5533 | 0.5533 | | |
| 0.2 | 1.5146 | 3.2292 | 0.6759 | 0.1226 | |
| 0.3 | 1.8773 | 4.0546 | 0.8254 | 0.1495 | 0.0269 |
| 0.4 | 2.3313 | 5.0626 | 1.0080 | 0.1826 | 0.0331 |
| 0.5 | 2.8969 | 6.2938 | 1.2312 | 0.2232 | 0.0406 |

The final result is:

$$y_6 = 2.8969 + 0.1[6.2938 + \tfrac{1}{2}(1.2312) + \tfrac{5}{12}(0.2232) + \tfrac{3}{8}(0.0406)]$$
$$= 2.8969 + 0.1(6.2938 + 0.6156 + 0.0930 + 0.0152)$$
$$= 2.8969 + 0.7018$$
$$= 3.599$$

Adams' method may be applied to a second-order equation of the form

$$y'' = f(x, y, y'),$$

with the initial conditions

$$y(x_0) = y_0, \quad y'(x_0) = y_0'.$$

Let $p = y'$ so that the given equation is replaced by the pair

146

of simultaneous equations

$$y' = p, \quad p' = f(x, y, p).$$

This system may be solved by means of the formulas

(21)
$$y_{n+1} = y_n + h(p_n + \tfrac{1}{2}\Delta p_n + \tfrac{5}{12}\Delta^2 p_n + \cdots),$$
$$p_{n+1} = p_n + h(f_n + \tfrac{1}{2}\Delta f_n + \tfrac{5}{12}\Delta^2 f_n + \cdots).$$

EXAMPLE 2. If $y(x)$ is the solution of the equation $y'' = x - y - y'$ for which $y(0) = 1$, $y'(0) = -1$, obtain values for $y(x)$ and $y'(x)$ at $x = 0.1, 0.2, 0.3$ by the Runge-Kutta formulas of the third order, and their values at $x = 0.4$ by Adams' formulas.

SOLUTION. The first of the following tables is for the Runge-Kutta method; the second for Adams' formulas.

| $x_n$ | $y_n$ | $y_n'$ | $l_1$ | $l_1'$ | $l_2$ | $l_2'$ | $l_3$ | $l_3'$ |
|---|---|---|---|---|---|---|---|---|
| 0.0 | 1.0000 | $-1.0000$ | $-0.1000$ | 0.0000 | $-0.1000$ | 0.0100 | $-0.0980$ | 0.0180 |
| 0.1 | 0.9003 | $-0.9903$ | $-0.0990$ | 0.0190 | $-0.0981$ | 0.0280 | $-0.0953$ | 0.0350 |
| 0.2 | 0.8026 | $-0.9627$ | $-0.0963$ | 0.0360 | $-0.0945$ | 0.0440 | $-0.0911$ | 0.0501 |
| 0.3 | 0.7084 | $-0.9190$ | | | | | | |

| $x_n$ | $y_n$ | $p_n$ | $\Delta p_n$ | $\Delta^2 p_n$ | $f_n$ | $\Delta f_n$ | $\Delta^2 f_n$ |
|---|---|---|---|---|---|---|---|
| 0.0 | 1.0000 | $-1.0000$ | | | 0.0000 | | |
| 0.1 | 0.9003 | $-0.9903$ | 0.0097 | | 0.1900 | 0.1900 | |
| 0.2 | 0.8026 | $-0.9627$ | 0.0276 | 0.0179 | 0.3601 | 0.1701 | $-0.0199$ |
| 0.3 | 0.7084 | $-0.9190$ | 0.0437 | 0.0161 | 0.5106 | 0.1505 | $-0.0196$ |

Substituting into (21) we obtain

$$y_4 = 0.7084 + 0.1(-0.9190 + 0.0218 + 0.0067) = 0.619,$$
$$p_4 = -0.9190 + 0.1(0.5106 + 0.0752 - 0.0082) = -0.861.$$

## EXERCISE 32

1–8. From the values previously found for $y_1, y_2, y_3, y_4$ in each of Problems 1–8 of Exercise 31, find $y_5$ by Adams' method.

9–12. From the values of $y_1, y_2, y_3, p_1, p_2, p_3$ in each of Problems 9–12 of Exercise 31, find $y_4$ and $p_4$ by Adams' method.

147

**50. Milne's method.** As in Article 49, Milne's method * requires for its application the knowledge of several approximate values of $y$. The method provides checks which show the degree of accuracy of the solution and which reveal errors in the calculations. Let

$$y_{n-3}, \; y_{n-2}, \; y_{n-1}, \; y_n$$

be approximate values of a solution $y(x)$ of the equation $y' = f(x, y)$ corresponding to the values

$$x_{n-3}$$
$$x_{n-2} = x_{n-3} + h$$
$$x_{n-1} = x_{n-2} + h$$
$$x_n = x_{n-1} + h$$

Then the approximate value $y_{n+1}$ of the solution corresponding to

$$x_{n+1} = x_n + h$$

is given by the so-called *predictor* formula

$$(22) \qquad y_{n+1} = y_{n-3} + \frac{4h}{3} \left( 2f_n - f_{n-1} + 2f_{n-2} \right).$$

As a check the value $f_{n+1} = f(x_{n+1}, y_{n+1})$ can then be substituted into the so-called *corrector* formula

$$(23) \qquad Y_{n+1} = y_{n-1} + \frac{h}{3} \left( f_{n+1} + 4f_n + f_{n-1} \right).$$

If the values of $y_{n+1}$ and $Y_{n+1}$ differ, but by not too much, the latter is the more trustworthy. If these values coincide to $k$ decimal places after being properly rounded off, the value of $y(x_{n+1})$ is likely to agree with the values of $y_{n+1}$ and $Y_{n+1}$ to the same number of places.

EXAMPLE 1. Use Milne's method to find the value of $y$ for $x = 0.6$ in Example 1 of Article 49.

SOLUTION. From the second table of the solution of the example

* W. E. Milne, *Numerical Calculus* (Princeton University Press, 1949), pp. 134–139.

we abstract the following information.

| $n$ | $x_n$ | $y_n$ | $f_n = x_n + 2y_n$ |
|---|---|---|---|
| 2 | 0.2 | 1.5146 | 3.2292 |
| 3 | 0.3 | 1.8773 | 4.0546 |
| 4 | 0.4 | 2.3313 | 5.0626 |
| 5 | 0.5 | 2.8969 | 6.2938 |

The approximate value $y_6$ of the ordinate $y(0.6)$ of the solution curve is given by the predictor formula (22):

$$y_6 = y_2 + \frac{0.4}{3} (2f_5 - f_4 + 2f_3)$$

$$= 1.5146 + \frac{0.4}{3} (12.5876 - 5.0626 + 8.1092)$$

$$= 3.599$$

The value of $f_6 = x_6 + 2y_6$ is 7.7984, so that by the corrector formula (23):

$$Y_6 = y_4 + \frac{0.1}{3} (f_6 + 4f_5 + f_4)$$

$$= 2.3313 + \frac{0.1}{3} (7.7984 + 25.1752 + 5.0626)$$

$$= 3.599$$

Milne's method can be readily extended to a second-order differential equation $y'' = f(x, y, y')$. Formula (22) is replaced by the pair of formulas:

$$(24) \quad \begin{aligned} y_{n+1}' &= y_{n-3}' + \frac{4h}{3} (2f_n - f_{n-1} + 2f_{n-2}) \\ y_{n+1} &= y_{n-1} + \frac{h}{3} (y_{n+1}' + 4y_n' + y_{n-1}') \end{aligned}$$

The analog of (23) is the pair of formulas:

$$(25) \quad \begin{aligned} Y_{n+1}' &= y_{n-1}' + \frac{h}{3} (f_{n+1} + 4f_n + f_{n-1}) \\ Y_{n+1} &= y_{n-1} + \frac{h}{3} (Y_{n+1}' + 4y_n' + y_{n-1}') \end{aligned}$$

If $Y_{n+1}$ and $y_{n+1}$ agree to $k$ decimal places, then their common value can be expected to be the value of $y(x_{n+1})$ correct to $k$ decimal places.

149

EXAMPLE 2. Solve Example 2 of Article 49 by use of Milne's method.

SOLUTION. We begin by listing the following information from the second table of the solution of the example referred to.

| $n$ | $x_n$ | $y_n$ | $y_n'$ | $f_n = x_n - y_n - y_n'$ |
|---|---|---|---|---|
| 0 | 0.0 | 1.0000 | $-1.0000$ | 0.0000 |
| 1 | 0.1 | 0.9003 | $-0.9903$ | 0.1900 |
| 2 | 0.2 | 0.8026 | $-0.9627$ | 0.3601 |
| 3 | 0.3 | 0.7084 | $-0.9190$ | 0.5106 |

The values of $y_4'$, $y_4$ given by the predictor formulas (24) are:

$$y_4' = y_0' + \frac{0.4}{3} (2f_3 - f_2 + 2f_1)$$

$$= -1.0000 + \frac{0.4}{3} (1.0212 - 0.3601 + 0.3800)$$

$$= -0.8612$$

$$y_4 = y_2 + \frac{0.1}{3} (y_4' + 4y_3' + y_2')$$

$$= 0.8026 + \frac{0.1}{3} (-0.8612 - 3.6760 - 0.9627)$$

$$= 0.6193$$

Since

$$f_4 = x_4 - y_4 - y_4' = 0.4 - 0.6193 + 0.8612 = 0.6419,$$

we find $Y_4'$ from (25) to be:

$$Y_4' = y_2' + \frac{0.1}{3} (f_4 + 4f_3 + f_2)$$

$$= -0.9627 + \frac{0.1}{3} (0.6419 + 2.0424 + 0.3601)$$

$$= -0.8612$$

Then from the second formula (25) we have:

$$Y_4 = y_2 + \frac{0.1}{3} (Y_4' + 4y_3' + y_2')$$

$$= 0.8026 + \frac{0.1}{3} (-0.8612 - 3.6760 - 0.9627)$$

$$= 0.6193$$

*Comparison of methods of Runge-Kutta, Adams, and Milne.* While the methods of Runge-Kutta and of Adams both provide means of starting and of continuing the solution, the following remarks should be made concerning the merits of the two. The complexity arising from Adams' method depends upon the difficulty encountered in determining the successive derivatives of the unknown function and upon the failure of the Taylor series to converge rapidly. The Runge-Kutta method determines the increments of the function once and for all by means of a definite set of formulas. There are no trial values, no repetitions, and no expansions in series. However, the computation of the increments is sometimes very laborious so that for the continuation of the solution already started a shift to the method of Adams or Milne may decrease the labor involved and may increase the accuracy of the solution.

## EXERCISE 33

1–8. From the values of $y_1$, $y_2$, $y_3$, $y_4$ in each of Problems 1–8 of Exercise 31, find $y_5$ by Milne's method.

9–12. From the values of $y_1$, $y_2$, $y_3$, $p_1$, $p_2$, $p_3$, in each of Problems 9–12 of Exercise 31, find $y_4$ and $p_4$ by Milne's method.

**51. Simultaneous equations.** The extension of the methods of the three preceding articles to systems of differential equations is easily made. The examples which follow illustrate such extension of two of these methods.

EXAMPLE 1. Using the fourth-order Runge-Kutta formulas, find the approximate values at $x = 0.1$, $0.2$, $0.3$ of the solution $y(x)$, $z(x)$ of the system $y' = y - 3z$, $z' = 2y + z$ for which $y(0) = 1$, $z(0) = -1$.

SOLUTION. The formulas, analogous to (14), which apply to the system $y' = f(x, y, z)$, $z' = g(x, y, z)$ are the following.

151

$$y_{n+1} = y_n + \tfrac{1}{6}(m_1 + 2m_2 + 2m_3 + m_4)$$
$$z_{n+1} = z_n + \tfrac{1}{6}(m_1' + 2m_2' + 2m_3' + m_4')$$

$$m_1 = hf(x_n, y_n, z_n)$$
$$m_1' = hg(x_n, y_n, z_n)$$
$$m_2 = hf(x_n + \tfrac{1}{2}h, y_n + \tfrac{1}{2}m_1, z_n + \tfrac{1}{2}m_1')$$
$$m_2' = hg(x_n + \tfrac{1}{2}h, y_n + \tfrac{1}{2}m_1, z_n + \tfrac{1}{2}m_1')$$
$$m_3 = hf(x_n + \tfrac{1}{2}h, y_n + \tfrac{1}{2}m_2, z_n + \tfrac{1}{2}m_2')$$
$$m_3' = hg(x_n + \tfrac{1}{2}h, y_n + \tfrac{1}{2}m_2, z_n + \tfrac{1}{2}m_2')$$
$$m_4 = hf(x_n + h, y_n + m_3, z_n + m_3')$$
$$m_4' = hg(x_n + h, y_n + m_3, z_n + m_3')$$

The results of the computation of these quantities are collected into tabular form:

| $x_n$ | $y_n, z_n$ | $m_1, m_1'$ | $m_2, m_2'$ | $m_3, m_3'$ | $m_4, m_4'$ |
|---|---|---|---|---|---|
| 0.0 | 1.00000 | 0.40000 | 0.40500 | 0.39850 | 0.39552 |
| | − 1.00000 | 0.10000 | 0.14500 | 0.14775 | 0.19448 |
| 0.1 | 1.40042 | 0.39604 | 0.38663 | 0.37876 | 0.36023 |
| | − 0.85334 | 0.19475 | 0.24409 | 0.24562 | 0.29506 |
| 0.2 | 1.78160 | 0.36070 | 0.33441 | 0.32547 | 0.28938 |
| | − 0.60847 | 0.29547 | 0.34632 | 0.34623 | 0.39519 |
| 0.3 | 2.10990 | | | | |
| | − 0.26251 | | | | |

The required solutions are 1.400, − 0.853; 1.782, − 0.608; 2.110, − 0.262.

EXAMPLE 2. From the results of Example 1, find by Milne's method approximate values of $y(0.4)$ and $z(0.4)$ for that example.

SOLUTION. The predictor formulas are

$$y_4 = y_0 + \frac{0.4}{3}(2f_3 - f_2 + 2f_1)$$

$$z_4 = z_0 + \frac{0.4}{3}(2g_3 - g_2 + 2g_1)$$

and the corrector formulas are

$$Y_4 = y_2 + \frac{0.1}{3}(f_4 + 4f_3 + f_2)$$

$$Z_4 = z_2 + \frac{0.1}{3}(g_4 + 4g_3 + g_2)$$

where $f_i = y_i - 3z_i$, $g_i = 2y_i + z_i$, $i = 1, 2, 3, 4$. From the table of

Example 1, we have

$$f_1 = 3.96043, \quad f_2 = 3.60701, \quad g_1 = 1.94750, \quad g_2 = 2.95473$$

and we find

$$f_3 = 2.89743, \quad g_3 = 3.95729.$$

Hence:

$$y_4 = 1.00000 + \frac{0.4}{9} (5.79486 - 3.60701 + 7.92086) = 2.34783$$

$$z_4 = -1.00000 + \frac{0.4}{3} (7.91458 - 2.95473 + 3.89500) = 0.18065$$

We now find $f_4 = 1.80588$, $g_4 = 4.87631$ and substitute these values into the corrector formulas:

$$Y_4 = 1.78160 + \frac{0.1}{3} (1.80588 + 11.58972 + 3.60701) = 2.34835$$

$$Z_4 = -0.60847 + \frac{0.1}{3} (4.87631 + 15.82916 + 2.95473) = 0.18020$$

The approximate values sought are, therefore, 2.348, 0.180.

## EXERCISE 34

Using the Runge-Kutta formulas of the third order, compute approximate values of $y(x)$ and $z(x)$ at $x = 0.1, 0.2, 0.3$. Round off to three decimal places.

1. $y' = x + z$, $z' = e^{-2y}$, $y(0) = 0$, $z(0) = 1$
2. $y' = e^{-2x} + 2z$, $z' = x + e^{-y}$, $y(0) = 0.2$, $z(0) = 1$
3. $y' = x + \sin z$, $z' = 2z - y$, $y(0) = 1$, $z(0) = 0$

Proceed as in Problems 1–3, using the Runge-Kutta formulas of the fourth order.

4. $y' = x + y + e^{-z}$, $z' = e^x + z$, $y(0) = z(0) = 1$
5. $y' = y + \cos z$, $z' = x - \sin y$, $y(0) = 0$, $z(0) = -0.5$

6–10. From the values of $y_1, y_2, y_3, z_1, z_2, z_3$ in each of Problems 1–5, compute the approximate values of $y(0.4)$ and $z(0.4)$, first by Adams', then by Milne's method.

# CHAPTER SIX

# Special differential equations
# of the second order

**52. Introduction.** Not many methods are available for solving nonlinear differential equations of order $n > 1$. However, certain types of equations of the second order can be attacked by devices which will be described in this chapter.

**53. Equations of the form $y'' = f(y)$.** The first step in the solution of the differential equation

$$(1) \qquad y'' = f(y)$$

is to multiply both members by $2y'$. The new equation is

$$(2) \qquad 2y'y'' = 2f(y)y'.$$

Since the left member equals $\dfrac{d}{dx}(y')^2$, integration of (2) with respect to $x$ gives us a so-called *first integral* of (1), namely

$$(y')^2 = 2 \int f(y) \, dy$$
$$= F(y) + c_1,$$

from which we get

$$y' = \pm \sqrt{F(y) + c_1}.$$

By separating variables we obtain the equivalent equation

$$dx = \frac{dy}{\pm \sqrt{F(y) + c_1}}.$$

The solution of (1) may then be written in the form

$$x + c_2 = \pm \int \frac{dy}{\sqrt{F(y) + c_1}}.$$

EXAMPLE. Solve the equation $y'' = y^{-3}$.

SOLUTION. After multiplication by $2y'$ the equation takes the form

$$\frac{d}{dx} (y')^2 = \frac{2y'}{y^3},$$

so that the first integral is found to be:

$$(y')^2 = \int \frac{2 \, dy}{y^3} = -\frac{1}{y^2} + c_1 = \frac{c_1 y^2 - 1}{y^2}$$

$$y' = \pm \frac{\sqrt{c_1 y^2 - 1}}{y}$$

Separation of variables leads to the equation

$$dx = \frac{y \, dy}{\pm \sqrt{c_1 y^2 - 1}},$$

whose solution is

$$x + c_2 = \frac{\pm \sqrt{c_1 y^2 - 1}}{c_1}.$$

## 54. Dependent variable absent. To solve the equation

$$(3) \qquad f(x, y', y'') = 0,$$

which does not contain $y$ explicitly, we substitute $p$ for $y'$, and hence $p'$ for $y''$. Equation (3) assumes the form

$$(4) \qquad f(x, p, p') = 0,$$

an equation of the first order in $p$. If $p = \phi(x, c_1)$ is the general solution of (4), then a second integration gives the general solution of the equation (3).

155

EXAMPLE. Find the general solution of the equation

$$(1 + x^2)y'' + 1 + (y')^2 = 0.$$

SOLUTION. Upon substituting $y' = p$, $y'' = p'$, the equation becomes

$$(1 + x^2)p' + 1 + p^2 = 0$$

$$\frac{dx}{1 + x^2} + \frac{dp}{1 + p^2} = 0$$

so that a first integral is

$$\text{Arc tan } x + \text{Arc tan } p = c.$$

Equating the tangents of the two members, we have

$$\frac{x + p}{1 - px} = \tan c = c_1,$$

which is equivalent to

$$p = \frac{dy}{dx} = \frac{c_1 - x}{1 + c_1 x}.$$

The general solution of the original differential equation is therefore:

$$y = \int \frac{c_1 - x}{1 + c_1 x}\, dx$$

$$= -\frac{x}{c_1} + \frac{c_1^2 + 1}{c_1^2} \ln (c_1 x + 1) + c_2$$

## 55. Independent variable absent.
An equation of the form

$$(5) \qquad\qquad f(y, y', y'') = 0,$$

in which $x$ does not appear explicitly, may be solved as follows.
Let $y' = p$, so that $y'' = \dfrac{dp}{dx} = \dfrac{dp}{dy}\dfrac{dy}{dx} = p\dfrac{dp}{dy}.$ Equation (5) becomes

$$f\left(y, p, p\frac{dp}{dy}\right) = 0,$$

a first-order equation in $p$, whose general solution may be written $p = \phi(y, c_1)$. The solution of (5) may then be found from the equation $y' = \phi(y, c_1)$.

156

EXAMPLE.  Solve the equation $yy'' + (y')^3 = 0$.

SOLUTION.  Let $y' = p$, $y'' = p\dfrac{dp}{dy}$.  Then:

$$yp\frac{dp}{dy} + p^3 = 0$$

$$p(y\,dp + p^2\,dy) = 0$$

For $p \neq 0$ this equation is equivalent to

$$y\,dp + p^2\,dy = 0,$$

whose solution is $p\,\ln\,(c_1 y) = 1$.  Since $p = \dfrac{dy}{dx}$, separation of variables leads to the equation

$$dx = \ln\,(c_1 y)\,dy,$$

which has the solution

$$x + c_0 = y[\ln\,(c_1 y) - 1] = y(\ln y + c_1')$$

From the equation $p = 0$ one obtains the additional solution

$$y = k.$$

## EXERCISE 35

Find the general solutions of the differential equations of Problems 1–28.

1. $\dfrac{d^2 y}{d\theta^2} = \cos\,\theta$

2. $y'' = k^2 y$

3. $\dfrac{d^2 x}{dt^2} + k^2 x = 0$

4. $y^3 y'' + 4 = 0$

5. $\dfrac{d^2 x}{dt^2} = \dfrac{k^2}{x^2}$

6. $xy'' = 1 + x^2$

7. $(1 - x)y'' = y'$

8. $(1 + x^2)y'' + 2x(y' + 1) = 0$

9. $y'' = (y')^3 + y'$

10. $xy'' + x = y'$

11. $\dfrac{d^2x}{dt^2} + t\dfrac{dx}{dt} = t^3$

12. $x^2y'' = xy' + 1$

13. $y'' = 1 + (y')^2$

14. $(1 - x^2)y'' + xy' = 1$

15. $y'' = \sqrt{1 + (y')^2}$

16. $y'' = (y')^2 + y'$

17. $\dfrac{d^2y}{dx^2} = y\dfrac{dy}{dx}$

18. $(1 + x^2)y'' + 1 + (y')^2 = 0$

19. $y'' + yy' = 0$

20. $y'' + 2(y')^2 = 0$

21. $yy'' + (y')^2 = 1$

22. $yy'' + 1 = (y')^2$

23. $y'' = y$

24. $yy'' + (y')^2 = yy'$

25. $2yy'' - (y')^2 = 0$

26. $y'' + 2(y')^2 = 2$

27. $y'' + y' = (y')^3$

28. $(y + 1)y'' = 3(y')^2$

In each of Problems 29–41, find the particular solution which satisfies the given conditions.

29. $\dfrac{d^2\theta}{dt^2} = \sec\theta\tan\theta$; $\theta = \dfrac{\pi}{4}$ and $\dfrac{d\theta}{dt} = 1$ when $t = 0$

30. $2y'' = e^y$; $y(0) = 0$, $y'(0) = 1$

31. $y'' = y^3$; $y(0) = -1$, $y'(0) = \dfrac{\sqrt{2}}{2}$

32. $y'' = (y')^2\cos x$; $y(0) = 2$, $y'(0) = 1$

33. $yy'' - y^2y' = (y')^2$; $y(0) = 2$, $y'(0) = 1$

34. $(1 + x^2)y'' + 1 + (y')^2 = 0$; $y(0) = y'(0) = 1$

35. $yy'' = y^3 + (y')^2$; $y(0) = 1$, $y'(0) = 2$

36. $[1 + (y')^2]^2 = y^2y''$; $y(0) = 3$, $y'(0) = \sqrt{2}$

37. $y'' = (y')^2\sin x$; $y(0) = 0$, $y'(0) = \frac{1}{2}$

38. $2yy'' = y^3 + 2(y')^2$; $y(0) = -1$, $y'(0) = 0$

39. $\dfrac{d^2x}{dt^2} - k^2x = 0$; $x = 0$, $\dfrac{dx}{dt} = v_0$ when $t = 0$

40. $yy'' = 2(y')^2 + y^2$; $y(0) = 1$, $y'(0) = \sqrt{3}$

41. $(1 - e^x)y'' = e^x y'$; $y(1) = 0$, $y'(1) = 1$

42. Find the equation of the family of curves each of which has the constant curvature $k$.

43. A curve passes through the point $P_0 : (0, 1)$ with slope zero. At any point $P$ of the curve the slope is three times the number of linear units in the arc $P_0 P$ of the curve. Determine the equation of the curve and find its slope at $x = 1$.

44. If a body whose weight is $w$ falls in a medium whose resistance to the motion is proportional to the square of the velocity, the differential equation of the motion is

$$\frac{w}{g}\frac{d^2 y}{dt^2} = w - k\left(\frac{dy}{dt}\right)^2,$$

assuming the positive $y$-axis to be directed downward. Find $v = \dfrac{dy}{dt}$ and $y$ as functions of $t$ if $v = v_1$ when $\dfrac{d^2 y}{dt^2} = 0$ and if $y(0) = v(0) = 0$.

45. A particle moves in a straight line with an acceleration whose expression in terms of position is

$$a = \frac{8}{(s + 3)^3},$$

where $s$ is the distance of the particle from the origin at the instant $t$. If the particle starts from rest at the origin, express (a) the velocity $v$ as a function of $t$, (b) $v$ as a function of $s$, and (c) $s$ as a function of $t$.

46. Assume that the acceleration of a body in the gravitational field of the earth varies inversely as the square of the distance from the earth's center and is $g$ feet per second per second at the surface of the earth. Let $R$ be the radius of the earth and take the positive sense of the motion downward. For the initial conditions $y = -R$ and $v = v_0$ when $t = 0$, express the velocity of the body as a function of $y$. For a given initial velocity find the velocity where $y = -2R$. How far will the body go? Find the "velocity of escape," i.e., the limit of $v$ as $y \to -\infty$.

47. Find the number of hours required for a body to fall to the earth's surface from a position 236,000 miles above it.

159

**56. The catenary.** Consider a cable of uniformly distributed weight $w$ pounds per foot suspended from two points $A$ and $B$ (Figure 16). The curve formed by the cable, called a *catenary*,

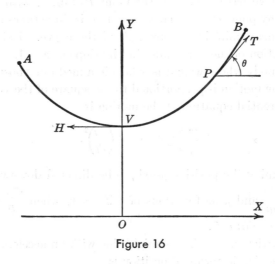

Figure 16

lies in a vertical plane which contains $A$ and $B$. Let a coordinate system be so chosen that the $y$-axis, directed vertically upward, passes through the lowest point $V$ of the cable. The position of the $x$-axis will be fixed later.

If $P$ is any point of the cable and $s$ is the length in feet of the portion $VP$, then the weight of $VP$ is $ws$ pounds. The three forces which keep the portion $VP$ in equilibrium are the tensions at $P$ and at $V$, acting tangentially to the curve, and the weight, which is directed downward. At $V$ the tension is directed horizontally, and since the algebraic sum of the horizontal components of the forces must be zero, we have

$$(6) \qquad T \cos \theta - H = 0,$$

where $T$ and $H$ are the magnitudes, measured in pounds, of the tensions at $P$ and $V$ respectively, and $\theta$ is the inclination of the tangent at $P$. Since the algebraic sum of the vertical components is also zero,

$$(7) \qquad T \sin \theta - ws = 0.$$

160

From the equations (6) and (7),

$$\tan \theta = \frac{ws}{H},$$

so that if the equation of the catenary is $y = f(x)$,

(8) $$\frac{dy}{dx} = \tan \theta = \frac{ws}{H}.$$

Since

$$\frac{ds}{dx} = \sqrt{1 + \left(\frac{dy}{dx}\right)^2},$$

differentiation of (8) with respect to $x$ gives us the differential equation of the catenary:

(9) $$\frac{d^2y}{dx^2} = \frac{w}{H}\sqrt{1 + \left(\frac{dy}{dx}\right)^2}.$$

The equation (9) may be solved by the method of Article 54. Let $p = \dfrac{dy}{dx}$, $\dfrac{dp}{dx} = \dfrac{d^2y}{dx^2}$, so that (9) becomes

(10) $$\frac{w}{H}\,dx = \frac{dp}{\sqrt{1 + p^2}}.$$

The solution of (10) for which $p = 0$ where $x = 0$ is

$$p = \frac{dy}{dx} = \sinh\frac{wx}{H}.$$

A second integration gives

(11) $$y = \frac{H}{w}\cosh\frac{wx}{H} + C.$$

For convenience we choose the location of the $x$-axis so that $y = \dfrac{H}{w}$ where $x = 0$. Then $C = 0$, and (11) takes the form

$$y = \frac{H}{w}\cosh\frac{wx}{H}.$$

161

**57. The pursuit curve.** Suppose a body $C_1$ moves along a curve $\Gamma_1$ with known speed and that a second body $C_2$ moves along a curve $\Gamma_2$ also with known speed. Then $\Gamma_2$ is called a *curve of pursuit* if at each instant the tangent to $\Gamma_2$ at the point occupied by $C_2$ passes through $C_1$. The problem of determining such a pursuit curve will be illustrated in the following example.

EXAMPLE. A bomber plane flying a course in a straight line with constant speed $v_B$ feet per second is under attack by a fighter plane which flies at a constant speed of $v_F$ feet per second. The nose of the fighter is always pointed at the bomber. Determine the path of the fighter plane.

SOLUTION. Introduce coordinate axes in space in such a manner that the bomber moves along the $y$-axis (Fig. 17) in the positive

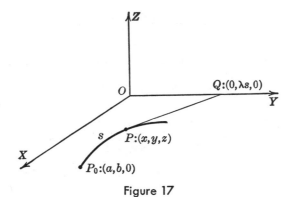

Figure 17

direction and assume that when $t = 0$, the bomber is at the origin of the coordinate system while the fighter is at the point $P_0 : (a, b, 0)$ in the $xy$-plane. It is intuitively evident that the curve of pursuit $\Gamma$ followed by the fighter will lie entirely in the $xy$-plane; that this is the case will be demonstrated in what follows. Let the pursuit curve $\Gamma$ be represented parametrically by equations $x = x(s)$, $y = y(s)$, $z = z(s)$, in terms of arc-length $s$ measured along $\Gamma$ from $P_0$. After $t$ seconds the fighter will be at the point $P : [x(s), y(s), z(s)]$ while the bomber, having gone a distance $v_B t$ along the $y$-axis, is at the point $Q : (0, \lambda s, 0)$, where

162

$s = v_F t$ and $\lambda = \dfrac{v_B}{v_F}$. The straight line $PQ$, whose direction cosines are proportional to $x(s)$, $y(s) - \lambda s$, $z(s)$, is tangent to $\Gamma$ at $P$ and hence has direction cosines $\dfrac{dx}{ds}, \dfrac{dy}{ds}, \dfrac{dz}{ds}$. We are thus led to the equations

$$k(s)\,\frac{dx}{ds} = x(s)$$

(a) 
$$k(s)\,\frac{dy}{ds} = y(s) - \lambda s$$

$$k(s)\,\frac{dz}{ds} = z(s)$$

where the factor of proportionality has the value
$$k(s) = \sqrt{[x(s)]^2 + [y(s) - \lambda s]^2 + [z(s)]^2}.$$
From the third equation of (a),
$$z(s) = z(0)e^{\int_0^s \frac{ds}{k(s)}}.$$
Since $z(0) = 0$, the function $z(s)$ is identically zero and hence the pursuit curve $\Gamma$ must lie entirely in the $xy$-plane.

From the first two equations of (a) the relation

(b) 
$$xp = y - \lambda s$$

is obtained, where $p = \dfrac{dy}{dx}$. Differentiation with respect to $x$ results in the equation

(c) 
$$x\,\frac{dp}{dx} = -\lambda\,\frac{ds}{dx}.$$

Since $s$ decreases as $x$ increases,
$$\frac{ds}{dx} = -\sqrt{1 + p^2}.$$

Hence (c) takes the form
$$x\,\frac{dp}{dx} = \lambda\sqrt{1 + p^2},$$

which is equivalent to

(d) 
$$\frac{dp}{\sqrt{1 + p^2}} = \frac{\lambda\,dx}{x}.$$

The general solution of $(d)$ may be written

$$\ln (p + \sqrt{1 + p^2}) = \ln x^\lambda + \ln C,$$

a nonlogarithmic form of which is

$(e)$ $$p + \sqrt{1 + p^2} = Cx^\lambda.$$

From the initial conditions $x = a$, $y = b$, $s = 0$, and from $(b)$ we find that the initial value of $p$ is $\dfrac{b}{a}$. Hence the value of the arbitrary constant in $(e)$ can be shown to be

$$C = a^{-(\lambda+1)}(b + \sqrt{a^2 + b^2}).$$

Equation $(e)$ may be solved for $p$:

$$p = \tfrac{1}{2}\left(Cx^\lambda - \frac{1}{Cx^\lambda}\right)$$

For $\lambda \neq 1$ a quadrature then gives

$$y = b + \tfrac{1}{2}\int_a^x \left(Cx^\lambda - \frac{1}{Cx^\lambda}\right) dx$$

$(f)$ $$y = \tfrac{1}{2}\left[\frac{Cx^{1+\lambda}}{1+\lambda} - \frac{x^{1-\lambda}}{C(1-\lambda)}\right] + B,$$

where the new arbitrary constant is

$$B = b - \tfrac{1}{2}\left[\frac{Ca^{1+\lambda}}{1+\lambda} - \frac{a^{1-\lambda}}{C(1-\lambda)}\right].$$

If $\lambda \neq 1$, the equation of the pursuit curve is $(f)$.

It is easily shown that if $\lambda = 1$, in which case the velocities $v_B$ and $v_F$ are equal, the equation of the pursuit curve becomes

$(g)$ $$y = \tfrac{1}{2}\left[\frac{Cx^2}{2} - \frac{\ln x}{C}\right] + B_1,$$

where $B_1 = b - \tfrac{1}{2}\left[\dfrac{Ca^2}{2} - \dfrac{\ln a}{C}\right]$.

**58. The relative pursuit curve.** If the motion of the pursuing body $C_2$ is described by reference to a coordinate system attached to the body $C_1$ and moving with it, the path traversed by $C_2$ is known as a *relative pursuit curve*.

EXAMPLE. In the example of the preceding article find the relative pursuit curve with respect to a polar coordinate system in the $xy$-plane in which the bomber is at the pole and the polar axis points in the direction of the bomber's flight.

SOLUTION. The velocity of the fighter in this moving coordinate system is represented (Fig. 18) by a vector which is the resultant of the vector $-v_B$ (the negative of the bomber's velocity with respect to the coordinate system of Article 57) and the velocity $v_F$ directed toward the pole. Hence the radial component of the fighter's velocity has magnitude

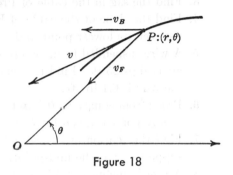

$$\frac{dr}{dt} = -v_F - v_B \cos \theta$$

while the magnitude of the transverse component is

$$r \frac{d\theta}{dt} = v_B \sin \theta.$$

**Figure 18**

From these equations we obtain the differential equation of the relative pursuit curve:

$$\frac{1}{r} dr = -\left(\frac{1}{\lambda} \csc \theta + \cot \theta\right) d\theta.$$

Its general solution is:

$$\ln Cr = -\left(\frac{1}{\lambda} \ln \tan \frac{\theta}{2} + \ln \sin \theta\right)$$

$$Cr = \frac{\left(\cot \dfrac{\theta}{2}\right)^{\frac{1}{\lambda}}}{\sin \theta}$$

In terms of the polar coordinates $(r_0, \theta_0)$ of the fighter at $t = 0$, the value of the arbitrary constant is

$$C = \frac{\left(\cot \dfrac{\theta_0}{2}\right)^{\frac{1}{\lambda}}}{r_0 \sin \theta_0}.$$

165

## EXERCISE 36

1. Show that the length of the catenary from its lowest point to a point whose abscissa is $x$ is given by $s = \dfrac{H}{w} \sinh \dfrac{wx}{H}$.

2. A cable 30 ft. long and weighing 5 lb. per foot hangs from two supports which are at the same level. Find its equation if the supports are 26 ft. apart.

3. Find the sag in the cable of Problem 2.

4. Find the slope of the cable of Problem 2 midway horizontally between its lowest point and a support.

5. A wire suspended from two pegs at the same level and 150 ft. apart dips 25 ft. Find the length of the wire if the weight of the wire is 0.1 lb./ft.

6. Prove from equations (6) and (7) of Article 56 that the tension at any point is given by $T = wy$.

7. Find the tension of the wire of Problem 5: (a) at a point of support, (b) at the mid-point.

8. A rope is inclined at 12° to the horizontal at its supports, and the sag is observed to be 13.4 ft. Find the length of the rope and its span.

9. A chain whose weight is negligible carries a load such that the load on any arc is proportional to the horizontal projection of the arc. Show that the chain hangs in a parabola.

10. Prove that for the curve of Problem 9 the tension varies as the square root of the height above the directrix.

11. Prove that the radius of curvature of the pursuit curve (f), Article 57, is given by the formula

$$R = \frac{x}{4\lambda}\left(Cx^\lambda + \frac{1}{Cx^\lambda}\right)^2.$$

12. Under what conditions is the relative pursuit curve of the example in Article 58 a parabola?

13. The centrifugal force $G$ acting upon the fighter plane of the example in Article 58 is given by

$$G = \frac{v_F v_B \sin \theta}{gr},$$

where $(r, \theta)$ are the coordinates of the plane in the relative pursuit curve. Show that $G$ is a maximum when $\theta$ is equal to the angle between the radius vector and the line tangent to the relative pursuit curve.

14. Show that the maximum value of $G$ in Problem 13 is

$$Cv_B v_F \frac{(4\lambda^2 - 1)}{4g\lambda^2} \left(\frac{2\lambda - 1}{2\lambda + 1}\right)^{\frac{1}{2\lambda}}.$$

# CHAPTER SEVEN

# Differential equations of the first order and not of the first degree

**59. Introduction.** A first-order differential equation which is not of the first degree need not define a unique value of the derivative at each point within the region of validity, so that Theorem 1 of Article 6 might not apply. Three methods of solving such equations will be presented. The first consists in solving the differential equation for the derivative, so as to replace the original equation by two or more equations each of the first degree. The two remaining methods apply to cases in which it is not convenient to solve for the derivative. We shall note the occasional appearance of an exceptional type of solution called a singular solution, whose geometric interpretation will be discussed in Article 63.

**60. Equations solvable for p.** If the differential equation can be readily solved for the derivative $p = \dfrac{dy}{dx}$, we are able to replace it by two or more equations of the first degree, to which the methods of Chapter Two might be applicable. The following example will illustrate the procedure.

EXAMPLE. Find the general solution of the equation

$$p^2 + py = px + xy.$$

SOLUTION. The equation can be written $(p - x)(p + y) = 0$, which is thus seen to be equivalent to the pair of first-degree equations:

$$p = \frac{dy}{dx} = x, \qquad p = \frac{dy}{dx} = -y$$

The general solutions of these equations are respectively:

(a) $\qquad 2y = x^2 + C, \qquad ye^x = C'$

The two families of curves which represent the solutions (a) constitute the family of integral curves of the original differential equation.

## 61. Equations solvable for y. If the differential equation

$$g(x, y, p) = 0$$

can be expressed in the form

(1) $\qquad y = f(x, p),$

we may differentiate (1) with respect to $x$ and obtain an equation free of $y$:

$$p = f_x(x, p) + f_p(x, p)\frac{dp}{dx}.$$

This is a differential equation of the first order and first degree. Its general solution is of the form

(2) $\qquad \phi(x, p, C) = 0.$

If $x = h(p, C)$ is a single-valued function which satisfies (2), then the equations $x = h(p, C)$, $y = f[h(p, C), p]$ constitute parametric equations of a family of integral curves of (1). Here a particular value of $C$ determines a particular curve of the family, and points of the curve are determined by specifying values of the parameter $p$. Each such function $x = h(p, C)$ serves in this manner to determine a family of solutions of the equation (1).

EXAMPLE 1. Solve the equation

$(a)$
$$y + px = p^2 x^4.$$

SOLUTION. Differentiating with respect to $x$, we have

$$p + p + x \frac{dp}{dx} = 4p^2 x^3 + 2px^4 \frac{dp}{dx},$$

which in factored form becomes

$(b)$
$$\left( 2p + x \frac{dp}{dx} \right) \left( 1 - 2px^3 \right) = 0.$$

We consider first the equation

$(c_1)$
$$2p + x \frac{dp}{dx} = 0,$$

and find its general solution

$(d_1)$
$$px^2 = C.$$

Since $(d_1)$ determines $x$ as a double-valued function of $p$ and $C$, it would appear that we have two families of solutions of $(a)$, namely:

$$x = \sqrt{\frac{C}{p}}, \quad y + px = p^2 x^4 \qquad x = -\sqrt{\frac{C}{p}}, \quad y + px = p^2 x^4$$

However, if these solutions are expressed in Cartesian coordinates by eliminating the parameter $p$, it is seen that the same equation

$(e_1)$
$$x(y - C^2) + C = 0$$

results from both pairs of parametric equations.

We consider the equation

$(c_2)$
$$1 - 2px^3 = 0$$

which comes from the second factor of $(b)$, and note that the derivative $\frac{dp}{dx}$ is absent, so that $(c_2)$ is not a differential equation in $p$ and $x$ as was $(c_1)$. We replace $p$ by $\frac{dy}{dx}$ and solve the resulting differential equation in $x$ and $y$, obtaining

$(d_2)$
$$y + \frac{1}{4x^2} = C.$$

Substitution of $(d_2)$ into the equation $(a)$ shows that the only curve of the family $(d_2)$ which is an integral curve of $(a)$ is

$(e_2)$ $$y + \frac{1}{4x^2} = 0.$$

It is readily verified that $(e_2)$ might also have been found by eliminating $p$ between $(a)$ and $(c_2)$. The solution $(e_2)$ is clearly not obtainable from the general solution $(e_1)$. Such a solution is called a *singular solution* of the differential equation $(a)$, and its geometrical significance will be discussed in Article 63.

EXAMPLE 2. Solve the equation

$(a)$ $$2xp - y + p^3 = 0.$$

SOLUTION. The result of differentiating $(a)$ is

$(b)$ $$p \mid \frac{dp}{dx} (2x + 3p^2) = 0,$$

whose solution can be found as follows:

$$p \, dx + 2x \, dp + 3p^2 \, dp = 0$$
$$p^2 \, dx + 2xp \, dp + 3p^3 \, dp = 0$$
$$p^2 x + \frac{3}{4} p^4 = \frac{C}{4}$$

$(c)$ $$4p^2 x + 3p^4 = C$$

Since the elimination of $p$ between $(c)$ and $(a)$ is awkward, we are content to consider the pair of equations $(a)$, $(c)$ as the general solution in parametric form. It will be noted that in this example no factor leading to a singular solution occurs in $(b)$.

## EXERCISE 37

In each of Problems 1–10, find the general solution by solving for $p$.

1. $4y^2 = p^2x^2$
2. $xyp^2 + (x + y)p + 1 = 0$
3. $1 + (2y - x^2)p - 2x^2yp^2 = 0$
4. $x(p^2 - 1) = 2yp$

5. $(1 - y^2)p^2 = 1$
6. $xyp^2 + (xy^2 - 1)p = y$
7. $y^2p^2 + xyp - 2x^2 = 0$
8. $y^2p^2 - 2xyp + 2y^2 = x^2$
9. $p^3 + (x + y - 2xy)p^2 - 2pxy(x + y) = 0$
10. $yp^2 + (y^2 - x^3 - xy^2)p - xy(x^2 + y^2) = 0$

In each of Problems 11–24, find the general solution by solving for $y$. Note singular solutions.

11. $y = px(1 + p)$      12. $y = x + 3 \ln p$
13. $y(1 + p^2) = 2$      14. $yp^2 - 2xp + y = 0$
15. $p^2 + y^2 = 1$      16. $(p^2 - 1)x = 2py$
17. $4x - 2py + p^2x = 0$      18. $2x^2y + p^2 = px^3$
19. $p^2y = 3px + y$      20. $8x + 1 = p^2y$
21. $p^2y + 2p + 1 = 0$      22. $(p^2 + 1)x = p(x + y)$
23. $x^2 - 3py + xp^2 = 0$      24. $y + 2px = p^2x$

25. Solve Problem 1 by solving for $y$.
26. Solve Problem 4 by solving for $y$.

**62. Equations solvable for x.** With a simple modification, the procedure explained in the preceding article can be used to obtain the solution of a differential equation solvable for $x$. Consider the following example.

EXAMPLE. Find the general solution of the equation

$$y = x - 2 \ln p.$$

SOLUTION. Solving for $x$, we have

(a) $$x = y + 2 \ln p.$$

Noting that $\dfrac{dx}{dy} = \dfrac{1}{p}$, we see that differentiation of (a) with re-

spect to $y$ gives $\dfrac{1}{p} = 1 + \dfrac{2 \dfrac{dp}{dy}}{p}$, which is equivalent to

172

(b)
$$1 = p + 2\frac{dp}{dy}.$$

After separating the variables, we find the solution of (b) to be $\ln (p - 1) + \frac{y}{2} = \ln C$. If we solve for $p$, this solution takes the form

(c)
$$p = 1 + Ce^{-\frac{y}{2}}.$$

Eliminating $p$ between (c) and (a), the general solution of (a) is obtained:

$$x - y = 2\ln (1 + Ce^{-\frac{y}{2}}).$$

## EXERCISE 38

Find the general solutions by solving for $x$. Note singular solutions.

1. $x = p^2 + p$
2. $x = y - p^3$
3. $x + 2py = p^2x$
4. $4x - 2py + xp^2 = 0$
5. $xp^3 = yp + 1$
6. $(p^2 + 1)y = 2px$
7. $2x + p^2x = 2py$
8. $x = py + p^2$
9. $4p^2x + 2px = y$
10. $y = px(p + 1)$
11. $2p^3x + 1 = p^2y$
12. $p^3 + pxy = 2y^2$
13. $3p^4x = p^3y + 1$
14. $2p^5 + 2px = y$
15. $p^{-2} + px = 2y$
16. $2y = 3px + 4 + 2\ln p$

17. Solve Problem 1 of Exercise 37 by the method of this article.
18. Solve Problem 4 of Exercise 37 by the method of this article.
19. Solve Problem 6 of Exercise 37 by the method of this article.

**63. Singular solutions and envelopes.** It has been shown that the general solution $y = \phi(x, C)$ of a differential equation of the first order is represented geometrically by a one-parameter family of integral curves. However, the equation might possess an integral curve $y = \psi(x)$ which is not a member of the family

173

$y = \phi(x, C)$   Such a function $\psi(x)$ is called a *singular* solution. If the family $y = \phi(x, C)$ has an envelope, it will be shown that this envelope is an integral curve which represents a singular solution. We proceed to the discussion of the envelope of a one-parameter family of curves.

Let the equation of the family be

(3) $$F(x, y, C) = 0,$$

where $C$ is the parameter of the family. If $C_1$ and $C_1 + \Delta C$ are neighboring values of the parameter, corresponding to two neighboring curves $\Gamma_1$ and $\Gamma_2$ of the family (Fig. 19), the coordi-

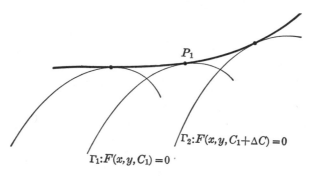

$\Gamma_2:F(x,y,C_1+\Delta C)=0$

$\Gamma_1:F(x,y,C_1)=0$

Figure 19

nates $x, y$ of a point of intersection of these curves must satisfy the equations:

(4) $$F(x, y, C_1) = 0, \quad F(x, y, C_1 + \Delta C) = 0$$

For the determination of such an intersection the equations (4) may be replaced by:

(5) $$F(x, y, C_1) = 0, \quad \frac{F(x, y, C_1 + \Delta C) - F(x, y, C_1)}{\Delta C} = 0$$

If $\Delta C$ is allowed to approach zero, the curve $\Gamma_2$ approaches $\Gamma_1$, and the point of intersection under consideration may approach a limit point $P_1$. The coordinates of this limit point must therefore satisfy the equations $F(x, y, C_1) = 0$, $F_C(x, y, C_1) = 0$.

The limit point $P_1$ is, of course, on the curve $\Gamma_1$. In the

174

favorable case there will be at least one such limit point on each curve of the family (3) and the locus of these points is defined to be the *envelope* of the family. The equations

(6) $$F(x, y, C) = 0, \quad F_C(x, y, C) = 0$$

may be regarded as parametric equations of the envelope in terms of the parameter $C$. The Cartesian equation of the envelope is found by eliminating $C$ between the equations (6).

> EXAMPLE. Find the envelope of the family of circles of constant radius $a$, whose centers lie on $OY$.
>
> SOLUTION. The equation of this family of circles is
>
> (a) $\qquad x^2 + (y - C)^2 = a^2$,
>
> where $C$ is the parameter. If we differentiate (a) partially with respect to $C$ and discard the constant factor, we have $y - C = 0$. When $C$ is eliminated between this equation and (a), the equation
>
> $$x^2 - a^2 = 0$$
>
> is obtained. Thus the envelope of the family (a) is the pair of straight lines paralled to $OY$ and tangent to each circle of the family. (Fig. 20.)

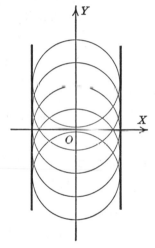

Figure 20

As in the example, the envelope of a family of curves is tangent to each curve $\Gamma$ of the family, the point of contact being a limit point on $\Gamma$. To show this, let $x = x(C)$, $y = y(C)$ be parametric equations of the envelope, obtained by solving (6) for $x$ and $y$ in terms of $C$. Then the equations

(7) $$\begin{aligned} F[x(C), y(C), C] &= 0, \\ F_C[x(C), y(C), C] &= 0 \end{aligned}$$

will be satisfied identically in $C$. Hence if $\Gamma_1$ is the curve $F(x, y, C_1) = 0$ of the family (3) determined by the parametric value $C_1$, the point whose coordinates are $x_1 = x(C_1)$, $y_1 = y(C_1)$

of the envelope also lies on $\Gamma_1$, as a consequence of the first identity (7). The slope of $\Gamma_1$ at this point has the value

$$-\frac{F_x(x_1, y_1, C_1)}{F_y(x_1, y_1, C_1)}.$$

Differentiation of the first identity (7) with respect to $C$ gives

$$F_x x_C + F_y y_C + F_C = 0,$$

which may be written

$$F_x x_C + F_y y_C = 0$$

by virtue of the second identity. Hence the slope $m_1$ of the envelope at the point $(x_1, y_1)$ is

$$m_1 = \frac{y_C(C_1)}{x_C(C_1)} = -\frac{F_x(x_1, y_1, C_1)}{F_y(x_1, y_1, C_1)},$$

so that the envelope and $\Gamma_1$ are tangent at $(x_1, y_1)$.

The equation (3) may be considered to be the primitive of a differential equation of the first order

$$(8) \qquad g(x, y, p) = 0.$$

The fact that the envelope of the family (3) is tangent at each of its points to an integral curve of (8) shows that the envelope is itself an integral curve of (8), because each point $(x, y)$ of the envelope and the slope $p$ of the envelope at this point constitute an element $(x, y, p)$ of the slope field defined by (8).

**64. The Clairaut equation.** The theory of Article 63 is well illustrated by equations of the form

$$(9) \qquad y = px + f(p),$$

which were first studied by Clairaut.* The general integral of (9) can be found by the method of Article 61. Differentiation of both members of (9) with respect to $x$ gives the equation

$$p = p + x\frac{dp}{dx} + f'(p)\frac{dp}{dx},$$

---

* Alexis Claude Clairaut (1713–1765). A precocious student of mathematics, he was the author of important investigations in theoretical mechanics and astronomy.

which may be written

(10) $$\frac{dp}{dx}\Big[x + f'(p)\Big] = 0.$$

The equation (10) is equivalent to the two equations:

(11) $$\frac{dp}{dx} = 0$$

(12) $$x + f'(p) = 0$$

Equation (11), which is a simple differential equation in the dependent variable $p$, has the solution $p = C$. Elimination of the parameter $p$ between this equation and (9) gives the general solution

(13) $$y = Cx + f(C).$$

Hence the general solution of the Clairaut equation (9) is readily obtained by replacing $p$ by $C$ in the equation.

The equation (12), on the other hand, is not a differential equation in the dependent variable $p$. It may be treated in either of two ways. In the first place we may regard (12) as a differential equation in the dependent variable $y$. If the general solution of this equation is $y = Y(x, K)$, it will be found that there exists a particular value $K = K_0$ for which $Y(x, K_0)$ is a solution of the original equation (9). This solution is not a particular solution of (9) since it is not a special case of the general solution (13).

Alternatively, this solution $Y(x, K_0)$ can be found more simply by eliminating the parameter $p$ between the equations:

$$x + f'(p) = 0, \quad y = px + f(p)$$

But this is exactly the process by which one obtains the equation of the envelope of the family (13). For differentiation of (13) with respect to $C$ gives

$$0 = x + f'(C)$$

and the envelope is found by eliminating $C$ between the equations:

$$x + f'(C) = 0, \quad y = Cx + f(C)$$

177

## EXERCISE 39

Find the equation of the envelope of the family of curves given in each of Problems 1–9. Draw the envelope and three curves of the family.

1. $x \cos \omega + y \sin \omega = p$, $p$ constant.
2. Circles of constant radius $a$ and with centers on $OX$.
3. Straight lines making a constant area $k$ with the coordinate axes.
4. Straight lines $y = mx + \dfrac{a}{m}$, $a$ constant.
5. Straight lines $4y = 4mx - (1 + 2m)^2$.
6. Parabolas $y^2 = Cx - C^{\frac{3}{2}}$.
7. Cubics $x^3 = Cy - C^2$.
8. Semicubical parabolas $y^2 = (x - C)^3$.
9. Cubics $y^3 = 3Cx^2 - 4C^3$.

Problems 10–20 are based on solutions of various problems of Exercises 37 and 38. In each case find the equation of the envelope of the family of curves represented by the general solution and identify the envelope with the singular solution.

10. Exercise 37, Problem 14.
11. Exercise 37, Problem 15.
12. Exercise 37, Problem 16.
13. Exercise 37, Problem 17.
14. Exercise 37, Problem 18.
15. Exercise 38, Problem 3.
16. Exercise 38, Problem 4.
17. Exercise 38, Problem 6.
18. Exercise 38, Problem 7.
19. Exercise 38, Problem 9.
20. Exercise 38, Problem 12.

21. Find the equation of the envelope of the family of ellipses of area $A$ whose axes lie on the coordinate axes.
22. Find the envelope of the family of circles having centers on the rectangular hyperbola $xy = 1$ and passing through the origin.

For each of the following Clairaut equations write the general solution by inspection. Find also the singular solution and identify it with the envelope of the family represented by the general solution.

23. $y = px + p^2$

24. $y = px + \dfrac{1}{p}$

25. $y = px - \sqrt{p}$

26. $y = px + \ln p$

27. $y = px + \dfrac{3}{p^2}$

28. $y = px - p^{\frac{2}{3}}$

29. $y = px + e^{-p}$

30. $(y - px)^2 = p^2 + 1$

31. $p^2x - py - 2 = 0$

32. $y^2 - 2pxy + p^2(x^2 - 1) = 0$

# CHAPTER EIGHT

# Solution in series

**65. Introduction.** According to the existence theorems which were stated without proof in Chapter One, an analytic differential equation possesses solutions which are themselves analytic; that is, they can be expressed as power series having nonzero intervals of convergence. Such expressions for the solutions may be desirable, either because no technique can be found for arriving at the solutions in finite terms or because, even if such a technique is available, it may be so laborious to apply as to be impracticable, and one may be content with the approximation to the solution which can be obtained by taking the first few terms of a power series.

Two methods of finding the solution as a power series will be described in Articles 66 and 67. The remainder of the chapter will be devoted to the exposition of a method due to Frobenius * for finding the solutions of a linear differential equation of the second order in terms of infinite series, when the coefficients of the differential equations have so-called singularities which make the existence theorems of Chapter One inapplicable. In particular, the method will be applied to two special differential

---

* Georg Frobenius (1849–1917), German mathematician, noted for his work in both algebra and analysis.

180

equations of considerable importance, the equations of Bessel * and of Legendre.†

**66. Solution in power series; first method.** To illustrate the method under discussion, consider a differential equation of the first order which we may suppose to have the form

(1) $$y' = f(x, y).$$

Let it be required to find the solution $y(x)$ of this equation for which $y(x_0) = y_0$. If $f(x, y)$ is analytic in the neighborhood of the point $(x_0, y_0)$, then it is known that the solution $y(x)$ can be expressed as a power series in $x - x_0$:

(2) $$y(x) = A_0 + A_1(x - x_0) + A_2(x - x_0)^2 + \cdots + A_n(x - x_0)^n + \cdots$$

The power series (2) must be the Taylor expansion of $y(x)$ about the point $x = x_0$, and the coefficients $A_n$, $n = 0, 1, 2, \ldots$, must therefore have the values

$$A_0 = y(x_0), \quad A_n = \frac{y^{(n)}(x_0)}{n!}, \quad n = 1, 2, \ldots.$$

Hence the coefficients of (2) may be found as follows. The value of $y'(x_0)$ is found from (1) to be

(3) $$y'(x_0) = f(x_0, y_0).$$

To find $y''(x_0)$, differentiate both members of (1) and obtain

(4) $$y'' = f_x(x, y) + f_y(x, y)y'.$$

After substitution of $x = x_0$ and $y = y_0$ the right member of (4) is completely determined since $y'(x_0)$ has already been found to have the value given by (3), so that

$$y''(x_0) = f_x(x_0, y_0) + f_y(x_0, y_0)f(x_0, y_0).$$

The process is continued by differentiating (4) so as to yield

---

* Friedrich Wilhelm Bessel (1784–1846), Prussian astronomer and Director of the observatory at Königsberg. He was led to the functions now named for him by his investigations into the perturbations of planetary motion.

† Adrien Marie Legendre (1752–1833). One of the most eminent mathematicians of his day, he made important contributions to the theory of numbers and the theory of elliptic functions.

181

$y'''(x_0)$, and so on. Frequently, after several stages a formula for $y^{(n)}(x_0)$ will suggest itself, which may then be verified by mathematical induction.

The method here described is readily extended to differential equations of order higher than the first.

EXAMPLE 1. Find the solution $y(x)$ of

(a) $$y' = x + 3xy$$

for which $y(0) = 1$.

SOLUTION. From (a) it is seen that $y'(0) = 0$. Differentiation of (a) yields

(b) $$y'' = 1 + 3y + 3xy',$$

so that

$$y''(0) = 4$$

and

$$A_2 = \frac{y''(0)}{2!} = 2.$$

From (b) we find

$$y''' = 6y' + 3xy''$$

and hence

$$y'''(0) = 0 \quad \text{and} \quad A_3 = \frac{y'''(0)}{3!} = 0.$$

Another differentiation gives

$$y^{(4)} = 9y'' + 3xy'''$$

so that

$$y^{(4)}(0) = 36 \quad \text{and} \quad A_4 = \frac{y^{(4)}(0)}{4!} = \frac{3}{2}.$$

The formula

$$y^{(n)} = 3(n-1)y^{(n-2)} + 3xy^{(n-1)}$$

suggests itself and is readily proved by induction, so that

$$y^{(n)}(0) = 3(n-1)y^{(n-2)}(0), \quad n = 2, 3, \ldots.$$

182

Thus:

$$y^{(2n-1)}(0) = 0, \quad n = 1, 2, \ldots$$
$$y''(0) = 4$$
$$y^{(4)}(0) = 3^2 \cdot 4$$
$$y^{(6)}(0) = 3^3 \cdot 4 \cdot 5$$
$$y^{(8)}(0) = 3^4 \cdot 4 \cdot 5 \cdot 7$$

It seems clear that $y^{(2n)}(0)$ is given by the formula

$$y^{(2n)}(0) = 4 \cdot 3^{n-1} \cdot 1 \cdot 3 \cdot 5 \cdots (2n-1),$$

and this may be verified by induction. Hence

$$A_{2n} = \frac{4 \cdot 3^{n-1} \cdot 1 \cdot 3 \cdot 5 \cdots (2n-1)}{(2n)!} = \frac{3^{n-1}}{2^{n-2}n!}, \quad n = 1, 2, \ldots,$$

and the desired solution is

$$y(x) = 1 + 2x^2 + \frac{3}{2} x^4 + \cdots + \frac{3^{n-1}}{2^{n-2}n!} x^{2n} + \cdots$$

EXAMPLE 2. Find the solution $y(x)$ of the equation

$$y''' = y^2 \ln x + y'$$

for which $y(1) = 1$, $y'(1) = 0$, $y''(1) = 1$.

SOLUTION. We have:

$$y^{(4)} = \frac{y^2}{x} + 2yy' \ln x + y''$$

$$y^{(5)} = -\frac{y^2}{x^2} + \frac{4yy'}{x} + 2(y'^2 + yy'') \ln x + y'''$$

Hence $y'''(1) = 0$, $y^{(4)}(1) = 2$, $y^{(5)}(1) = -1$, and the Taylor expansion of the solution about the point $x = 1$ may be written

$$y(x) = 1 + \frac{(x-1)^2}{2!} + \frac{2(x-1)^4}{4!} - \frac{(x-1)^5}{5!} + \cdots,$$

correct to terms of order five.

**67. Solution in power series; second method.** The method to be considered here will be readily understood from its application to the examples of Article 66.

EXAMPLE 1. Find the solution $y(x)$ of

$$y' = x + 3xy$$

for which $y(0) = 1$.

SOLUTION. Let

(a) $\qquad y(x) = A_0 + A_1 x + A_2 x^2 + \cdots + A_n x^n + \cdots$

represent the power series expansion of the solution about $x = 0$. Then

(b) $\qquad y'(x) = A_1 + 2A_2 x + \cdots + nA_n x^{n-1} + \cdots.$

Substitution of (a) and (b) into the differential equation gives:

$$A_1 + 2A_2 x + \cdots + nA_n x^{n-1} + (n+1)A_{n+1} x^n + \cdots$$
$$= x + 3x(A_0 + A_1 x + A_2 x^2 + \cdots + A_n x^n + \cdots)$$
$$= (3A_0 + 1)x + 3(A_1 x^2 + A_2 x^3 + \cdots + A_{n-1} x^n + A_n x^{n+1} + \cdots)$$

Since the power series in the two members of the last equation are identically equal, coefficients of like powers of $x$ in the two members must be the same. Hence $A_1 = 0$, $2A_2 = 3A_0 + 1$, and

$$(n+1)A_{n+1} = 3A_{n-1}, \quad n = 2, 3, \ldots.$$

From this last relation one finds $A_3 = A_1 = 0$, $5A_5 = 3A_3 = 0$, and in general $(2n - 1)A_{2n-1} = 0, \quad n = 1, 2, \ldots.$ Also

$$A_4 = \frac{3}{4} A_2 = \frac{3}{2 \cdot 4} (3A_0 + 1)$$

$$A_6 = \frac{3}{6} A_4 = \frac{3^2}{2 \cdot 4 \cdot 6} (3A_0 + 1)$$

and by induction

$$A_{2n} = \frac{3^{n-1}}{2^n n!} (3A_0 + 1), \quad n = 1, 2, \ldots.$$

Hence the general solution is

$$y(x) = A_0 + (3A_0 + 1)\left(\frac{1}{2} x^2 + \frac{3}{2 \cdot 4} x^4 + \frac{3^2}{2 \cdot 4 \cdot 6} x^6 + \cdots\right).$$

Since $A_0 = y(0) = 1$, the particular solution desired is

$$y(x) = 1 + 4\left(\frac{1}{2} x^2 + \frac{3}{2 \cdot 4} x^4 + \frac{3^2}{2 \cdot 4 \cdot 6} x^6 + \cdots\right)$$

or $\qquad y(x) = 1 + 2x^2 + \frac{3}{2} x^4 + \frac{3^2}{2(2 \cdot 3)} x^6 + \cdots.$

EXAMPLE 2.   Find the solution $y(x)$ of the equation

(a) $$y''' = y^2 \ln x + y'$$

for which $y(1) = 1$, $y'(1) = 0$, $y''(1) = 1$.

SOLUTION.   By virtue of the initial conditions we may write the solution in the form

(b) $$y(x) = 1 + \tfrac{1}{2}(x - 1)^2 + A_3(x - 1)^3 + A_4(x - 1)^4$$
$$+ A_5(x - 1)^5 + \cdots,$$

where $A_3$, $A_4$, $A_5$, ... are to be determined.   From (b) we get by differentiation:

(c) $$y'(x) = (x - 1) + 3A_3(x - 1)^2 + 4A_4(x - 1)^3 + 5A_5(x - 1)^4 + \cdots$$

(d) $$y'''(x) = 6A_3 + 24A_4(x - 1) + 60A_5(x - 1)^2 + \cdots$$

The function $\ln x$ has the expansion

$$\ln x = (x - 1) - \tfrac{1}{2}(x - 1)^2 + \cdots \qquad 0 < x \leq 2,$$

and by squaring (b) we find $y^2(x)$ to be

$$y^2 = 1 + (x - 1)^2 + \cdots,$$

so that the product term $y^2 \ln x$ has the expansion

(e) $$y^2 \ln x = (x - 1) - \tfrac{1}{2}(x - 1)^2 + \cdots.$$

The undetermined coefficients of the solution (b) are found from the identity which results by substituting the series (c), (d), and (e) into the equation (a).   This identity is

$$6A_3 + 24A_4(x - 1) + 60A_5(x - 1)^2 + \cdots$$
$$= [(x - 1) - \tfrac{1}{2}(x - 1)^2 + \cdots] + [(x - 1) + 3A_3(x - 1)^2 + \cdots].$$

Equating coefficients of like powers of $x - 1$, we have

$$6A_3 = 0, \quad 24A_4 = 2, \quad 60A_5 = -\tfrac{1}{2} + 3A_3,$$

so that

$$A_3 = 0, \quad A_4 = \tfrac{1}{12}, \quad A_5 = -\tfrac{1}{120},$$

and the required solution is

$$y(x) = 1 + \tfrac{1}{2}(x - 1)^2 + \tfrac{1}{12}(x - 1)^4 - \tfrac{1}{120}(x - 1)^5 + \cdots,$$

which coincides with the solution found in Example 2 of the preceding article.

$$1. \; y'' + 2xy' + 2y = 0$$
$$2. \; (1+x^2)y'' - 4xy' + 6y = 0$$

SOLUTION IN SERIES

Each of the following differential equations with its associated initial condition or conditions defines a particular solution in the form of a power series in $x - a$ where $a$ is the given initial value of $x$. Find the terms of this particular solution up to and including the term of the specified order $k$.

1. $y' = (1 - y)^{\frac{1}{2}}$; $y(0) = 0$, $k = 2$

2. $y' = xy - x^2$; $y(0) = 2$, $k = 5$

3. $y' = x^2 - y^2$; $y(1) = 0$, $k = 5$

4. $y' = 3x + \dfrac{y}{x}$; $y(1) = 3$, $k = 4$

5. $y' = \ln xy$; $y(1) = 1$, $k = 5$

6. $y' = 1 + y^2$; $y(1) = -1$, $k = 5$

7. $y' = x^2 + y^2$; $y(2) = 0$, $k = 6$

8. $y' = \sqrt{1 + xy}$; $y(0) = 1$, $k = 4$

9. $y' = \cos x + \sin y$; $y\left(\dfrac{\pi}{2}\right) = \dfrac{\pi}{2}$, $k = 5$

10. $y'' - y = \sin x$; $y(0) = 1$, $y'(0) = 2$, $k = 7$

11. $y'' - 2y = e^{2x}$; $y(0) = y'(0) = 2$, $k = 7$

12. $y'' + 2yy' = 0$; $y(0) = 0$, $y'(0) = 1$, $k = 7$

13. $y'' = \sin y$; $y(0) = \dfrac{\pi}{4}$, $y'(0) = 0$, $k = 7$

14. $y'' + \frac{1}{2}(y')^2 - y = 0$; $y(0) = y'(0) = 1$, $k = 7$

15. $y'' = \sin xy$; $y\left(\dfrac{\pi}{2}\right) = y'\left(\dfrac{\pi}{2}\right) = 1$, $k = 5$

16. $y'' = \cos xy$; $y\left(\dfrac{\pi}{2}\right) = y'\left(\dfrac{\pi}{2}\right) = 1$, $k = 5$

$$(x+1)y' - (7+2)y = 0 \qquad y($$

**68. Singular points of second-order linear equations.** Consider the second-order linear equation

(5) $$R_0 y'' + R_1 y' + R_2 y = Q,$$

where $R_0$, $R_1$, $R_2$, and $Q$ are functions of $x$. This equation may be changed into the form

$$y'' + p_1 y' + p_2 y = q$$

by dividing (5) by the leading coefficient $R_0$.

186

The point $x = x_0$ is said to be an *ordinary* point of the differential equation (5) if both $p_1$ and $p_2$ can be expanded in power series in an interval about $x_0$. Otherwise $x = x_0$ is called a *singular* point of (5). If

$$(x - x_0)p_1 \quad \text{and} \quad (x - x_0)^2 p_2$$

can both be expanded in power series in an interval about $x = x_0$, the point $x = x_0$ is called a *regular* singular point. Singular points which are not regular are called *irregular*.

Consider, for example, the equation

$$(x - 1)^4 x^2 y'' - 3(x - 1)xy' - 5y = 0.$$

The point $x = 0$ is a regular singular point, while the point $x = 1$ is an irregular singular point. All other values of $x$ are ordinary points.

It may be shown that if $x = x_0$ is an ordinary point of (5), the methods described in Articles 66 and 67 enable one to find two linearly independent solutions of the form

$$\sum_{n=0}^{\infty} A_n (x - x_0)^n.$$

If $x = x_0$ is a regular singular point of (5), at least one solution of the form

$$(x - x_0)^k \sum_{n=0}^{\infty} A_n (x - x_0)^n$$

can be found, where $k$ need not be an integer. If $x = x_0$ is an irregular singular point of (5), the problem is more complicated and will not be considered in this book.

## 69. The method of Frobenius.

We shall consider solutions of the homogeneous differential equation

$$(6) \qquad R_0(x)y'' + R_1(x)y' + R_2(x)y = 0$$

near a regular singular point, and we shall assume this point to be the origin since no loss of generality is thereby involved. It should be noted that the method to be explained is also effective for a solution in the neighborhood of an ordinary point.

Equation (6) can be written in the form

$$(7) \qquad P_0(x)y'' + \frac{1}{x} P_1(x)y' + \frac{1}{x^2} P_2(x)y = 0,$$

where $P_0(x)$, $P_1(x)$, and $P_2(x)$ are functions which can be expanded in Maclaurin series in intervals about $x = 0$:

$$P_0(x) = a_{00} + a_{01}x + a_{02}x^2 + \cdots$$
$$P_1(x) = a_{10} + a_{11}x + a_{12}x^2 + \cdots$$
$$P_2(x) = a_{20} + a_{21}x + a_{22}x^2 + \cdots$$

It will be assumed that $P_0(0) = a_{00}$ is different from zero. We seek solutions of (7) of the form

$$(8) \qquad y = x^k \sum_{n=0}^{\infty} A_n x^n$$
$$= A_0 x^k + A_1 x^{k+1} + \cdots, \quad A_0 \neq 0.$$

If the series (8) is substituted into the left member of (7), we obtain

$$(a_{00} + a_{01}x + a_{02}x^2 + \cdots)[k(k-1)A_0 x^{k-2} + (k+1)kA_1 x^{k-1} + (k+2)(k+1)A_2 x^k + \cdots]$$
$$+ (a_{10} + a_{11}x + a_{12}x^2 + \cdots)[kA_0 x^{k-2} + (k+1)A_1 x^{k-1} + (k+2)A_2 x^k + \cdots]$$
$$+ (a_{20} + a_{21}x + a_{22}x^2 + \cdots)[A_0 x^{k-2} + A_1 x^{k-1} + A_2 x^k + \cdots].$$

When the indicated multiplications have been performed and the result arranged in ascending powers of $x$, this expression takes the form

$$(9) \qquad \begin{aligned} &[a_{00}k(k-1) + a_{10}k + a_{20}]A_0 x^{k-2} \\ &+ \{[a_{00}(k+1)k + a_{10}(k+1) + a_{20}]A_1 \\ &\quad + [a_{01}k(k-1) + a_{11}k + a_{21}]A_0\}x^{k-1} \\ &+ \{[a_{00}(k+2)(k+1) + a_{10}(k+2) + a_{20}]A_2 \\ &\quad + [a_{01}(k+1)k + a_{11}(k+1) + a_{21}]A_1 \\ &\quad + [a_{02}k(k-1) + a_{12}k + a_{22}]A_0\}x^k + \cdots. \end{aligned}$$

In order that (8) shall be a solution of the differential equation (7), the expression (9) must vanish identically for all values of $x$ in an interval about $x = 0$. This requires that the coefficient of each power of $x$ in (9) shall be zero. The equation

$$[a_{00}k^2 + (a_{10} - a_{00})k + a_{20}]A_0 = 0,$$

which expresses the vanishing of the coefficient of $x^{k-2}$, will be satisfied if $k$ is chosen to be a root of the *indicial equation*

(10) $$f(k) = a_{00}k^2 + (a_{10} - a_{00})k + a_{20} = 0.$$

The roots $k_1$, $k_2$ of this quadratic equation will be called the *indicial exponents* associated with the point $x = 0$.

When the indicial exponent $k_1$ is substituted into the expression (9), the equations which result from setting the coefficients of

$$x^{k-1}, \quad x^k, \quad x^{k+1}, \quad \cdots$$

equal to zero serve to determine each coefficient $A_n$ in terms of the preceding coefficients and hence in terms of $A_0$. The series (8) formed with the coefficients so determined can be shown to converge on an interval about $x = 0$ and to represent on this interval a solution $A_0 y_1(x)$ of the differential equation (7). The procedure fails if there is a positive integer $n$ such that $k_1 + n$ is equal to the second indicial exponent $k_2$. The modifications necessary in this case are discussed in Article 71.

If $k_2$ is distinct from $k_1$ and if $k_2$ is not the sum of $k_1$ and a positive integer, then $k_2$ serves in a similar manner to define a second solution $y_2(x)$ of the differential equation (7). It can be shown that $y_1(x)$ and $y_2(x)$ are linearly independent, so that the general solution of (7) is

$$y = c_1 y_1(x) + c_2 y_2(x).$$

EXAMPLE 1. Solve the differential equation

(a) $$(2x^2 + x^3)y'' + (x + 3x^2)y' - (1 + 4x)y = 0$$

by the method of Frobenius.

SOLUTION. The equation

(b) $\qquad (2 + x)y'' + \dfrac{1}{x}(1 + 3x)y' - \dfrac{1}{x^2}(1 + 4x)y = 0,$

which is obtained by dividing (a) by $x^2$, shows that $x = 0$ is a regular singular point. Assume therefore that a solution of (a) is expressible in the form

(c) $\quad y(x) = A_0 x^k + A_1 x^{k+1} + \cdots + A_n x^{k+n} + \cdots, \quad A_0 \neq 0.$

The first and second derivatives of (c) are then:

$y'(x) = kA_0 x^{k-1} + (k + 1)A_1 x^k + \cdots + (k + n)A_n x^{k+n-1} + \cdots$

$y''(x) = k(k - 1)A_0 x^{k-2} + (k + 1)kA_1 x^{k-1} + \cdots$
$$\qquad\qquad\qquad + (k + n)(k + n - 1)A_n x^{k+n-2} + \cdots$$

Substitution of the series for $y(x)$, $y'(x)$, $y''(x)$ into the left member of (b) produces the expression

(d)
$$[2k(k - 1) + k - 1]A_0 x^{k-2}$$
$$+ \{[2k(k + 1) + k]A_1 + [k(k - 1) + 3k - 4]A_0\}x^{k-1} + \cdots$$
$$+ \{[2(k + n)(k + n - 1) + k + n - 1]A_n$$
$$+ [(k+n-1)(k+n-2)+3(k+n-1)-4]A_{n-1}\}x^{k+n-2} + \cdots.$$

The indicial equation is

$$f(k) = 2k(k - 1) + k - 1 = 2k^2 - k - 1 = 0;$$

its roots are $k = 1$ and $k = -\frac{1}{2}$. For either of these values of $k$ the coefficient of $x^{k-2}$ will vanish. The vanishing of the coefficient of $x^{k-1}$ is expressed by the equation

$$[2k(k + 1) + k]A_1 + [k(k - 1) + 3k - 4]A_0 = 0,$$

and in general the vanishing of the coefficient of

$$x^{k+n-2}, \quad n = 1, 2, \ldots,$$

is assured by the condition

(e)
$$[2(k + n)(k + n - 1) + k + n - 1]A_n$$
$$+ [(k + n - 1)(k + n - 2) + 3(k + n - 1) - 4]A_{n-1} = 0,$$
$$n = 1, 2, \ldots.$$

We first choose $k = 1$. In this case the condition $(e)$ becomes

$$n(2n + 3)A_n + (n^2 + 2n - 4)A_{n-1} = 0, \quad n = 1, 2, \ldots,$$

and we may solve for $A_n$:

$(f)$ $\qquad A_n = - \dfrac{n^2 + 2n - 4}{n(2n + 3)} A_{n-1}, \quad n = 1, 2, \ldots$

From $(f)$ we find successively:

$$A_1 = \tfrac{1}{5}A_0$$
$$A_2 = - \tfrac{2}{7}A_1 = - \tfrac{2}{25}A_0$$
$$A_3 = - \tfrac{11}{27}A_2 = \tfrac{22}{945}A_0$$

. . . . . . .

Hence a particular solution corresponding to $k = 1$ is

$$y_1(x) = x(1 + \tfrac{1}{5}x - \tfrac{2}{35}x^2 + \tfrac{22}{945}x^3 - \cdots).$$

For $k = - \tfrac{1}{2}$ the relation $(e)$ reduces to

$$A_n = - \frac{4n^2 - 4n - 19}{4n(2n - 3)} A_{n-1}, \quad n = 1, 2, \ldots,$$

from which we find:

$$A_1 = - \tfrac{19}{4}A_0$$
$$A_2 = \tfrac{11}{8}A_1 = - \tfrac{209}{32}A_0$$
$$A_3 = - \tfrac{5}{36}A_2 = \tfrac{1045}{1152}A_0$$

. . . . . . .

Hence a second particular solution is

$$y_2(x) = x^{-\frac{1}{2}}(1 - \tfrac{19}{4}x - \tfrac{209}{32}x^2 + \tfrac{1045}{1152}x^3 - \cdots).$$

The general solution is

$$c_1 y_1(x) + c_2 y_2(x).$$

By means of the notation

(11) $\qquad \begin{aligned} g_i(k) &= a_{0i}(k - i)(k - i - 1) + a_{1i}(k - i) + a_{2i} \\ &= a_{0i}(k - i)^2 + (a_{1i} - a_{0i})(k - i) + a_{2i}, \quad i = 1, 2, \ldots, \end{aligned}$

and (10), the expression (9) can be written in the form

$$f(k)A_0 x^{k-2} + [A_1 f(k+1) + A_0 g_1(k+1)]x^{k-1}$$

(12) $\qquad + [A_2 f(k+2) + A_1 g_1(k+2) + A_0 g_2(k+2)]x^k + \cdots$

$$+ \Big[A_n f(k+n) + \sum_{i=1}^{n} A_{n-i} g_i(k+n)\Big]x^{k+n-2} + \cdots.$$

Hence the condition that the coefficients of $x^{k-1}$, $x^k$, $x^{k+1}$, ... shall vanish is given by the equations

(13) $\quad A_n f(k+n) = -\sum_{i=1}^{n} A_{n-i} g_i(k+n), \quad n = 1, 2, \ldots$

The relations (13) are the *recursion formulas* for the coefficients $A_n$. If we divide both members of (13) by $f(k+n)$ and apply the resulting formulas sequentially beginning with $n = 1$, it is clear that each coefficient $A_n$ can be expressed in the form

(14) $\qquad A_n = A_0 B_n(k), \quad n = 1, 2, \ldots,$

where the functions $B_n(k)$ are readily seen to be rational functions of $k$. If $k$ is replaced by an indicial exponent $k_1$ in (14), it is seen that each coefficient $A_n$ will have a well-defined value expressible in terms of $A_0$, unless $f(k_1 + n) = 0$ for some positive integer $n$, that is, unless the second indicial exponent $k_2$ is the sum of $k_1$ and a positive integer.

EXAMPLE 2. Use the recursion formulas (13) to solve the equation

$$3x^2 y'' + x(2 - x)y' - (2 + x^2)y = 0.$$

SOLUTION. We write the equation in the form

$$3y'' + \frac{1}{x}(2 - x)y' - \frac{1}{x^2}(2 + x^2)y = 0,$$

which shows that $x = 0$ is a regular singular point, and that the functions $P_0$, $P_1$, $P_2$ of (7) are 3, $2 - x$, and $-(2 + x^2)$, respectively. Hence $a_{00} = 3$, $a_{10} = 2$, $a_{11} = -1$, $a_{20} = -2$, $a_{22} = -1$, and all other coefficients $a_{ij}$ are zero. The indicial equation (10) is therefore

$$f(k) = 3k^2 - k - 2 = (k - 1)(3k + 2) = 0,$$

the roots of which are

$$1, -\tfrac{2}{3}.$$

The only functions $g_i$ of (11) which do not vanish identically are $g_1(k) = 1 - k$, $g_2(k) = -1$, so that the recursion formulas become

(a) $\quad A_1 = \dfrac{A_0}{3k+5}, \quad A_n = \dfrac{A_{n-1}}{3k+3n+2} + \dfrac{A_{n-2}}{(k+n-1)(3k+3n+2)}, \quad n > 1.$

For the indicial exponent $k = 1$, these formulas reduce to

$$A_1 = \frac{1}{8} A_0, \quad A_n = \frac{A_{n-1}}{3n + 5} + \frac{A_{n-2}}{n(3n + 5)}, \quad n = 2, 3, \ldots,$$

from which we have

$$A_1 = \frac{1}{8} A_0$$

$$A_2 = \frac{1}{11} A_1 + \frac{1}{22} A_0 = \frac{5A_0}{88}$$

$$A_3 = \frac{1}{14} A_2 + \frac{1}{42} A_1 = \frac{13A_0}{1848}$$

$$A_4 = \frac{1}{17} A_3 + \frac{1}{68} A_2 = \frac{157A_0}{125664}$$

$$\cdot \quad \cdot \quad \cdot \quad \cdot \quad \cdot \quad \cdot \quad \cdot$$

so that one particular integral of the differential equation is

$$(b) \quad y_1(x) = x\left[1 + \frac{x}{8} + \frac{5x^2}{88} + \frac{13x^3}{1848} + \frac{157x^4}{125664} + \cdots\right].$$

For the indicial exponent $k = -\frac{2}{3}$ the recursion formulas $(a)$ become

$$A_1 = \frac{1}{3} A_0, \quad A_n = \frac{A_{n-1}}{3n} + \frac{A_{n-2}}{n(3n - 5)}, \quad n = 2, 3, \ldots.$$

From these formulas we get the following expressions:

$$A_1 = \tfrac{1}{3}A_0$$
$$A_2 = \tfrac{1}{6}A_1 + \tfrac{1}{2}A_0 = \tfrac{5}{9}A_0$$
$$A_3 = \tfrac{1}{9}A_2 + \tfrac{1}{12}A_1 = \tfrac{29}{324}A_0$$
$$A_4 = \tfrac{1}{12}A_3 + \tfrac{1}{28}A_2 = \tfrac{743}{27216}A_0$$

$$\cdot \quad \cdot \quad \cdot \quad \cdot \quad \cdot \quad \cdot \quad \cdot$$

Hence a second particular integral is

$$(c) \quad y_2(x) = x^{-\frac{2}{3}}\left[1 + \frac{x}{3} + \frac{5x^2}{9} + \frac{29x^3}{324} + \frac{743x^4}{27216} + \cdots\right].$$

The general solution of the differential equation is

$$c_1 y_1(x) + c_2 y_2(x).$$

EXAMPLE 3. Solve the differential equation

$$5x^2 y'' + xy' - (1 - x^3)y = 0.$$

SOLUTION. Division by $x^2$ shows that the origin is a regular singular point and that the only nonvanishing coefficients $a_{ij}$ of the functions $P_0$, $P_1$, $P_2$ in (7) are $a_{00} = 5$, $a_{10} = 1$, $a_{20} = -1$, $a_{23} = 1$. The indicial equation is therefore

$$f(k) = 5k^2 - 4k - 1 = (k - 1)(5k + 1) = 0,$$

and $g_3 = 1$. The functions $g_1$, $g_2$ vanish identically, as do all $g_i$ for $i > 3$. The recursion formulas (13) become:

$$A_1 = A_2 = 0, \quad A_n = \frac{-A_{n-3}}{(k + n - 1)(5k + 5n + 1)}, \quad n > 2$$

For the indicial exponent $k = 1$ the recursion formulas show that

$$A_n = \frac{-A_{n-3}}{n(5n + 6)}, \quad n = 3, 6, 9, \ldots,$$

all other $A_n$ being zero. Hence

$$A_3 = \frac{-A_0}{9 \cdot 7}, \quad A_6 = \frac{A_0}{9^2 \cdot 2! \cdot 7 \cdot 12}, \quad A_9 = \frac{-A_0}{9^3 \cdot 3! \cdot 7 \cdot 12 \cdot 17}, \cdots,$$

$$A_{3m} = \frac{(-1)^m A_0}{9^m \cdot m! \cdot 7 \cdot 12 \cdots (5m + 2)},$$

so that the particular integral which corresponds to $k = 1$ is

$$y_1(x) = x\left[1 - \frac{x^3}{9 \cdot 7} + \frac{x^6}{9^2 \cdot 2 \cdot 7 \cdot 12} - \cdots \right.$$
$$\left. + (-1)^m \frac{x^{3m}}{9^m \cdot m! \cdot 7 \cdot 12 \cdots (5m + 2)} + \cdots \right].$$

The recursion formulas for $k = -\frac{1}{5}$ show that

$$A_n = \frac{-A_{n-3}}{n(5n - 6)}, \quad n = 3, 6, 9, \ldots,$$

all other $A_n$ being zero. We have

$$A_3 = -\frac{A_0}{9 \cdot 3}, \quad A_6 = \frac{A_0}{9^2 \cdot 2! \cdot 3 \cdot 8}, \cdots,$$

$$A_{3m} = \frac{(-1)^m A_0}{9^m \cdot m! \cdot 3 \cdot 8 \cdots (5m - 2)},$$

and the second particular integral is

$$y_2(x) = x^{-\frac{1}{3}}\left[1 - \frac{x^3}{9 \cdot 3} + \frac{x^6}{9^2 \cdot 2! \cdot 3 \cdot 8} - \cdots\right.$$

$$\left. + (-1)^m \frac{x^{3m}}{9^m \cdot m! \cdot 3 \cdot 8 \cdots (5m-2)} + \cdots\right].$$

The general solution is

$$c_1 y_1(x) + c_2 y_2(x).$$

# EXERCISE 41

In each of Problems 1–10 show that the origin is a regular singular point. Substitute the series $(c)$ of Example 1 into the differential equation and find the general solution as in that example.

1. $2xy'' + 5y' + xy = 0$
2. $3x(2 + 3x)y''\quad 4y' + 4y = 0$
3. $x^2(4 + x)y'' + 7xy' - y = 0$
4. $2x^2y'' + (x - x^2)y' - y = 0$
5. $2x^2y'' + 5xy' + (1 + x)y = 0$
6. $9x^2y'' + (2 + 3x)y = 0$
7. $(2x^2 + x^3)y'' - xy' + (1 - x)y = 0$
8. $2x^2y'' - 3(x + x^2)y' + (2 + 3x)y = 0$
9. $3x^2y'' + (5x - x^2)y' + (2x^2 - 1)y = 0$
10. $4x^2y'' + x(x^2 - 4)y' + 3y = 0$

11. Show that the substitution $t = \dfrac{1}{x}$, which implies that

$$\frac{dy}{dt} = -x^2\frac{dy}{dx} \quad \text{and} \quad \frac{d^2y}{dt^2} = x^4\frac{d^2y}{dx^2} + 2x^3\frac{dy}{dx},$$

transforms the differential equation

$$(a) \qquad\qquad 2t^4\frac{d^2y}{dt^2} - t^3\frac{dy}{dt} + y = 0$$

into the equation of Problem 1. From the particular integrals already found for that problem find the corresponding integrals of the equation $(a)$. Then show that $(a)$ can be solved by assuming a solution of the form

$$y = t^k[A_0 + A_1t^{-1} + A_2t^{-2} + \cdots].$$

195

In Problems 12, 13, 14 proceed as in Problem 11. The transformed differential equation is that of the earlier problem indicated.

12. $2t^3 \dfrac{d^2y}{dt^2} - t^2 \dfrac{dy}{dt} + (1+t)y = 0.$   Problem 5.

13. $9t^3 \dfrac{d^2y}{dt^2} + 18t^2 \dfrac{dy}{dt} + (2t+3)y = 0.$   Problem 6.

14. $2t^3 \dfrac{d^2y}{dt^2} + (7t^2 + 3t) \dfrac{dy}{dt} + (2t+3)y = 0.$   Problem 8.

Using the formulas (10) and (11), set up the recursion relations (13) for each of the problems which follow and find the general solution.

15. $2x^2y'' - 3(x + x^2)y' + 2y = 0$
16. $9x^2y'' + 9(x - x^2)y' + (x - 1)y = 0$
17. $4x^2(1 - x)y'' + 3x(1 + 2x)y' - 3y = 0$
18. $2x^2(1 - 3x)y'' + 5xy' - 2y = 0$
19. $4x^2(1 + x)y'' - 5xy' + 2y = 0$
20. $(4 + x)x^2y'' + x(x - 1)y' + y = 0$
21. $(8 - x)x^2y'' + 6xy' - y = 0$
22. $2x^2y'' + x(1 + x^2)y' - (1 + x)y = 0$
23. $2x^2y'' - xy' + (1 + x^2)y = 0$
24. $3x^2y'' + 2xy' + (x^2 - 2)y = 0$
25. $x^2(3 + x^2)y'' + 5xy' - (1 + x)y = 0$
26. $2xy'' - (1 + x^3)y' + y = 0$

**70. Indicial exponents equal.** If the two roots of the indicial equation are equal, the theory of Article 69 leads to only one solution of the differential equation (7). In order to find a second solution which is independent of the first, we employ the following procedure.

When the expressions (14) are substituted for the coefficients $A_n$ in the series (8) a function

(15) $$y(x, k) = A_0 x^k \sum_{n=0}^{\infty} B_n(k)x^n$$

results, where it is understood that $B_0(k) = 1$. From the manner in which the expressions (14) are derived from the recursion formulas (13) it is clear that when the substitutions are made the expression (9) reduces to

$$A_0 f(k) x^{k-2}.$$

Hence when $y$, $y'$, and $y''$ in the differential equation (7) are replaced by $y(x, k)$, $y_x(x, k)$, and $y_{xx}(x, k)$, one obtains the identity

$$(16) \quad P_0(x) \frac{\partial^2}{\partial x^2} y(x, k) + \frac{1}{x} P_1(x) \frac{\partial}{\partial x} y(x, k)$$

$$+ \frac{1}{x^2} P_2(x) y(x, k) = A_0 f(k) x^{k-2}.$$

Differentiation of the identity (16) partially with respect to $k$ gives

$$(17) \quad P_0(x) \frac{\partial^2}{\partial x^2} \left[ \frac{\partial}{\partial k} y(x, k) \right] + \frac{1}{x} P_1(x) \frac{\partial}{\partial x} \left[ \frac{\partial}{\partial k} y(x, k) \right]$$

$$+ \frac{1}{x^2} P_2(x) \left[ \frac{\partial}{\partial k} y(x, k) \right] = A_0 \frac{\partial}{\partial k} \left[ f(k) x^{k-2} \right].$$

If $k_1$ is the double root of the indicial equation,

$$f(k) = a_{00}(k - k_1)^2,$$

so that

$$\frac{\partial}{\partial k} \left[ f(k) x^{k-2} \right] = a_{00} \left[ 2(k - k_1) + (k - k_1)^2 \ln x \right] x^{k-2}.$$

Hence the right member of (17) vanishes for $k = k_1$ so that

$$\frac{\partial}{\partial k} y(x, k),$$

when evaluated for $k = k_1$, furnishes a solution $y_2(x)$ of the differential equation (7). Moreover, since (15) can be written

$$y(x, k) = A_0 x^k + A_0 \sum_{n=1}^{\infty} B_n(k) x^{k+n},$$

197

it is seen that

$$\frac{\partial}{\partial k} y(x, k) = A_0 x^k \ln x + A_0 \sum_{n=1}^{\infty} \left[ B_n(k) x^{k+n} \ln x + B_n{}'(k) x^{k+n} \right]$$

$$= \left[ A_0 x^k + A_0 \sum_{n=1}^{\infty} B_n(k) x^{k+n} \right] \ln x + A_0 \sum_{n=1}^{\infty} B_n{}'(k) x^{k+n},$$

where

$$B_n{}'(k) = \frac{d}{dk} B_n(k).$$

Noting that the value of the coefficient of $\ln x$ for $k = k_1$ is $y_1(x)$, we have

$$y_2(x) = \left[ \frac{\partial}{\partial k} y(x, k) \right]_{k=k_1} = y_1(x) \ln x + \sum_{n=1}^{\infty} B_n{}'(k_1) x^{k_1+n},$$

and it can be shown that the solutions $y_1(x)$ and $y_2(x)$ are linearly independent.

EXAMPLE. Find the general solution of the differential equation $x^2 y'' - 3xy' + 4(x + 1)y = 0$.

SOLUTION. Writing the equation in the form

$$y'' - \frac{3}{x} y' + \frac{4x + 4}{x^2} y = 0,$$

we see that $x = 0$ is a regular singular point and that $P_0(x) = 1$, $P_1(x) = -3$, $P_2(x) = 4x+4$. Also $a_{00} = P_0(0) = 1$, $a_{10} = P_1(0) = -3$, $a_{20} = P_2(0) = 4$, and $a_{21} = 4$, while the remaining $a_{ij}$ are zero. Hence the indicial equation is $f(k) = k^2 - 4k + 4 = 0$, while $g_1(k) = 4$ and $g_i(k) = 0$ for $i > 1$. The recursion formulas may be written

$$A_n = \frac{-4}{(k + n - 2)^2} A_{n-1}, \quad n = 1, 2, \ldots,$$

and hence:

$$A_1 = -\frac{4}{(k - 1)^2} A_0$$

$$A_2 = -\frac{4}{k^2} A_1 = \frac{4^2}{(k - 1)^2 k^2} A_0$$

In general,

$$A_n = A_0 B_n(k) = \frac{(-1)^n 4^n}{[(k-1)k(k+1) \cdots (k+n-2)]^2} A_0,$$

and

$$B_n(k) = \frac{(-1)^n 4^n}{[(k-1)k(k+1) \cdots (k+n-2)]^2}, \quad n > 0.$$

The function $y(x, k)$ is therefore given by the series

$$y(x, k) = A_0 x^k \left\{ 1 - \frac{4}{(k-1)^2} x + \frac{4^2}{[(k-1)k]^2} x^2 - \cdots \right.$$

$$\left. + \frac{(-1)^n 4^n}{[(k-1)k(k+1) \cdots (k+n-2)]^2} x^n + \cdots \right\}.$$

Putting $k = 2$, $A_0 = 1$, we obtain the particular solution

$$y_1(x) = x^2 \left\{ 1 - 4x + \frac{4^2}{(2!)^2} - \cdots + \frac{(-1)^n 4^n}{(n!)^2} x^n + \cdots \right\}.$$

To compute $B_n'(k)$, we write

$$\ln | B_n(k) |$$
$$= n \ln 4 - 2[\ln (k-1) + \ln k + \cdots + \ln (k+n-2)]$$

and hence

$$\frac{d}{dk} | B_n(k) | = -2 | B_n(k) | \left[ \frac{1}{k-1} + \frac{1}{k} + \cdots + \frac{1}{k+n-2} \right].$$

Consequently

$$B_n'(2) = -2B_n(2) \left( 1 + \frac{1}{2} + \cdots + \frac{1}{n} \right),$$

so that the first three values of $B_n'(2)$ are:

$$B_1'(2) = -2B_1(2) = 8$$
$$B_2'(2) = -2B_2(2)(1 + \tfrac{1}{2}) = -12$$
$$B_3'(2) = -2B_3(2)(1 + \tfrac{1}{2} + \tfrac{1}{3}) = \tfrac{176}{27}$$

A second independent particular solution is therefore

$$y_2(x) = y_1(x) \ln x + x^2(8x - 12x^2 + \tfrac{176}{27}x^3 - \cdots).$$

**71. Indicial exponents differing by an integer.** Suppose that the roots $k_1$, $k_2$ of the indicial equation are such that $k_2 - k_1$ is a positive integer $N$. In this case

$$f(k) = a_{00}(k - k_1)(k - k_2) = a_{00}(k - k_1)(k - k_1 - N)$$

and the recursion formulas (13) take the form

$$(18) \quad a_{00}(k + n - k_1)(k + n - k_1 - N)A_n = -\sum_{i=1}^{n} A_{n-i}g_i(k + n),$$

$$i = 1, 2, \ldots.$$

For $k = k_1$ the formulas (18) become

$$(19) \quad a_{00}n(n - N)A_n = -\sum_{i=1}^{n} A_{n-i}g_i(k_1 + n), \quad i = 1, 2, \ldots,$$

and each of the coefficients $A_1$, $A_2$, $\ldots$, $A_{N-1}$ can be computed in terms of the preceding coefficients and hence in terms of $A_0$. However, for $n = N$ the coefficient of the left member of (19) is zero and (19) fails to determine $A_N$.

It may happen that the right member of (19) is also zero for $n = N$. In this case the coefficient $A_N$ can be left arbitrary. The succeeding coefficients $A_n$, $n > N$, can then be calculated in terms of $A_0$ and $A_N$ by successive applications of (19). The function $y(x)$ obtained by using these coefficients in the series (8) is then the general solution of the differential equation (7), since it depends upon two independent arbitrary constants $A_0$ and $A_N$. Hence the solution $y_2(x)$ corresponding to the indicial exponent $k_2$ is not independent of $y_1(x)$ but can be obtained from it by giving appropriate values to $A_0$ and $A_N$.

EXAMPLE 1. Find the general solution of the differential equation

$$x^2y'' + (x - 2x^2)y' + (x^2 - x - 1)y = 0.$$

SOLUTION. The equation may be written in the form

$$y'' + \frac{1 - 2x}{x} y' + \frac{x^2 - x - 1}{x^2} y = 0$$

from which we see that $x = 0$ is a regular singular point. We have

$$P_0(x) = 1, \quad P_1(x) = 1 - 2x, \quad P_2(x) = x^2 - x - 1,$$

so that

$$a_{00} = P_0(0) = 1, \quad a_{10} = P_1(0) = 1, \quad a_{20} = P_2(0) = -1;$$

also $a_{11} = -2$, $a_{21} = -1$, and $a_{22} = 1$, while the remaining $a_{ij}$ are zero. The indicial equation is $f(k) = k^2 - 1 = 0$ and has the roots $k_1 = -1$, $k_2 = 1$; $g_1(k) = 1 - 2k$, $g_2(k) = 1$, and $g_i(k) = 0$ for $i > 2$. The recursion formulas are

(a)
$$(k+2)kA_1 = (2k+1)A_0$$
$$(k+n+1)(k+n-1)A_n = (2k+2n-1)A_{n-1} - A_{n-2}, \quad n=2, 3, \ldots,$$

which upon substitution of $k = -1$ become:

$$A_1 = A_0$$
(b) $\quad n(n-2)A_n = (2n-3)A_{n-1} - A_{n-2}, \quad n = 2, 3, \ldots$

The left member of (b) vanishes for $n = 2$ and so does the right member. Hence we may leave the coefficient $A_2$ arbitrary. Successive calculations give:

$$A_3 = A_2 - \frac{2}{3!} A_0$$

$$A_4 = \frac{5A_3 - A_2}{2 \cdot 4} = \frac{1}{2!} A_2 - \frac{5}{4!} A_0$$

$$A_5 = \frac{7A_4 - A_3}{3 \cdot 5} = \frac{1}{3!} A_2 - \frac{9}{5!} A_0$$

$$A_6 = \frac{9A_5 - A_4}{4 \cdot 6} = \frac{1}{4!} A_2 - \frac{14}{6!} A_0$$

By induction we find

$$A_n = \frac{1}{(n-2)!} A_2 - \frac{(n-2)(n+1)}{2 \cdot n!} A_0, \quad n = 3, 4, \ldots.$$

The general solution is therefore:

$$y(x) = x^{-1}\left\{ A_0(1+x) + A_2 x^2 + \left(A_2 - \frac{2}{3!} A_0\right)x^3 + \left(\frac{1}{2!}A_2 - \frac{5}{4!}A_0\right)x^4 + \cdots \right.$$
$$\left. + \left[\frac{1}{(n-2)!}A_2 - \frac{(n-2)(n+1)}{2 \cdot n!}A_0\right]x^n + \cdots \right\}$$

$$= A_0 x^{-1}\left[1 + x - \frac{2}{3!}x^3 - \frac{5}{4!}x^4 - \cdots - \frac{(n-2)(n+1)}{2 \cdot n!}x^n - \cdots\right]$$
$$+ A_2 x\left[1 + x + \frac{1}{2!}x^2 + \cdots + \frac{1}{(n-2)!}x^{n-2} + \cdots\right]$$

201

The coefficient of $A_2$ in the expression for $y(x)$ is the solution corresponding to the remaining indicial exponent. This can be verified easily, for substitution of $k = 1$ into $(a)$ gives us

$$A_1 = A_0, \quad n(n+2)A_n = (2n+1)A_{n-1} - A_{n-2}, \quad n = 2, 3, \ldots$$

Hence we find:

$$A_2 = \frac{1}{2 \cdot 4} (5A_1 - A_0) = \frac{1}{2!} A_0$$

$$A_3 = \frac{1}{3 \cdot 5} (7A_2 - A_1) = \frac{1}{3!} A_0$$

Then by induction

$$A_n = \frac{1}{n!} A_0, \quad n = 1, 2, \ldots,$$

so that the solution is

$$y_2(x) = x \left[ 1 + x + \frac{x^2}{2!} + \cdots + \frac{x^n}{n!} + \cdots \right].$$

But $y_2(x)$ is clearly a member of the family of solutions represented by $y(x)$.

When the right member of (19) does not vanish for $n = N$, we can obtain a solution $y_1(x)$ corresponding to the indicial exponent $k_1$ by the following modification of the procedure described in Article 70. Consider the function

$$Y(x, k) = (k - k_1)y(x, k),$$

where $y(x, k)$ is the function defined by equation (15) of Article 70. Substitution into the differential equation (7) gives

$$P_0(x) \frac{\partial^2}{\partial x^2} Y(x, k) + \frac{1}{x} P_1(x) \frac{\partial}{\partial x} Y(x, k) + \frac{1}{x^2} P_2(x) Y(x, k)$$
$$= A_0(k - k_1) f(k) x^{k-2},$$

and differentiation with respect to $k$ gives

(20)
$$P_0(x) \frac{\partial^2}{\partial x^2} \left[ \frac{\partial}{\partial k} Y(x, k) \right] + \frac{1}{x} P_1(x) \frac{\partial}{\partial x} \left[ \frac{\partial}{\partial k} Y(x, k) \right]$$
$$+ \frac{1}{x^2} P_2(x) \left[ \frac{\partial}{\partial k} Y(x, k) \right] = A_0 \frac{\partial}{\partial k} \left[ (k - k_1) f(k) x^{k-2} \right].$$

Since $f(k) = a_{00}(k - k_1)(k - k_1 - N)$,

$$\frac{\partial}{\partial k}\left[(k - k_1)f(k)x^{k-2}\right] = a_{00}\left[2(k - k_1)(k - k_1 - N) + (k - k_1)^2\right]x^{k-2}$$
$$+ (k - k_1)f(k)x^{k-2}\ln x$$

so that the right member of (20) is zero for $k = k_1$. Consequently the function $\frac{\partial}{\partial k}Y(x, k)$, when evaluated for $k = k_1$, will furnish a solution of the differential equation (7), provided that this function is well defined. That it is well defined may be seen as follows. From the definition of $Y(x, k)$ and from (15) we see that the function $Y(x, k)$ can be represented by the series

$$(21) \qquad Y(x, k) = A_0 x^k \sum_{n=0}^{\infty} C_n(k) x^n$$

where $C_n(k) = (k - k_1)B_n(k)$. From (18) and (14) it easily follows that

$$(22) \quad a_{00}(k+n-k_1)(k+n-k_1-N)B_n(k) = -\sum_{i=1}^{n} B_{n-i}(k)g_i(k+n),$$

and hence

$$(23) \quad a_{00}(k+n-k_1)(k+n-k_1-N)C_n(k) = -\sum_{i=1}^{n} C_{n-i}(k)g_i(k+n)$$
$$= -(k-k_1)\sum_{i=1}^{n} B_{n-i}(k)g_i(k+n),$$

where $n = 1, 2, \ldots$. For values of $n < N$, (22) furnishes well-defined values of $B_n(k_1)$, and the second equation (23) shows that $C_n(k_1) = 0$ for such values of $N$. Substitution of $n = N$ into (22) shows that $B_N(k)$ becomes infinite as $k$ approaches $k_1$, and since the term in $B_N$ occurs in the right member of (22) for $n > N$, it is clear that as $k$ tends to $k_1$ the functions $B_n(k)$ become infinite for $n > N$. However, as is seen from the second equation (23), $C_N(k)$ approaches a finite limit as $k$ approaches $k_1$. The first equation (23) shows that for $n > N$ the limit of $C_n(k)$ as $k$ approaches $k_1$ exists. From the fact that $C_n(k)$ are

203

rational functions of $k$ it is evident that their derivatives $\dfrac{\partial C_n}{\partial k}$ also have finite limits as $k$ approaches $k_1$. Hence

$$A_0 y_1(x) = \left[ \frac{\partial}{\partial k} Y(x, k) \right]_{k=k_1} = \left\{ \frac{\partial}{\partial k} \left[ (k - k_1) y(x, k) \right] \right\}_{k=k_1}$$

is a solution of the differential equation (7).

A second solution $y_2(x)$ corresponding to the indicial exponent $k_2$ can be found without difficulty by the method of Article 69, but this is unnecessary since it can be shown that $y_2(x)$ will occur incidentally in the calculation of $y_1(x)$.

EXAMPLE 2. Find the general solution of the differential equation

$$x^2 y'' - (x^2 + 4x) y' + 4y = 0.$$

SOLUTION. Writing the equation in the form

$$y'' - \frac{x + 4}{x} y' + \frac{4}{x^2} y = 0$$

we see that the origin is a regular singular point with $P_0(x) = 1$, $P_1(x) = -4 - x$, $P_2(x) = 4$. Hence $a_{00} = 1$, $a_{10} = -4$, $a_{20} = 4$, $a_{11} = -1$, and the remaining $a_{ij}$ are zero. The indicial equation is $k^2 - 5k + 4 = 0$ and its roots, $k_1 = 1$, $k_2 = 4$, differ by an integer. Further, $g_1(k) = 1 - k$ and $g_i(k) = 0$ for $i > 1$. Hence the recursion formulas become

$$A_n = \frac{k + n - 1}{(k + n - 1)(k + n - 4)} A_{n-1}$$

$$= \frac{1}{k + n - 4} A_{n-1}, \quad n = 1, 2, \ldots,$$

so that we find successively:

$$A_1 = \frac{1}{k - 3} A_0$$

$$A_2 = \frac{1}{k - 2} A_1 = \frac{1}{(k - 3)(k - 2)} A_0$$

$$A_3 = \frac{1}{k - 1} A_2 = \frac{1}{(k - 3)(k - 2)(k - 1)} A_0$$

$$A_4 = \frac{1}{k} A_3 = \frac{1}{(k - 3)(k - 2)(k - 1)k} A_0$$

By induction, we have

$$A_n = A_0 B_n(k)$$

$$= \frac{1}{(k-3)(k-2)(k-1)k \cdots (k+n-4)} A_0, \quad n = 1, 2, \ldots$$

Consequently, putting $C_n(k) = (k-1)B_n(k)$, we find:

$$C_1(k) = \frac{k-1}{k-3}$$

$$C_2(k) = \frac{k-1}{(k-3)(k-2)}$$

$$C_3(k) = \frac{1}{(k-3)(k-2)}$$

and for $n \geqq 4$ we have

$$C_n(k) = \frac{1}{(k-3)(k-2)k(k+1) \cdots (k+n-4)}.$$

Differentiation with respect to $k$ gives:

$$C_1'(k) = -\frac{2}{(k-3)^2}$$

$$C_2'(k) = -\frac{k^2 - 2k - 1}{(k-3)^2(k-2)^2}$$

$$C_3'(k) = -\frac{2k - 5}{(k-3)^2(k-2)^2}$$

· · · · · · · · · · · · ·

$$C_n'(k) = -C_n(k) \left[ \frac{1}{k-3} + \frac{1}{k-2} + \frac{1}{k} + \frac{1}{k+1} + \cdots \right.$$

$$\left. + \frac{1}{k+n-4} \right], \quad n = 4, 5, \ldots$$

Hence if we define $Y(x, k) = (k-1)y(x, k)$, where

$$y(x, k) = A_0 x^k \left[ 1 + \sum_{n=1}^{\infty} B_n(k)x^n \right],$$

then we find

$$Y(x, k) = A_0 x^k \left[ (k-1) + \sum_{n=1}^{\infty} C_n(k)x^n \right],$$

and consequently

205

$$\frac{\partial Y(x, k)}{\partial k} = A_0 x^k \ln x \left[ (k - 1) + \sum_{n=1}^{\infty} C_n(k) x^n \right]$$
$$+ A_0 x^k \left[ 1 + \sum_{n=1}^{\infty} C_n'(k) x^n \right].$$

Putting $k = 1$, we have

$$y_1(x) = x \ln x \left[ \frac{1}{2!} x^3 + \frac{1}{2!} \sum_{n=4}^{\infty} \frac{x^n}{(n - 3)!} \right]$$
$$+ x \left[ 1 - \frac{x}{2} + \frac{x^2}{2} + \frac{3x^3}{4} + \frac{x^4}{4} - \frac{x^6}{36} + \cdots \right].$$

The coefficient of $\ln x$ is

$$\frac{x^4}{2!} \left( 1 + \frac{x}{1!} + \frac{x^2}{2!} + \cdots + \frac{x^n}{n!} + \cdots \right) = \frac{x^4 e^x}{2},$$

and it is readily verified that $y_2(x) = x^4 e^x$ is the solution of the differential equation which corresponds to the indicial exponent $k_2 = 4$.

## EXERCISE 42

Find the general solution of each of the following differential equations.

1. $xy'' + y' + 2y = 0$
2. $xy'' + y' + 2xy = 0$
3. $x^2 y'' - 3xy' + 4(1 + x)y = 0$
4. $x^2 y'' - x(1 + x)y' + y = 0$
5. $x^2 y'' - x(2x + 3)y' + 4y = 0$
6. $x^2(1 - x^2)y'' - 5xy' + 9y = 0$
7. $x^2 y'' + x(x^2 - 1)y' + (1 - x^2)y = 0$
8. $x^2 y'' + x(2x - 1)y' + x(x - 1)y = 0$
9. $x^2 y'' - x^2 y' + (x^2 - 2)y = 0$
10. $x^2 y'' + 2x^2 y' - (3x^2 + 2)y = 0$
11. $x^2(1 - x)y'' + x(1 + x)y' - 9y = 0$
12. $(x - x^2)y'' - 3y' + 2y = 0$
13. $x^2 y'' + x(x - 7)y' + (x + 12)y = 0$
14. $x^2(x + 1)y'' + x(x - 4)y' + 4y = 0$
15. $x^2 y'' + x(3 - x^2)y' - 3y = 0$

**72. The nonhomogeneous equation.** As in Chapter Four, the general solution of the nonhomogeneous equation

$$(24) \qquad P_0(x)y'' + \frac{1}{x}P_1(x)y' + \frac{1}{x^2}P_2(x)y = Q(x)$$

will be found by adding a particular integral of (24) to the general solution of the homogeneous equation (7). In what follows, the function $Q(x)$ will be assumed to be a polynomial

$$a_0 + a_1x + \cdots + a_m x^m.$$

A particular integral of (24) is of the form

$$y_p(x) = Y_0(x) + Y_1(x) + \cdots + Y_m(x),$$

where $Y_j(x)$ is a particular integral of the equation

$$P_0(x)y'' + \frac{1}{x}P_1(x)y' + \frac{1}{x^2}P_2(x)y = a_jx^j.$$

If any coefficient $a_j$ is zero, the corresponding integral $Y_j$ is taken to be identically zero. Each particular integral $Y_j(x)$ will be found by a method analogous to that of Article 69. The following example shows the details of the procedure.

EXAMPLE. Find a particular integral of the differential equation

$$(a) \qquad xy'' + (5 - x^3)y' - x^2y = x^2 - 2x^3.$$

SOLUTION. Assume that the particular integral has the form

$$(b) \quad y = A_0x^k + A_1x^{k+1} + \cdots + A_nx^{k+n} + \cdots, \quad A_0 \neq 0.$$

If this series and those for $y'$ and $y''$ are substituted into the left member of $(a)$, the following expression results:

$$k(k + 4)A_0x^{k-1} + (k + 1)(k + 5)A_1x^k + (k + 2)(k + 6)A_2x^{k+1}$$
$$(c) \qquad + [(k + 3)(k + 7)A_3 - (k + 1)A_0]x^{k+2} + \cdots$$
$$+ [(k + n)(k + n + 4)A_n - (k + n - 2)A_{n-3}]x^{k+n-1} + \cdots$$

A particular integral $Y_2$ of the equation

$$(d) \qquad xy'' + (5 - x^3)y' - x^2y = x^2$$

is found by equating the expression $(c)$ identically to $x^2$. This means that the leading term of $(c)$ must equal $x^2$ and that the

207

coefficient of each succeeding term of (c) must vanish. These conditions are met by taking

$$k - 1 = 2, \quad k(k + 4)A_0 = 1, \quad A_1 = A_2 = 0,$$

and by using the recursion formulas

(e) $\qquad A_n = \dfrac{(k + n - 2)}{(k + n)(k + n + 4)} A_{n-3}, \quad n = 3, 4, \ldots$

Since $k = 3$, these conditions are equivalent to

$$A_0 = \tfrac{1}{21}, \quad A_1 = A_2 = 0,$$

and

$$A_n = \dfrac{n + 1}{(n + 3)(n + 7)} A_{n-3}, \quad n = 3, 4, \ldots,$$

from which the further coefficients $A_j$ are found sequentially:

$$A_3 = \frac{4}{6 \cdot 10} A_0 = \frac{1}{315}, \quad A_4 = A_5 = 0,$$

$$A_6 = \frac{7}{9 \cdot 13} A_3 = \frac{1}{5265}, \quad A_7 = A_8 = 0, \cdots$$

Hence

$$Y_2(x) = \tfrac{1}{21}x^3 + \tfrac{1}{315}x^6 + \tfrac{1}{5265}x^9 + \cdots.$$

A particular integral $Y_3(x)$ corresponding to the right member $- 2x^3$ is obtained similarly. In this case

$$k = 4, \quad A_0 = - \tfrac{1}{16}, \quad A_1 = A_2 = 0,$$

and the recursion formulas (e) become

$$A_n = \dfrac{n + 2}{(n + 4)(n + 8)} A_{n-3}, \quad n = 3, 4, \ldots,$$

from which $A_3 = \dfrac{-5}{1232}$, $A_4 = A_5 = 0$, $A_6 = \dfrac{-1}{4312}$, $A_7 = A_8 = 0$,

$A_9 = \dfrac{-1}{86632}, \cdots$. Hence

$$Y_3(x) = - \tfrac{1}{16}x^4 - \tfrac{5}{1232}x^7 - \tfrac{1}{4312}x^{10} - \tfrac{1}{86632}x^{13} - \cdots.$$

A particular integral of the given differential equation (a) is therefore

$$y(x) = Y_2(x) + Y_3(x).$$

Find a particular integral in series form for each of the following equations.

1. $xy'' + 3y' - y = x$
2. $xy'' + y' - 2xy = x^2$
3. $xy'' - xy' + y = x^3$
4. $(1 - 2x)y'' + 4xy' - 4y = x^2 - x$
5. $x^2y'' + xy' + (x + 12)y = x^2 + x$
6. $x^2(x + 1)y'' + x(x^2 + 3)y' + y = x - 2x^2$
7. $3x^2y'' + x(5 - x)y' + (2x^2 - 1)y = x - x^3$
8. $9x^2y'' + (2 + 3x)y = x^2 + x^4$
9. $9x^2y'' + 10xy' + y = x - 1$.
10. $2x^2y'' + (x - x^2)y' - y = 1 + x^3$. Interpret the arbitrary constant.
11. $(1 - x^2)y'' + 2xy' - 2y = 6(1 - x^2)^2$
12. $(x^2 + 2x)y'' - (2 + 2x)y' + 2y = x^2(x + 2)^2$
13. $2x^2y'' + 5xy' + (1 + x)y = x(1 + x + x^2)$
14. $(2x^2 + x^3)y'' - xy' + (1 - x)y = x^2(1 + x)^2$

**73. The Legendre equation.** The differential equation

(25) $$(1 - x^2)y'' - 2xy' + m(m + 1)y = 0$$

is known as *Legendre's equation*. The solutions of this equation are of great importance in both pure and applied mathematics, particularly in connection with boundary value problems associated with the sphere.

We shall find the general solution of (25) for each value of the parameter $m$. It will be found convenient to assume that the solution can be written as a series proceeding in descending powers of $x$:

(26) $$y = A_0x^k + A_1x^{k-1} + \cdots + A_nx^{k-n} + \cdots, \quad A_0 \neq 0$$

When (26) is substituted into the equation (25), the left member becomes

(27) $$B_0x^k + B_1x^{k-1} + \cdots + B_nx^{k-n} + \cdots,$$

whose coefficients have the forms:

$$B_0 = [m(m+1) - k(k+1)]A_0$$
$$B_1 = [m(m+1) - (k-1)k]A_1$$
$$B_2 = \{[m(m+1) - (k-2)(k-1)]A_2 + (k-1)kA_0\}$$

$$\cdot \quad \cdot \quad \cdot \quad \cdot \quad \cdot \quad \cdot \quad \cdot \quad \cdot$$

$$B_n = \{[m(m+1) - (k-n)(k-n+1)]A_n$$
$$+ (k-n+1)(k-n+2)A_{n-2}\}, \quad n = 2, 3, \ldots$$

Hence (27) must vanish identically if (26) is to be a solution of the differential equation (25). The condition $B_0 = 0$ is satisfied by choosing $k$ to be a root of the indicial equation

$$(28) \quad k(k+1) - m(m+1) = (k-m)(k+m+1) = 0.$$

The condition $B_1 = 0$ can be met by requiring that $A_1 = 0$. The condition $B_n = 0$ for $n \geqq 2$ leads to the recursion formulas

$$(29) \quad A_n = \frac{(k-n+2)(k-n+1)}{(k-n-m)(k-n+m+1)} A_{n-2}, \quad n = 2, 3, \ldots.$$

The roots of the indicial equation (28) are $m$ and $-m-1$. When either of these roots is substituted into (29) the coefficients $A_n$, $n \geqq 2$, can be determined successively. Since $A_1 = 0$, it follows from (29) that $A_n = 0$ if $n$ is odd. At this stage only particular solutions are desired, so that $A_0$ is put equal to unity.

If $m$ is not an integer, the two series

$$(30) \quad y_m = x^m \left[ 1 - \frac{m(m-1)}{2(2m-1)} x^{-2} + \frac{m(m-1)(m-2)(m-3)}{2 \cdot 4 \cdot (2m-1)(2m-3)} x^{-4} - \cdots \right],$$

$$(31) \quad y_{-m-1} = x^{-m-1} \left[ 1 + \frac{(m+1)(m+2)}{2(2m+3)} x^{-2} \right.$$
$$\left. + \frac{(m+1)(m+2)(m+3)(m+4)}{2 \cdot 4 \cdot (2m+3)(2m+5)} x^{-4} + \cdots \right],$$

thus obtained converge for $|x| > 1$ and represent linearly independent functions. The general solution of (25) is then

$$y = c_1 y_m + c_2 y_{-m-1}.$$

The series (30) terminates if $m$ is a positive integer. For example, if $m = 3$, $y_3 = x^3(1 - \frac{3}{5}x^{-2})$.

For a given positive integer $m$ the polynomial obtained by multiplying $y_m(x)$ by $\dfrac{(2m)!}{2^m(m!)^2}$ is called the *Legendre polynomial* of degree $m$:

$$P_m(x) = \frac{(2m)!}{2^m(m!)^2} y_m(x)$$

We define the Legendre polynomial of degree zero to be $P_0(x) = 1$. This is seen to be consistent with the series (30).

**74. The Bessel equation.** The important equation

(32) $$x^2y'' + xy' + (x^2 - m^2)y = 0,$$

known as *Bessel's equation*, can also be solved by a method based on infinite series. In the following treatment of this equation attention will be limited to cases in which the parameter $m$ is a nonnegative real number.

A solution of the form

(33) $$y = A_0x^k + A_1x^{k+1} + \cdots + A_nx^{k+n} + \cdots$$

will be sought. When this series and its first and second derivatives are substituted into the left member of (32) the resulting expression has $x^k$ as lowest power of $x$. This expression must vanish identically if the series (33) is to be a solution of (32). The coefficient of $x^k$ is $[k(k-1) + k - m^2]A_0$, so that the indicial equation is

(34) $$k^2 - m^2 = 0,$$

and the indicial exponents are $k = \pm m$. The coefficient of $x^{k+1}$, which is $[(k+1)^2 - m^2]A_1$, can be made to vanish by choosing $A_1 = 0$. The vanishing of the coefficient of $x^{k+n}$ leads to the recursion formulas

(35) $$A_n = \frac{-A_{n-2}}{(k+n+m)(k+n-m)}, \quad n = 2, 3, \ldots.$$

Since $A_1 = 0$, it follows from (35) that $A_n = 0$ if $n$ is odd. Of course, $A_0$ may be taken as unity if a particular solution is desired.

For the indicial exponent $k = m$ we have the solution

$$(36) \quad y_1(x, m) = x^m \left[ 1 - \frac{\left(\frac{x}{2}\right)^2}{1 \cdot (1+m)} + \frac{\left(\frac{x}{2}\right)^4}{1 \cdot 2 \cdot (1+m)(2+m)} - \cdots \right.$$
$$\left. + \frac{(-1)^n \left(\frac{x}{2}\right)^{2n}}{n!(1+m)(2+m) \cdots (n+m)} + \cdots \right].$$

If $m$ is neither a positive integer nor zero, from the second indicial exponent $k = -m$ we have the following solution independent of (36):

$$(37) \quad y_2(x, m) = x^{-m} \left[ 1 - \frac{\left(\frac{x}{2}\right)^2}{1 \cdot (1-m)} + \frac{\left(\frac{x}{2}\right)^4}{1 \cdot 2 \cdot (1-m)(2-m)} - \cdots \right.$$
$$\left. + \frac{(-1)^n \left(\frac{x}{2}\right)^{2n}}{n!(1-m)(2-m) \cdots (n-m)} + \cdots \right].$$

If $m$ is a positive and nonintegral real number, the general solution of the Bessel equation (32) is

$$y(x, m) = c_1 y_1(x, m) + c_2 y_2(x, m).$$

It will be observed from (37) that the function $y_2(x, m)$ does not exist if $m$ is a positive integer. In this case a solution $Y_2(x, m)$ which is independent of $y_1(x, m)$ can be found by the method described in Article 71. Further, it can be shown that when $m = 0$ so that $y_1(x, m)$ and $y_2(x, m)$ are identical, a solution of (32) which is independent of (36) can be found by the method employed in Article 70.

If $m$ is a positive integer or zero, the function $y_1(x, m)$ in (36) is, except for a constant factor, the *Bessel function* of the *first kind*, of order $m$:

$$J_m(x) = \frac{y_1(x, m)}{2^m m!} = \sum_{n=0}^{\infty} \frac{(-1)^n x^{m+2n}}{2^{m+2n} n!(m+n)!}.$$

In particular, the Bessel function of order zero is

$$J_0(x) = 1 - \frac{x^2}{2^2} + \frac{x^4}{2^4 (2!)^2} - \cdots.$$

The Bessel function $J_{-m}(x)$ with a negative integral subscript may be defined by means of the relation

$$J_{-m}(x) = (-1)^m J_m(x), \quad m = 1, 2, \cdots.$$

Thus $J_{-2m}(x) = J_{2m}(x)$ and $J_{-(2m-1)}(x) = -J_{2m-1}(x)$.

## EXERCISE 44

1. Write the expressions for $P_5(x)$, $P_6(x)$, and $P_7(x)$.

2. Prove that $\int_{-1}^{1} [P_4(x)]^2 \, dx = \frac{2}{9}$.

3. Prove that $\int_{-1}^{1} P_m(x) \cdot P_n(x) \, dx = 0$, $m \neq n$, for the first four Legendre polynomials.

4. Prove that $\int_{-1}^{1} P_3(x) R(x) \, dx = 0$, where $R(x)$ is any quadratic function in $x$.

5. Show that all the roots of the equations

$$P_n(x) = 0, \quad n = 1, 2, 3, 4, 5,$$

lie between $-1$ and $1$.

6. Show that $\int_{-1}^{1} P_5(x) P_6'(x) \, dx = 2$.

7. Show that $\int_{-1}^{1} x P_4(x) P_3(x) \, dx = \frac{8}{63}$.

8. Prove the identity $P_{m+1}'(x) - (m+1)P_m(x) = x P_m'(x)$. *Hint:* First express the identity in terms of the functions $y_{m+1}'(x)$, $y_m(x)$, and $y_m'(x)$ [see equation (30)], and divide out a suitable constant factor.

9. Prove the identity $x P_m'(x) = P_{m-1}'(x) + m P_m(x)$. *Note:* Use the hint of Problem 8.

10. Prove the identity $(x^2 - 1)P_m'(x) = m x P_m(x) - m P_{m-1}(x)$. *Note:* Use the hint of Problem 8.

11. Evaluate to four decimal places: (a) $J_0(0.3)$; (b) $J_0(0.4)$; (c) $J_0'(0.2)$.

12. Evaluate to four decimal places: (a) $J_1(0.2)$; (b) $J_1(0.3)$; (c) $J_1'(0.2)$; (d) $J_1'(0.4)$.

13. Show that $\sqrt{\dfrac{2}{\pi x}} \cdot \sin x$ satisfies Bessel's equation with $m = \dfrac{1}{2}$.

213

Prove the following identities.

14. $J_0'(x) = -J_1(x)$

15. $J_{m+1}(x) + J_{m-1}(x) = \dfrac{2m}{x} J_m(x)$

16. $J_m'(x) = \dfrac{m}{x} J_m(x) - J_{m+1}(x)$

17. $J_m'(x) = J_{m-1}(x) - \dfrac{m}{x} J_m(x)$

18. $J_2(x) = J_0(x) + 2J_0''(x)$

19. $J_2(x) = J_0''(x) - \dfrac{1}{x} J_0'(x)$

20. $\dfrac{d}{dx} \left[ x^{m+1} J_{m+1}(x) \right] = x^{m+1} J_m(x)$

21. $\dfrac{d}{dx} \left[ x^{-m} J_m(x) \right] = - x^{-m} J_{m+1}(x)$

# Systems of partial differential equations

**75. Introduction.** In this chapter and the one which follows, attention will be paid to the problem of solving partial differential equations. The reader will recall from Chapter One that a partial differential equation of the first order

$$f(x, y, z, z_x, z_y) = 0$$

is an equation involving an unknown function $z(x, y)$ of the two independent variables $x, y$, together with the partial derivatives $z_x, z_y$ of this function. Partial differential equations occur both in pure and applied mathematics. Equations of the first order, for example, are met in the study of dynamics, while equations of the second and higher orders are encountered in connection with the boundary value problems that arise in the theory of elasticity, electromagnetic theory, and elsewhere. In this chapter we shall be concerned primarily with systems of first-order partial differential equations of the form

$$z_x = P(x, y, z), \quad z_y = Q(x, y, z).$$

**76. Completely integrable systems.** As described in Article 5, an ordinary differential equation of the first order, $y' = f(x, y)$, is characterized by a slope field such that through each point $(x, y)$ of the region $R$ in which $f(x, y)$ is defined there passes a

SYSTEMS OF PARTIAL DIFFERENTIAL EQUATIONS

line segment of slope $y' = f(x, y)$, and the integral curves of the equation are those which at each point are tangent to the line segment through the point.

It is natural to generalize this notion of a slope field to space of three dimensions by substituting for the segment of a tangent line through the point $(x, y)$ a portion of an oriented plane through $(x, y, z)$, that is, a plane through $(x, y, z)$ with a directed normal. Through each point $(x, y, z)$ of a region $R$ of space there now passes a directed line segment which represents the positive direction of the normal to the oriented plane through that point. We are thus led to the following problem: to find a surface in the region $R$ whose normal at each point coincides with the normal of the slope field at that point. If $P(x, y, z)$, $Q(x, y, z)$, $-1$ are direction numbers of the normal through $(x, y, z)$, the problem becomes that of finding a function $z(x, y)$ such that

$$z_x(x, y) = P[x, y, z(x, y)], \quad z_y(x, y) = Q[x, y, z(x, y)].$$

Consider the simultaneous pair of partial differential equations of the first order

(1) $$z_x = P(x, y, z), \quad z_y = Q(x, y, z).$$

The functions $P(x, y, z)$, $Q(x, y, z)$, together with their partial derivatives, are assumed to be continuous in a certain region $R$ of space. A *solution* of the equations (1) is a function $z(x, y)$ which together with its partial derivatives $z_x(x, y)$, $z_y(x, y)$ is continuous in a region $G$ of the $xy$-plane and which is such that

(2) $$z_x(x, y) = P[x, y, z(x, y)], \quad z_y(x, y) = Q[x, y, z(x, y)],$$

identically for $(x, y)$ in $G$.

Since the right members of (2) have continuous partial derivatives of the first order, the derivatives $z_{xy}(x, y)$ and $z_{yx}(x, y)$ exist and are given by:

$$z_{xy} = P_y[x, y, z(x, y)] + P_z[x, y, z(x, y)]z_y$$
$$= P_y[x, y, z(x, y)] + P_z[x, y, z(x, y)]Q[x, y, z(x, y)]$$
$$z_{yx} = Q_x[x, y, z(x, y)] + Q_z[x, y, z(x, y)]z_x$$
$$= Q_x[x, y, z(x, y)] + Q_z[x, y, z(x, y)]P[x, y, z(x, y)]$$

216

Since $z_{xy}(x, y)$ and $z_{yx}(x, y)$ are continuous, they must be equal. Hence the equality

$$(3) \qquad P_y + P_z Q = Q_x + Q_z P$$

is a necessary condition which must be satisfied on every integral surface $z(x, y)$ of the equations (1).

Equations of the form (1) which satisfy the condition (3) identically in $R$ are said to form a *completely integrable system.* It will be shown in Article 77 that the condition (3) is also sufficient to insure that the system (1) has solutions.

EXAMPLE. Show that the system

$$z_x = \frac{z}{y}, \quad z_y = -\frac{zx}{y^2}$$

is completely integrable.

SOLUTION. In this case

$$P(x, y, z) = \frac{z}{y}, \quad Q(x, y, z) = -\frac{zx}{y^2}.$$

Hence:

$$P_y + P_z Q = -\frac{z}{y^2} + \frac{1}{y}\left(-\frac{zx}{y^2}\right) = -\frac{z}{y^2} - \frac{zx}{y^3}$$

$$Q_x + Q_z P = -\frac{z}{y^2} - \frac{x}{y^2}\left(\frac{z}{y}\right) = -\frac{z}{y^2} - \frac{zx}{y^3}$$

Thus the condition (3) is satisfied, and the equations form a completely integrable system.

## 77. Solving completely integrable systems.

In case the system (1) is completely integrable, the solution may readily be found by the following device. Consider one of the two equations, say $z_x = P(x, y, z)$, as an *ordinary* differential equation for $z$ in terms of the independent variable $x$, the variable $y$ acting as a parameter. Suppose the general solution of this equation to be

$$(4) \qquad z = g(x, y, c)$$

where the arbitrary "constant" of integration $c$ may depend

217

on the variable $y$. Then

$$z_y = g_y + g_c \frac{dc}{dy},$$

and in order that the second equation of (2) may be satisfied one must have

$$g_y + g_c \frac{dc}{dy} = Q[x, y, g(x, y, c)].$$

Since $g_c \neq 0$, this equation is equivalent to

(5)
$$\frac{dc}{dy} = \frac{Q[x, y, g(x, y, c)] - g_y}{g_c}.$$

Equation (5) may be regarded as an ordinary differential equation for the determination of the function $c(y)$, provided that the right member of (5) does not depend on $x$. That this is actually the case follows from the integrability condition (3); for:

$$\frac{\partial}{\partial x} \left\{ \frac{Q[x, y, g(x, y, c)] - g_y}{g_c} \right\}$$

$$= \frac{Q_x + Q_z g_x - g_{yx}}{g_c} - \frac{(Q - g_y)g_{cx}}{g_c^2}$$

$$= \frac{Q_x + Q_z P - \dfrac{\partial}{\partial y} P[x, y, g(x, y, c)]}{g_c}$$

$$\quad - \frac{(Q - g_y)\dfrac{\partial}{\partial c} P[x, y, g(x, y, c)]}{g_c^2}$$

$$= \frac{Q_x + Q_z P - (P_y + P_z g_y)}{g_c} - \frac{(Q - g_y)P_z g_c}{g_c^2}$$

$$= \frac{Q_x + Q_z P - P_y - P_z g_y - P_z Q + P_z g_y}{g_c}$$

$$= \frac{Q_x + Q_z P - (P_y + P_z Q)}{g_c} = 0.$$

Hence equation (5) has a general solution $c = c(y, a)$ which depends on an arbitrary constant $a$. Substitution of $c(y, a)$ into (4) yields a solution

$$z = z(x, y, a) = g[x, y, c(y, a)]$$

of the system (1) containing one arbitrary constant. This can be shown to be the general solution of the completely integrable system (1). Thus condition (3) is sufficient to insure that the system (1) has solutions, as was stated in Article 76.

The following example will serve to make clear the details of this method.

EXAMPLE 1. Find the general solution of the completely integrable system

(a) $$z_x = \frac{z}{y}, \quad z_y = -\frac{zx}{y^2}.$$

SOLUTION. Treating the first equation as an ordinary differential equation for the determination of $z$ as a function of $x$, with $y$ acting as a parameter, we have:

$$\frac{z_x}{z} = \frac{1}{y}$$

$$\ln z = \frac{x}{y} + \ln c$$

(b) $$z = ce^{\frac{x}{y}}$$

Here the arbitrary "constant" $c$ has the right to depend on $y$. Differentiation with respect to $y$ yields

(c) $$z_y = c_y e^{\frac{x}{y}} - \frac{cx}{y^2} e^{\frac{x}{y}}.$$

Substitution of (b) and (c) into the second equation of the system (a) yields

$$c_y e^{\frac{x}{y}} - \frac{cx}{y^2} e^{\frac{x}{y}} = -\frac{cx}{y^2} e^{\frac{x}{y}},$$

which is equivalent to $c_y = 0$. Hence $c = a$, where $a$ is an arbitrary constant. The general solution of the system (a) is therefore

$$z = ae^{\frac{x}{y}}.$$

EXAMPLE 2. Find the general solution of the system

(a) $$z_x = \frac{z^2 + y^2 - x^2}{2xz}, \quad z_y = -\frac{y}{z}.$$

SOLUTION. A simple computation shows that

$$P_y + P_zQ = Q_x + Q_zP = \frac{y(z^2 + y^2 - x^2)}{2xz^3},$$

so that the system is completely integrable. The second and simpler of the equations (a) may be written

$$zz_y = -y,$$

and hence:

$$z^2 = -y^2 + c$$
$$z = (c - y^2)^{\frac{1}{2}}$$

Here the arbitrary "constant" $c$ has a right to depend on $x$. By choosing the positive radical for $z$, we have limited ourselves to finding solutions of (a) for which $z > 0$. The student will notice that the right members of (a) are discontinuous for $z = 0$, so that it is necessary to make the choice $z > 0$ (or $z < 0$) in order to remain in a region of points $(x, y, z)$ in which the proof made above is valid. We have

$$z_x = \frac{c_x}{2(c - y^2)^{\frac{1}{2}}}.$$

Substitution into the first equation of the system gives

$$\frac{c_x}{2(c - y^2)^{\frac{1}{2}}} = \frac{c - x^2}{2x(c - y^2)^{\frac{1}{2}}},$$

from which it follows that

$$c_x - \frac{c}{x} = -x.$$

This is a linear differential equation, whose solution is

$$c = ax - x^2.$$

Hence the general solution of the completely integrable system (a) is

$$z = (ax - x^2 - y^2)^{\frac{1}{2}}.$$

Check each of the following systems for complete integrability. Find the general solution if one exists.

1. $z_x = 2x$, $z_y = 2y$

2. $z_x = \dfrac{-\ln k}{x^2 y}$, $z_y = \dfrac{-\ln k}{xy^2}$

3. $z_x = \cos xy$, $z_y = \dfrac{xy \cos xy - \sin xy}{y^2}$

4. $z_x = \dfrac{-2(1+z)}{x}$, $z_y = \dfrac{-(1+z)}{y}$

5. $z_x = \dfrac{2y^2}{z-1}$, $z_y = \dfrac{2xyz}{z-1}$

6. $z_x = \dfrac{-2z}{x}$, $z_y = \dfrac{-4yz}{1+y^2}$

7. $z_x = -2xe^{-z}\sin y$, $z_y = -x^2 e^{-z}\cos y$

8. $z_x = \dfrac{y\cos x - \sin z}{1+\cos x}$, $z_y = \dfrac{\sin x}{1+x\cos z}$

9. $z_x = \dfrac{1+z^2}{xz}$, $z_y = \dfrac{1+z^2}{z}$

10. $z_x = \dfrac{2x\cot z}{x^2+1}$, $z_y = \dfrac{\cot z}{xy^2}$

11. $z_x = \dfrac{2xz}{1+x^2}$, $z_y = 2z\csc 2y$

12. $z_x = e^{-\frac{z}{y}}\tan x$, $z_y = \dfrac{z}{y} - 1$

13. $z_x = \dfrac{z}{x-x^2-z^2}$, $z_y = \dfrac{2y(x^2+z^2)}{x^2+z^2-x}$

14. $z_x = \dfrac{2xye^{x^2-z}}{1+ye^{x^2-z}}$, $z_y = \dfrac{e^{x^2-z}}{1+ye^{x^2-z}}$

**78. Completely integrable systems in several variables.** The treatment of the preceding article can readily be extended to the case where more than two independent variables are present.

For concreteness consider a system:

(6)
$$u_x = P(x, y, z, u)$$
$$u_y = Q(x, y, z, u)$$
$$u_z = R(x, y, z, u)$$

Such a system will be called *completely integrable* in case the conditions

(7)
$$P_y + P_u Q = Q_x + Q_u P$$
$$Q_z + Q_u R = R_y + R_u Q$$
$$R_x + R_u P = P_z + P_u R$$

are satisfied identically in $x$, $y$, $z$, $u$. If the system (6) is completely integrable, then there exists a solution $u(x, y, z, a)$ which depends upon an arbitrary constant $a$. This is the general solution of the system (6).

The proof of this result is similar to that given in the preceding article. The method of attack will be made sufficiently clear by considering an example.

EXAMPLE. Find the general solution of the completely integrable system

$$u_x = yu, \quad u_y = xu, \quad u_z = \frac{u}{z}.$$

SOLUTION. Consider the first equation of the system, $u_x = yu$, as an ordinary differential equation for $u$ in terms of the independent variable $x$, with $y$ and $z$ regarded as parameters. The solution of this equation is readily found:

$$\frac{u_x}{u} = y$$

$$\ln u = xy + \ln c$$
$$u = ce^{xy}$$

where $c$, the "constant" of integration, is to be considered as a function of $y$ and $z$. The partial derivative of $u$ with respect to $y$ is

$$u_y = ce^{xy} + c_y x e^{xy}.$$

When $u$ and $u_y$ are substituted into the second equation of the original system, we obtain

$$c_y e^{xy} + cxe^{xy} = cxe^{xy},$$

so that $c_y = 0$ and hence $c$ is independent of $y$ but may still depend on $z$. Differentiation of $u$ with respect to $z$ and substitution into the third equation of the system gives

$$u_z = c_z e^{xy} = \frac{ce^{xy}}{z},$$

so that $c$ must satisfy the differential equation $c_z = \dfrac{c}{z}$. The solution of this equation is $c = az$, where $a$ is an arbitrary constant, and hence the general solution of the original system is

$$u = aze^{xy}.$$

## EXERCISE 46

Show that each of the following systems is completely integrable and find the general solution.

1. $u_x = -zy \sin xy, \quad u_y = -zx \sin xy, \quad u_z = \cos xy$

2. $u_x = \dfrac{u}{x}, \quad u_y = \dfrac{u}{y}, \quad u_z = u \cot z$

3. $u_x = \dfrac{u}{x}, \quad u_y = u, \quad u_z = \dfrac{u}{z}$

4. $u_x = u, \quad u_y = u \cot y, \quad u_z = \dfrac{u}{z}$

5. $u_x = \dfrac{2u}{x}, \quad u_y = \dfrac{3u}{y}, \quad u_z = \dfrac{u}{z}$

6. $u_x = \dfrac{2u}{x}, \quad u_y = u \sec y \csc y, \quad u_z = \dfrac{u}{z}$

7. $u_x = \dfrac{1}{x} + ye^{xy}, \quad u_y = \dfrac{1}{y} + xe^{xy}, \quad u_z = \dfrac{1}{z}$

8. $u_x = \dfrac{y}{1+x^2y^2}, \quad u_y = \dfrac{x}{1+x^2y^2} + z^2 e^{yz^2}, \quad u_z = 2yze^{yz^2}$

9. $u_x = \dfrac{y \cos xy - z \sin xz}{2u}, \quad u_y = \dfrac{x \cos xy}{2u}, \quad u_z = \dfrac{-x \sin xz}{2u}$

10. $u_x = \dfrac{yz \cos xyz}{3u^2}, \quad u_y = \dfrac{xz \cos xyz}{3u^2}, \quad u_z = \dfrac{xy \cos xyz}{3u^2}$

**79. Total differential equations.** The equations (1) of Article 76 may be interpreted as saying that the total differential $dz$ of the function $z(x, y)$ has the value $P(x, y, z)\, dx + Q(x, y, z)\, dy$, that is,

$$P(x, y, z)\, dx + Q(x, y, z)\, dy - dz = 0.$$

This is an instance of an equation of the type

(8) $\quad L(x, y, z)\, dx + M(x, y, z)\, dy + N(x, y, z)\, dz = 0$

which is known as a *total differential equation*. If a function $\Phi(x, y, z)$ can be found such that

(9) $\qquad \dfrac{\partial \Phi}{\partial x} = L, \qquad \dfrac{\partial \Phi}{\partial y} = M, \qquad \dfrac{\partial \Phi}{\partial z} = N,$

then the equation (8) is said to be *exact*, and its solution is $\Phi(x, y, z) = a$, where $a$ is an arbitrary constant.

From (9) it follows that

$$\Phi_{xy} = L_y, \quad \Phi_{yx} = M_x,$$
$$\Phi_{xz} = L_z, \quad \Phi_{zx} = N_x,$$
$$\Phi_{yz} = M_z, \quad \Phi_{zy} = N_y,$$

assuming that the required derivatives exist and are continuous. Hence a necessary condition that the equation (8) be exact is that the functions $L, M, N$ satisfy the identities

(10) $\qquad M_z - N_y = 0, \quad N_x - L_z = 0, \quad L_y - M_x = 0.$

The conditions (10) are also sufficient to make the equation (8) exact. This may be demonstrated by exhibiting the solution $\Phi(x, y, z) = a$ of equation (8) as follows:

(11) $\quad \Phi(x, y, z) = \displaystyle\int_{x_0}^{x} L(\xi, y, z)\, d\xi + \int_{y_0}^{y} M(x_0, \eta, z)\, d\eta$

$$+ \int_{z_0}^{z} N(x_0, y_0, \zeta)\, d\zeta,$$

where $x_0, y_0, z_0$ are arbitrary numbers for which the integrals in (11) are defined. To verify that (11) is the solution of (8), we note that

$$\Phi_x(x, y, z) = L(x, y, z).$$

Then
$$\Phi_y(x, y, z) = \int_{x_0}^{x} L_y(\xi, y, z) \, d\xi + M(x_0, y, z)$$
$$= \int_{x_0}^{x} M_x(\xi, y, z) \, d\xi + M(x_0, y, z)$$

by virtue of the last of the conditions (10). Hence:

$$\Phi_y(x, y, z) = [M(x, y, z) - M(x_0, y, z)] + M(x_0, y, z)$$
$$= M(x, y, z)$$

Further,

$$\Phi_z(x, y, z) = \int_{x_0}^{x} L_z(\xi, y, z) \, d\xi + \int_{y_0}^{y} M_z(x_0, \eta, z) \, d\eta + N(x_0, y_0, z)$$
$$= \int_{x_0}^{x} N_x(\xi, y, z) \, d\xi + \int_{y_0}^{y} N_y(x_0, \eta, z) \, d\eta + N(x_0, y_0, z)$$

in consequence of the first two conditions (10). Hence:

$$\Phi_z(x, y, z) = [N(x, y, z) - N(x_0, y, z)] + [N(x_0, y, z) - N(x_0, y_0, z)]$$
$$+ N(x_0, y_0, z)$$
$$= N(x, y, z)$$

EXAMPLE. Show that the equation

$$(z^2 - y) \, dx + (2y - x) \, dy + 2xz \, dz = 0$$

is exact and find its integral.

SOLUTION. We have $L = z^2 - y$, $M = 2y - x$, $N = 2xz$, and hence:

$$M_z = 0, \quad N_x = 2z, \quad L_y = -1$$
$$N_y = 0, \quad L_z = 2z, \quad M_x = -1$$

The equation is therefore exact.

$$\Phi(x, y, z) = \int_{x_0}^{x} (z^2 - y) \, d\xi + \int_{y_0}^{y} (2\eta - x_0) \, d\eta + \int_{z_0}^{z} 2\zeta x_0 \, d\zeta$$
$$= (z^2 - y)(x - x_0) + y^2 - y_0^2 - x_0(y - y_0) + (z^2 - z_0^2)x_0$$
$$= (z^2 - y)x + y^2 - (z_0^2 - y_0)x_0 - y_0^2$$

If we take $x_0 = y_0 = z_0 = 0$, we find the solution of the equation in the form

$$(z^2 - y)x + y^2 = a$$

where $a$ is an arbitrary constant. This solution may be found by inspection if the differential equation is written in the form

$$(z^2 - y) \, dx + x(2z \, dz - dy) + 2y \, dy = 0$$

since the first two terms are clearly equal to $d[x(z^2 - y)]$ while the third term is $d(y^2)$.

Test the following equations for exactness and integrate when exact.

1. $2xy\, dx + (x^2 + 2yz)\, dy + y^2\, dz = 0$
2. $(y^2 + 1)\, dx + (2xy - \tan z)\, dy - y \sec^2 z\, dz = 0$
3. $(z + a)^{-1}(dx + dy) + (z + a)^{-2}(x + y)\, dz = 0$
4. $\dfrac{1 + x}{x}\, dx - \dfrac{1}{z}\, dy + \dfrac{y + z}{z^2}\, dz = 0$
5. $(xyz + 3x^2y)\, dx + (x^2z + x)\, dy + (x^2y + z)\, dz = 0$
6. $\dfrac{y - 2xz - 2x^3z}{1 + x^2}\, dx + (z + \text{Arctan } x)\, dy + (y - x^2 - 1)\, dz = 0$
7. $xy^2z^2\, dx + 3xy^2z\, dy - x(y^3 + z)\, dz = 0$
8. $e^z\, dx + e^z\, dy + (x + y)e^z\, dz = 0$
9. $(y \cos xy - \sin y)\, dx + (x \cos xy - x \cos y)\, dy + 2z\, dz = 0$
10. $(2ye^{2x} - 3e^y)\, dx + (e^{2x} - 3xe^y)\, dy + e^z\, dz = 0$
11. $(e^y + yze^{zz})\, dx + (e^{2x} - 3e^y)\, dy + 2ze^z\, dz = 0$
12. $\left(yz + \dfrac{1}{x}\right) dx + \left(zx + \dfrac{1}{y}\right) dy + \left(xy + \dfrac{1}{z}\right) dz = 0$
13. $(\sin y + yz \cos xz)\, dx + (x + z + \sin xz)\, dy$
    $\qquad\qquad\qquad\qquad + (\sin y + xy \cos xz)\, dz = 0$
14. $(2xe^z + yze^{xy})\, dx + (2ye^z + xze^{xy})\, dy + [(x^2 + y^2)e^z + e^{xy}]\, dz = 0$

**80. Integrating factors.** In case the functions $L(x, y, z)$, $M(x, y, z)$, $N(x, y, z)$ do not satisfy the conditions (10), it may nevertheless be possible to find a function $\mu(x, y, z)$ such that the total differential equation formed with the functions $L_1 = \mu L$, $M_1 = \mu M$, $N_1 = \mu N$ is exact. The function $\mu$ is then called an *integrating factor* for the total differential equation

(12) $\qquad\qquad L\, dx + M\, dy + N\, dz = 0$

and the equation is said to be *integrable*.

If (12) is integrable and $\mu$ is an integrating factor, it follows by definition that there is a function $\Phi(x, y, z)$ such that:

(13) $\qquad \Phi_x = L_1 = \mu L, \quad \Phi_y = M_1 = \mu M, \quad \Phi_z = N_1 = \mu N$

The functions $L_1$, $M_1$, $N_1$ must then satisfy the conditions (10) of the preceding article. That is:

$$\frac{\partial}{\partial z}(\mu M) = \frac{\partial}{\partial y}(\mu N), \quad \frac{\partial}{\partial x}(\mu N) = \frac{\partial}{\partial z}(\mu L), \quad \frac{\partial}{\partial y}(\mu L) = \frac{\partial}{\partial x}(\mu M)$$

These equations may be written:

$$\mu(M_z - N_y) = \mu_y N - \mu_z M$$
$$\mu(N_x - L_z) = \mu_z L - \mu_x N$$
$$\mu(L_y - M_x) = \mu_x M - \mu_y L$$

Let these equations be multiplied by $L$, $M$, and $N$ respectively and added. It is easy to see that the right member of the resulting equation is identically zero. The left member is

$$\mu[L(M_z - N_y) + M(N_x - L_z) + N(L_y - M_x)].$$

In a region $R$ of points $(x, y, z)$ in which the integrating factor $\mu(x, y, z)$ is never zero, it may be concluded that a necessary condition that the total differential equation (12) be integrable is that the condition

(14) $\qquad L(M_z - N_y) + M(N_x - L_z) + N(L_y - M_x) = 0$

be satisfied identically for $x$, $y$, $z$ in $R$.

Conversely, a total differential equation whose coefficients $L$, $M$, $N$ satisfy (14) is integrable. To show this, consider the system of partial differential equations:

(15)
$$z_x = P = -\frac{L}{N}$$
$$z_y = Q = -\frac{M}{N}$$

In order to apply the integrability condition (3) to the system (15), we find:

$$Q_x + Q_z P = -\frac{NM_x - MN_x}{N^2} + \frac{(NM_z - MN_z)L}{N^3}$$
$$P_y + P_z Q = -\frac{NL_y - LN_y}{N^2} + \frac{(NL_z - LN_z)M}{N^3}$$

Subtracting the second equation from the first, we have

$$(Q_x + Q_z P) - (P_y + P_z Q)$$
$$= \frac{1}{N^2} \left[ L(M_z - N_y) + M(N_x - L_z) + N(L_y - M_x) \right],$$

and since the bracket expression vanishes as a result of (14), we see that the condition (3) is satisfied. The completely integrable system (15) then has a general solution $z = z(x, y, a)$. Let this equation be solved for $a$ in terms of $x$, $y$, $z$:

(16) $$a = \Phi(x, y, z)$$

Then $a \equiv \Phi[x, y, z(x, y, a)]$ so that differentiation with respect to $x$ and $y$ results in the equations

$$0 = \Phi_x + \Phi_z z_x = \Phi_x - \Phi_z \frac{L}{N}$$

$$0 = \Phi_y + \Phi_z z_y = \Phi_y - \Phi_z \frac{M}{N}$$

from which it follows that

(17) $$\frac{\Phi_x}{L} = \frac{\Phi_y}{M} = \frac{\Phi_z}{N}.$$

If the common value of the three ratios in (17) is designated by $\mu$, then $\Phi_x = \mu L$, $\Phi_y = \mu M$, $\Phi_z = \mu N$, and (12) is integrable.

EXAMPLE 1. Show that the equation

$$(y^2 + z^2 - x^2) \, dx - 2xy \, dy - 2xz \, dz = 0$$

is integrable and find an integrating factor.

SOLUTION. In this case,

$$L = y^2 + z^2 - x^2, \quad M = -2xy, \quad N = -2xz,$$

and

$$L(M_z - N_y) + M(N_x - L_z) + N(L_y - M_x)$$
$$= (y^2 + z^2 - x^2)(0 - 0) - 2xy(-2z - 2z) - 2xz(2y + 2y) = 0.$$

Thus the equation is integrable and we are led to the completely integrable system

$$z_x = \frac{y^2 + z^2 - x^2}{2xz}, \quad z_y = -\frac{y}{z}.$$

This is precisely the system considered in Example 2 of Article 77 and its solution was found there to be

$$z = (ax - x^2 - y^2)^{\frac{1}{2}}.$$

When we solve this equation for $a$ we get

$$a = \frac{x^2 + y^2 + z^2}{x}$$

so that the function $\Phi$ of equation (10) in this case becomes $\Phi(x, y, z) = \dfrac{x^2 + y^2 + z^2}{x}$. The partial derivatives of $\Phi$ are

$$\Phi_x = \frac{x^2 - y^2 - z^2}{x^2}, \quad \Phi_y = \frac{2y}{x}, \quad \Phi_z = \frac{2z}{x},$$

so that the integrating factor given by (17) is

$$\mu = \frac{\Phi_x}{L} = \frac{\Phi_y}{M} = \frac{\Phi_z}{N} = \frac{-1}{x^2}.$$

Sometimes an integrating factor can be found by inspection, although no general rules can be laid down. The student must acquire facility in finding integrating factors through practice.

EXAMPLE 2. Find an integrating factor for the equation

$$zy\, dx = zx\, dy + y^2\, dz$$

by inspection, and integrate.

SOLUTION. Here $L = zy$, $M = -zx$, $N = -y^2$, and

$$L(M_z - N_y) + M(N_x - L_z) + N(L_y - M_x)$$
$$= zy(-x + 2y) - xz(0 - y) - y^2(z + z) = 0.$$

Thus the equation is integrable. It may be written

$$(a) \qquad z(y\, dx - x\, dy) = y^2\, dz$$

and it is clear that $\dfrac{1}{y^2 z}$ is an integrating factor. When this factor is multiplied into the differential equation ($a$), the result is the exact equation $\dfrac{y\, dx - x\, dy}{y^2} - \dfrac{dz}{z} = 0$, whose solution is found to be

$$\frac{x}{y} - \ln z = a.$$

229

In Problems 1–8 find an integrating factor by inspection and solve.

1. $x \, dy - y \, dx - 2x^2z \, dz = 0$
2. $(1 - z^2)(x \, dy + y \, dx) + xy \, dz = 0$
3. $(z - 2x) \, dx + (z - 2y) \, dy + (x + y) \, dz = 0$
4. $x(z \, dx + x \, dz) + y(z \, dy + y \, dz) = 0$
5. $dx + xz \, dy + xy \, dz = 0$
6. $zy \, dx = zx \, dy + y^2 \, dz$
7. $z \csc yz \, dx + z \, dy + (y + x \csc yz) \, dz = 0$
8. $\dfrac{z}{x^2 + z^2} \, dx + \dfrac{z}{y\sqrt{y^2 - z^2}} \, dy - \left( \dfrac{x}{x^2 + z^2} + \dfrac{1}{\sqrt{y^2 - z^2}} \right) dz = 0$

Verify that each of the following equations is integrable, solve, and find an integrating factor.

9. $(y^2 + yz) \, dx + (xz + z^2) \, dy + (y^2 - xy) \, dz = 0$
10. $(2x^2 + 2xy + 2xz^2 + 1) \, dx + dy + 2z \, dz = 0$
11. $yz^2 \, dx + (y^2z - xz^2) \, dy - y^2(y + z) \, dz = 0$
12. $(yz - 2xy^2z) \, dx + (xz - 2x^2yz) \, dy + 2xy \, dz = 0$
13. $z(\ln y - y) \, dx + z(\ln z - x) \, dy + y \, dz = 0$
14. $(y^2 + yz + z^2) \, dx + (z^2 + zx + x^2) \, dy + (x^2 + xy + y^2) \, dz = 0$

**81. Compatible systems.** A pair of partial differential equations of the first order, written in the implicit form

(18)
$$F(x, y, z, p, q) = 0,$$
$$G(x, y, z, p, q) = 0,$$

where $p = z_x$ and $q = z_y$, are said to be *compatible* in case every solution $z(x, y)$ of one equation is also a solution of the other.

If the equations (18) are solved for $p$ and $q$ in terms of the remaining variables,* one secures equations in the *explicit* form:

(19) $\qquad z_x = p = P(x, y, z), \quad z_y = q = Q(x, y, z)$

---

* This can be done if the Jacobian $\begin{vmatrix} F_p & F_q \\ G_p & G_q \end{vmatrix}$ is different from zero.

In order for the system (18) to be compatible, it is necessary and sufficient that the system (19) be completely integrable. Thus the condition for compatibility of the system (18) is found as a consequence of the known condition for the complete integrability of the system (19).

When the functions $P(x, y, z)$, $Q(x, y, z)$ are substituted into equations (18), one obtains

$$(20) \quad \begin{aligned} F[x, y, z, P(x, y, z), Q(x, y, z)] = 0 \\ G[x, y, z, P(x, y, z), Q(x, y, z)] = 0 \end{aligned}$$

as identities in $x, y, z$. By differentiating the first identity partially with respect to $x, y$, and $z$, the equations

$$(21) \quad \begin{aligned} F_x + F_p P_x + F_q Q_x = 0 \\ F_y + F_p P_y + F_q Q_y = 0 \\ F_z + F_p P_z + F_q Q_z = 0 \end{aligned}$$

arc obtained. If the third equation in this set is multiplied by $P$ and the result added to the first equation, one has

$$(22) \quad F_x + F_z P + F_p(P_x + P_z P) + F_q(Q_x + Q_z P) = 0.$$

Similarly, multiplication of the third equation (21) by $Q$ and addition of the result to the second equation yields

$$(23) \quad F_y + F_z Q + F_p(P_y + P_z Q) + F_q(Q_y + Q_z Q) = 0.$$

Analogous treatment of the second identity (20) leads to the equations:

$$(24) \quad G_x + G_z P + G_p(P_x + P_z P) + G_q(Q_x + Q_z P) = 0$$

$$(25) \quad G_y + G_z Q + G_p(P_y + P_z Q) + G_q(Q_y + Q_z Q) = 0$$

Equations (22) and (24) are linear in the quantities $P_x + P_z P$ and $Q_x + Q_z P$ and one finds that

$$(26) \quad Q_x + Q_z P = \Delta^{-1}[G_p(F_x + F_z P) - F_p(G_x + G_z P)],$$

where $\Delta = F_p G_q - F_q G_p$ is assumed to be different from zero. Equations (23) and (25) lead similarly to the result

$$(27) \quad P_y + P_z Q = \Delta^{-1}[F_q(G_y + G_z Q) - G_q(F_y + F_z Q)].$$

231

The condition (3) shows that the left members of (26) and (27) are equal if and only if the system (19) is completely integrable, or, equivalently, if the system (18) is compatible. Hence (18) is compatible if and only if the right members of (26) and (27) are equal. Since this result must hold for every set of values $x, y, z, p, q$ which satisfies both equations (18), we conclude that the equations (18) are compatible if and only if the expression

$$[F, G] = F_p(G_x+G_z p)+F_q(G_y+G_z q)-G_p(F_x+F_z p)-G_q(F_y+F_z q)$$

vanishes for every set $x, y, z, p, q$ which satisfies the system (18).

EXAMPLE. Show that the equations

(a) $$xp - yq = x, \quad x^2 p + q = xz$$

are compatible and find the solution $z = z(x, y)$ for which $y = 0$ and $z = 4$ at $x = 1$.

SOLUTION. Let $F = xp - yq - x$, $G = x^2 p + q - xz$. Then

$$\begin{aligned}[F, G] &= x(2xp - z - xp) - y(- xq) - x^2(p - 1) - (- q)\\ &= (x^2 p + q - xz) - x(xp - yq - x)\\ &= G - xF.\end{aligned}$$

Hence $[F, G]$ vanishes for any set $x, y, z, p, q$ which satisfies the equations (a) and therefore these equations are compatible. Equations (a) are equivalent to

(b) $$z_x = p = \frac{1 + yz}{1 + xy}, \quad z_y = q = \frac{x(z - x)}{1 + xy}.$$

The first of these equations may be written

(c) $$z_x - \frac{y}{1 + xy} z = \frac{1}{1 + xy},$$

and is seen to be a linear first-order equation in $x$ and $z$, $y$ acting as a parameter. An integrating factor is readily found to be $\dfrac{1}{1 + xy}$ and the solution of (c) can be obtained in the form

(d) $$z = -\frac{1}{y} + c(1 + xy),$$

232

where $c$ can be a function of $y$. Differentiating $(d)$ with respect to $y$ and substituting the result and $(d)$ into the second equation $(b)$, we have:

$$\frac{1}{y^2} + c_y(1 + xy) + cx = \frac{x}{y}(cy - 1)$$

$$c_y(1 + xy) = -\frac{1}{y^2}(1 + xy)$$

$$c_y = -\frac{1}{y^2}$$

Hence $c = y^{-1} + a$, and the general solution of $(a)$ is

$$z = -y^{-1} + (y^{-1} + a)(1 + xy) = x + a(1 + xy).$$

Putting $x = 1$, $y = 0$, $z = 4$, we find $a = 3$, so that the desired solution is

$$z - x + 3(1 + xy)$$

## EXERCISE 49

In each of the following problems verify that the equations are compatible and solve.

1. $xp - y^2q = x + z$, $\quad x^2p + y^3zq = xz(1 - y)$

2. $2px - q^2 = 4z$, $\quad p - q = \dfrac{2(z + xy + y^2)}{x}$

3. $xp + yq = z + x$, $\quad ypq = z$

4. $p^2 + q^2 = z^2(x^2 + y^2)$, $\quad xp - yq = 0$

5. $xp + yq = z$, $\quad yp - xq = 0$

6. $yp + xq = z$, $\quad p + q = 0$

7. $p^2 + q^2 = \dfrac{1 + z^2}{z^2}$, $\quad zq = y$

8. $xp - q = z - y$, $\quad xp - zq = 1 - y$

# CHAPTER TEN

# Partial differential equations
# of the first order

**82. Introduction.** In this chapter we shall be concerned mainly with a single partial differential equation

(1) $$f(x, y, z, p, q) = 0$$

of the first order. We seek a solution of this equation, that is, a function $z(x, y)$ which is defined and has continuous partial derivatives $p = z_x(x, y)$ and $q = z_y(x, y)$ in some region $R$ of points $(x, y)$, and which is such that in $R$

$$f[x, y, z(x, y), \; z_x(x, y), \; z_y(x, y)] \equiv 0.$$

An equation such as (1) may be derived from a primitive (cf. Article 4) in the following manner. Let $z = \phi(x, y, a, b)$ be a function of the independent variables $x$, $y$, depending upon the two parameters $a$ and $b$. If we then eliminate $a$ and $b$ from the three equations

$$z = \phi(x, y, a, b), \quad p = \phi_x(x, y, a, b), \quad q = \phi_y(x, y, a, b)$$

we obtain an equation of the form (1). The function

$$\phi(x, y, a, b),$$

which depends on two essential parameters, is called a *complete integral* of the resulting partial differential equation.

234

EXAMPLE. Find a partial differential equation of the first order which has

$$z = ae^{bx} \sin by$$

as a complete integral.

SOLUTION. From the equations

$$p = z_x = abe^{bx} \sin by$$
$$q = z_y = abe^{bx} \cos by$$

we find that

$$\tan by = \frac{p}{q}.$$

Since $b = \frac{p}{z}$, we have

$$\tan\left(\frac{py}{z}\right) = \frac{p}{q}$$

as the desired equation.

**83. Linear equations.** In order to solve an equation of the type (1), it will be convenient first to consider an equation which is linear and homogeneous in the derivatives of the unknown function $z$ with coefficients which are functions of the independent variables only. It is no more difficult, and more useful for our purpose, to suppose that $z$ is a function of $n$ independent variables $x_1, x_2, \ldots, x_n$, rather than of just the two variables $x, y$. The equation to be studied is then of the form

$$(2) \qquad A_1 \frac{\partial z}{\partial x_1} + A_2 \frac{\partial z}{\partial x_2} + \cdots + A_n \frac{\partial z}{\partial x_n} = 0$$

in which the coefficients $A_i$, $i = 1, 2, \ldots, n$, are functions of $x_1, x_2, \ldots, x_n$.

To solve the equation (2), consider the system of ordinary differential equations

$$(3) \qquad \frac{dx_1}{A_1} = \frac{dx_2}{A_2} = \cdots = \frac{dx_n}{A_n},$$

which may be written

$$(4) \qquad \frac{dx_2}{dx_1} = \frac{A_2}{A_1}, \quad \frac{dx_3}{dx_1} = \frac{A_3}{A_1}, \quad \ldots, \quad \frac{dx_n}{dx_1} = \frac{A_n}{A_1}.$$

**235**

The general solution of this system of equations will be of the form

(5)
$$x_2 = X_2(x_1, c_1, c_2, \ldots, c_{n-1})$$
$$x_3 = X_3(x_1, c_1, c_2, \ldots, c_{n-1})$$
$$\cdot \quad \cdot \quad \cdot \quad \cdot \quad \cdot \quad \cdot \quad \cdot \quad \cdot$$
$$x_n = X_n(x_1, c_1, c_2, \ldots, c_{n-1})$$

where $c_1, c_2, \ldots, c_{n-1}$ are arbitrary constants. When solved for the parameters $c_i$, the equations (5) may be written in the form:

(6)
$$\phi_1(x_1, x_2, \ldots, x_n) = c_1$$
$$\phi_2(x_1, x_2, \ldots, x_n) = c_2$$
$$\cdot \quad \cdot \quad \cdot \quad \cdot \quad \cdot \quad \cdot \quad \cdot$$
$$\phi_{n-1}(x_1, x_2, \ldots, x_n) = c_{n-1}$$

Each of the functions $\phi_i(x_1, x_2, \ldots, x_n)$, $i = 1, 2, \ldots, n - 1$, is then a solution of equation (2). For example,

$$\phi_1(x_1, X_2, X_3, \ldots, X_n) = c_1$$

identically in $x_1, c_1, c_2, \ldots, c_{n-1}$. Differentiation with respect to $x_1$ gives

$$\frac{\partial \phi_1}{\partial x_1} + \frac{\partial \phi_1}{\partial x_2} \frac{dX_2}{dx_1} + \frac{\partial \phi_1}{\partial x_3} \frac{dX_3}{dx_1} + \cdots + \frac{\partial \phi_1}{\partial x_n} \frac{dX_n}{dx_1} = 0,$$

and by means of (4) this may be written

$$A_1 \frac{\partial \phi_1}{\partial x_1} + A_2 \frac{\partial \phi_1}{\partial x_2} + \cdots + A_n \frac{\partial \phi_1}{\partial x_n} = 0.$$

It can be shown that any solution of (2) can be expressed as a function of the particular solutions (6).

It is easy to reduce the case of the nonhomogeneous equation

(2′)
$$A_1 \frac{\partial z}{\partial x_1} + A_2 \frac{\partial z}{\partial x_2} + \cdots + A_n \frac{\partial z}{\partial x_n} = C$$

to that of the homogeneous equation (2). No greater difficulty is encountered if we suppose that the coefficients $A_1, A_2, \ldots, A_n$ and $C$ are functions of the dependent variable $z$ as well as of the independent variables $x_1, x_2, \ldots, x_n$. The equation (2′) is then referred to as a *quasi-linear* equation.

**236**

The solution of (2′) is found by considering the problem of finding a solution

$$\psi(x_1, x_2, \ldots, x_n, z)$$

of the linear homogeneous equation

$$A_1 \frac{\partial \psi}{\partial x_1} + A_2 \frac{\partial \psi}{\partial x_2} + \cdots + A_n \frac{\partial \psi}{\partial x_n} + C \frac{\partial \psi}{\partial z} = 0$$

in the $n + 1$ independent variables $x_1, x_2, \ldots, x_n, z$. Such a solution may be found by the techniques described at the beginning of this article, the equations (3) taking the form

$$(3') \qquad \frac{dx_1}{A_1} = \frac{dx_2}{A_2} = \cdots = \frac{dx_n}{A_n} = \frac{dz}{C}.$$

Then the equation

$$\psi(x_1, x_2, \ldots, x_n, z) = a,$$

in which $a$ is an arbitrary constant, may be solved for $z$, provided $\psi_z \neq 0$, and yields a solution

$$z = Z(x_1, x_2, \ldots, x_n, a)$$

of (2′). This can be shown as follows. Since

$$\psi[x_1, x_2, \ldots, x_n, Z(x_1, x_2, \ldots, x_n, a)] \equiv a$$

we have by differentiation

$$\frac{\partial \psi}{\partial x_i} + \frac{\partial \psi}{\partial z} \frac{\partial Z}{\partial x_i} = 0, \quad i = 1, 2, \ldots, n.$$

When these equations are solved for $\dfrac{\partial Z}{\partial x_i}$, $i = 1, 2, \ldots, n$, and the results substituted into (2′) we obtain

$$A_1 \frac{\partial Z}{\partial x_1} + A_2 \frac{\partial Z}{\partial x_2} + \cdots + A_n \frac{\partial Z}{\partial x_n} - C$$

$$= \frac{-1}{\dfrac{\partial \psi}{\partial z}} \left( A_1 \frac{\partial \psi}{\partial x_1} + A_2 \frac{\partial \psi}{\partial x_2} + \cdots + A_n \frac{\partial \psi}{\partial x_n} + C \frac{\partial \psi}{\partial z} \right) = 0.$$

237

EXAMPLE 1.  Find two particular solutions of the linear equation

$$x_1 \frac{\partial z}{\partial x_1} + x_1 x_2 \frac{\partial z}{\partial x_2} + x_3 \frac{\partial z}{\partial x_3} = 0.$$

SOLUTION.  The equations (3) are

$$\frac{dx_1}{x_1} = \frac{dx_2}{x_1 x_2} = \frac{dx_3}{x_3},$$

which are equivalent to:

$$\frac{dx_2}{dx_1} = x_2, \quad \frac{dx_3}{dx_1} = \frac{x_3}{x_1}$$

The general solution of these equations is:

$$x_2 = c_1 e^{x_1}, \quad x_3 = c_2 x_1$$

Hence

$$\phi_1 = x_2 e^{-x_1}, \quad \phi_2 = x_3 x_1^{-1}$$

are the desired solutions.

EXAMPLE 2.  Find a solution of the quasi-linear equation

$$x_1 z_{x_1} + (z + x_3) z_{x_2} + (z + x_2) z_{x_3} = x_2 + x_3.$$

SOLUTION.  The equations (3') take the form

(a) $$\frac{dx_1}{x_1} = \frac{dx_2}{z + x_3} = \frac{dx_3}{z + x_2} = \frac{dz}{x_2 + x_3}.$$

Each of the fractions in the equations (a) is equal to

$$\frac{l_1 \, dx_1 + l_2 \, dx_2 + l_3 \, dx_3 + l_4 \, dz}{l_1 x_1 + l_2(z + x_3) + l_3(z + x_2) + l_4(x_2 + x_3)}$$

for arbitrary values of the multipliers $l_1$, $l_2$, $l_3$, $l_4$, not all zero. Putting $l_1 = 0$, $l_2 = -1$, $l_3 = 0$, $l_4 = 1$, we therefore may write

$$\frac{dx_1}{x_1} = -\frac{dz - dx_2}{x_2 - z}.$$

The solution of this equation is readily found by the following steps.

$$\frac{dx_1}{x_1} = -\frac{d(z - x_2)}{z - x_2}$$

$$\ln x_1 = -\ln (z - x_2) + \ln C$$

(b) $$x_1(z - x_2) = C.$$

238

From the equation $(b)$ we find

$$z = x_2 + \frac{C}{x_1},$$

which is readily verified to be a solution of the original equation.

## EXERCISE 50

Form the first-order partial differential equations whose complete integrals are the following.

1. $z = ax + by + ab$
2. $ax^2 + by^2 = 2xyz$
3. $ax^2 - by^2 = 2z$
4. $z = bx^a y^{1-a}$
5. $6az = (x + y)^3 + 3a^2(y - x) + b$
6. $(x - a \cos b)^2 + (y - a \sin b)^2 + z^2 = a^2$
7. $(z + a^2)^3 = (x + ay + b)^2$
8. $z = ay - \frac{1}{a} \cos ax + b$
9. $z = e^{ax+by}$
10. $(z + b)^2 = y^2(4x^2 + a)$
11. $z = \left( \frac{ax}{2} + \frac{y^2}{4a} + b \right)^2$
12. $z = ae^{\frac{1}{x}} + be^{\frac{1}{y}}$

Find two particular solutions for each of the following equations.

13. $\dfrac{\partial z}{\partial x_1} + \dfrac{\partial z}{\partial x_2} + \dfrac{\partial z}{\partial x_3} = 0$

14. $x_1 \dfrac{\partial z}{\partial x_1} + \dfrac{\partial z}{\partial x_2} - x_2 \dfrac{\partial z}{\partial x_3} = 0$

15. $x_1 x_2 x_3 \dfrac{\partial z}{\partial x_1} + x_2 \dfrac{\partial z}{\partial x_2} - x_3 \dfrac{\partial z}{\partial x_3} = 0$

16. $\dfrac{\partial z}{\partial x_1} + \dfrac{\partial z}{\partial x_2} - \sqrt{x_3} \dfrac{\partial z}{\partial x_3} = 0$

17. $x_2 \dfrac{\partial z}{\partial x_1} - x_1 \dfrac{\partial z}{\partial x_2} - (1 + x_3^2) \dfrac{\partial z}{\partial x_3} = 0$

18. $x \dfrac{\partial z}{\partial x} + y \dfrac{\partial z}{\partial y} + x = 0$

19. $yz \dfrac{\partial z}{\partial x} + xz \dfrac{\partial z}{\partial y} = xy$

20. $x^2 \dfrac{\partial z}{\partial x} - y^2 \dfrac{\partial z}{\partial y} + 2z = 0$

21. $x^2 p + yq = z$

22. $z \dfrac{\partial z}{\partial x} - x \dfrac{\partial z}{\partial y} = xz$

**84. Method of Lagrange-Charpit.\*** We return now to the problem of solving the equation $f(x, y, z, p, q) = 0$. To accomplish this, we seek a function $g(x, y, z, p, q)$ such that the pair of partial differential equations

(7) $\qquad f(x, y, z, p, q) = 0, \quad g(x, y, z, p, q) = a$

will be compatible for every value of the arbitrary constant $a$ in the sense defined in Article 81; that is,

(8) $[f, g] = f_p(g_x+g_z p)+f_q(g_y+g_z q)-g_p(f_x+f_z p)-g_q(f_y+f_z q)$
$\qquad = f_p g_x+f_q g_y+(f_p p+f_q q)g_z+(-f_x-f_z p)g_p+(-f_y-f_z q)g_q=0.$

This equation is a linear partial differential equation for the unknown function $g$, the independent variables being $x, y, z, p, q$. In this case, the equations (3) become

(9) $\qquad \dfrac{dx}{f_p} = \dfrac{dy}{f_q} = \dfrac{dz}{pf_p + qf_q} = \dfrac{dp}{-f_x - f_z p} = \dfrac{dq}{-f_y - f_z q},$

and a solution $g(x, y, z, p, q)$ of equation (8) may be found by the method of the preceding article. If the resulting pair of equations (7) has the solution

$$p = P(x, y, z, a), \quad q = Q(x, y, z, a),$$

the system

(10) $\qquad z_x = P(x, y, z, a), \quad z_y = Q(x, y, z, a)$

---

\* Lagrange's method of solution for partial differential equations of the first order was improved upon by Paul Charpit (?–1784).

is completely integrable, according to the discussion of Article 81. Hence (10) will have a solution $z = z(x, y, a, b)$ and this solution will be a complete integral of the equation

$$f(x, y, z, p, q) = 0.$$

EXAMPLE. Find a complete integral of the equation $pq - z = 0$.
SOLUTION. The equation (8) takes the form

$$q(g_u + g_z p) + p(g_y + q_z q) + pq_p + qg_q = 0,$$

and the equations (9) become

$$\frac{dx}{q} = \frac{dy}{p} = \frac{dz}{2pq} = \frac{dp}{p} = \frac{dq}{q}$$

which may be written:

$$\frac{dy}{dx} = \frac{p}{q}, \quad \frac{dz}{dx} = 2p, \quad \frac{dp}{dx} = \frac{p}{q}, \quad \frac{dq}{dx} = 1$$

It is sufficient to integrate the last of these equations. We thus obtain a particular integral $q = x$. We may adjoin to $pq - z = 0$ the equation $q - x = a$ and the resulting system is compatible. Solving for $p$ and $q$ we secure the completely integrable system

$$z_x = \frac{z}{x + a}, \quad z_y = x + a,$$

whose general solution is

$$z = (x + a)(y + b).$$

This is the desired complete integral.

## EXERCISE 51

Find a complete integral for each of the following equations.

1. $px + qy = 2z$          2. $xp - yq = 0$
3. $px - qy = z$           4. $q(px - z) = y$
5. $px + q = z$            6. $pq + xp + yq - z = 0$
7. $p^2 + q^2 = x^2$       8. $pq + z = x$
9. $xp^2 + yq^2 = 1$       10. $p^2 + pq + x - y = 0$
11. $p^2 - q^2 + z = 0$    12. $p^2 + q^2 - xz = 0$

**85. Integrating factors for ordinary differential equations.** It was stated in Article 15 that every ordinary differential equation of the first order and first degree has an integrating factor. If the equation is

(11) $$M(x, y) \, dx + N(x, y) \, dy = 0,$$

this means that there exists a function $\mu(x, y)$ not identically zero such that $\mu(M \, dx + N \, dy) = 0$ is exact, that is

$$\frac{\partial}{\partial y}(\mu M) = \frac{\partial}{\partial x}(\mu N).$$

We are thus led to a partial differential equation of the first order for $\mu$, which may be written

(12) $$N\mu_x - M\mu_y + \mu(N_x - M_y) = 0.$$

This is an instance of equation (2′) of Article 83 and the equations (3′) of that article become

(13) $$-\frac{dx}{N} = \frac{dy}{M} = \frac{d\mu}{\mu(N_x - M_y)}.$$

It might seem that the integration of (13) is no less complicated than the original problem of integrating the equation (11), and ordinarily this is indeed true. However, it will be recalled that it is not necessary to find the general solution of the system (13) but that a single integral relation suffices to complete the solution of (12). Sometimes such a relation can be found by inspection. We shall consider several cases where this is true.

*Case 1.* If $\dfrac{N_x - M_y}{N}$ is a function $\phi(x)$ of $x$ alone, then the equation

$$-\frac{N_x - M_y}{N} \, dx = \frac{d\mu}{\mu}$$

yields a first integral of (13), and

$$\mu = e^{-\int \phi(x) \, dx}$$

is a solution of (12) and hence an integrating factor of (11).

242

*Case 2.* If $\dfrac{N_x - M_y}{M}$ is a function $\psi(y)$ of $y$ alone, then the equation

$$\frac{N_x - M_y}{M}\, dy = \frac{d\mu}{\mu}$$

gives a first integral of (13), and

$$\mu = e^{\int \psi(y)\, dy}$$

is an integrating factor of (11).

*Case 3.* If $M$ and $N$ are homogeneous of the same degree $n$, then $\dfrac{1}{xM + yN}$ is an integrating factor of (11). The proof is made as follows. Equation (11) may be written

$$\frac{nM\, dx + nN\, dy}{xM + yN} = 0,$$

which can be replaced by

(14) $$\frac{(xM_x + yM_y)\, dx + (xN_x + yN_y)\, dy}{xM + yN} = 0$$

because by Euler's theorem on homogeneous functions we have

$$xM_x + yM_y = nM, \quad xN_x + yN_y = nN$$

The equations (13) may be written

$$\frac{-\, d\mu}{\mu} = \frac{(N_x - M_y)\, dx}{N} = \frac{-\,(N_x - M_y)\, dy}{M}.$$

On the other hand we have by composition

$$\frac{(N_x - M_y)\, dx}{N} = \frac{-\,(N_x - M_y)\, dy}{M}$$

$$= \frac{y(N_x - M_y)\, dx - x(N_x - M_y)\, dy}{xM + yN},$$

so that

(15) $$\frac{y(N_x - M_y)\, dx - x(N_x - M_y)\, dy}{xM + yN} = \frac{-\, d\mu}{\mu}.$$

When the expressions $xM_x \, dx + yM_y \, dx + xN_x \, dy + yN_y \, dy$ and $M \, dx + N \, dy$, which are zero by (14) and (11) respectively, are added to the numerator of the left member of (15), the latter can be written

$$x(M_x \, dx + M_y \, dy) + y(N_x \, dx + N_y \, dy) + M \, dx + N \, dy,$$

so that

$$-\frac{d\mu}{\mu} = \frac{d(xM + yN)}{xM + yN}.$$

A particular solution of this equation is

$$\mu = \frac{1}{xM + yN}.$$

*Case 4.* When (11) is linear in $y$ and $\dfrac{dy}{dx}$, it may be written in the form

$$[yP(x) - Q(x)] \, dx + dy = 0,$$

so that

$$M = yP(x) - Q(x), \quad N = 1,$$

and

$$\frac{d\mu}{\mu} = -\frac{N_x - M_y}{N} \, dx = P \, dx.$$

Hence we get the familiar integrating factor

$$\mu = e^{\int P(x) \, dx}.$$

## EXERCISE 52

Find an integrating factor for each of the equations in Problems 1–8 and integrate.

1. $(y^4 - 5y) \, dx + (7xy^3 - 5x + y) \, dy = 0$
2. $(x^2 - xy + y^2) \, dx + (x^2 - xy) \, dy = 0$
3. $(6x^2y + 2xy + 3y^2) \, dx + (x^2 + y) \, dy = 0$

4. $(x^2y + y^3)\, dx - 2x^3\, dy = 0$
5. $(y^4 - 2x^3y)\, dx + (x^4 - 2xy^3)\, dy = 0$
6. $(3xy - 8y + x^2)\, dx + (x^2 - 5x + 6)\, dy = 0$
7. $(x^3y^3 + y^3 - 2x^2y + x)\, dx + (3xy^2 - 2)\, dy = 0$
8. $(2xy^2 + 3y - 1)\, dx + (x^2y^3 + 3xy^2 + 2x^2y - xy + 3x)\, dy = 0$

9. If $M = yf(xy)$ and $N = xg(xy)$ where $f$ and $g$ are functions of the product $xy$, show that $(Mx - Ny)^{-1}$, if not identically zero, is an integrating factor of $M\, dx + N\, dy = 0$.

Find an integrating factor for each of the following equations.

10. $(x + x^3y^2)\, dy + (x^2y^3 - y)\, dx = 0$
11. $(2xy^2 + x^2y^3)\, dx + x^4y^3\, dy = 0$
12. $(y + 2x^{\frac{1}{2}}y^{\frac{3}{2}})\, dx + 3x^{\frac{3}{2}}y^{\frac{1}{2}}\, dy = 0$
13. $y\,(\cos xy + 1)\, dx + x\,(\sin xy + 1)\, dy = 0$
14. $ye^{xy}\, dx + x\,(\ln x + \ln y)\, dy = 0$

**86. Cauchy's Problem.** It will be remembered that for an ordinary differential equation $g(x, y, y') = 0$ with $g_{y'} \neq 0$ a solution $y = y(x)$ is uniquely determined if one prescribes a point $(x_0, y_0)$ through which the integral curve must pass. An analogous result holds for a partial differential equation

(16) $$f(x, y, z, p, q) = 0$$

of the first order. In this case an integral surface $z = z(x, y)$ is determined by the prescription that it is to pass through a given curve. The problem of finding the integral surface $z = z(x, y)$ of equation (16) which passes through a given curve $C$ is known as Cauchy's Problem.

It is possible to determine the desired integral surface from a complete integral of equation (16), by taking the envelope of those surfaces defined by the complete integral which are tangent to the given curve. However, we shall describe another method due to Cauchy which constructs the solution out of so-called characteristic strips. We turn now to an explanation of this method.

Consider a curve $C$ defined by parametric equations:

$$x = \xi(v), \quad y = \eta(v), \quad z = \zeta(v), \quad v_1 \leqq v \leqq v_2$$

We shall suppose that the curve is continuous and has a continuously turning tangent, that is, that the functions $\xi$, $\eta$, $\zeta$ and their derivatives are continuous on the interval $v_1 \leqq v \leqq v_2$, and that $\xi'^2 + \eta'^2 + \zeta'^2$ vanishes nowhere on this interval. At each point of the curve let there be given a normal to the curve whose direction numbers $\pi$, $\kappa$, $-1$ are defined by functions $\pi(v)$, $\kappa(v)$ which also have continuous derivatives on the interval $v_1 \leqq v \leqq v_2$. Then

$$\pi(v)\xi'(v) + \kappa(v)\eta'(v) - \zeta'(v) = 0, \quad v_1 \leqq v \leqq v_2$$

expresses the fact that the direction $\pi(v):\kappa(v):-1$ is orthogonal to the direction $\xi'(v):\eta'(v):\zeta'(v)$ of the curve at each point.

The curve and the strip of normals defined by the functions $\xi(v)$, $\eta(v)$, $\zeta(v)$, $\pi(v)$, $\kappa(v)$ determine a *characteristic strip* for the equation (16) if these functions satisfy the differential equations

$$\frac{dx}{f_p} = \frac{dy}{f_q} = \frac{dz}{pf_p + qf_q} = \frac{dp}{-f_x - f_z p} = \frac{dq}{-f_y - f_z q} = du$$

when substituted for $x$, $y$, $z$, $p$, $q$, respectively.

Consider a curve and a strip of normals defined by functions $\xi(v)$, $\eta(v)$, $\zeta(v)$, $\pi(v)$, $\kappa(v)$ which satisfy the equation

$$f[\xi(v), \eta(v), \zeta(v), \pi(v), \kappa(v)] = 0, \quad v_1 \leqq v \leqq v_2$$

and suppose that they do *not* form a characteristic strip. Then it can be shown that there is a unique solution of (16) of the form $z = z(x, y)$ which passes through the given curve and whose surface normal at each point of the curve coincides with the normal of the strip at that point; that is, for $v_1 \leqq v \leqq v_2$:

$$z[\xi(v), \eta(v)] = \zeta(v)$$
$$z_x[\xi(v), \eta(v)] = \pi(v)$$
$$z_y[\xi(v), \eta(v)] = \kappa(v)$$
$$f[x, y, z(x, y), z_x(x, y), z_y(x, y)] = 0$$

The surface $z = z(x, y)$ is found as follows. Consider the differential equations of the characteristic strip:

$$\frac{dx}{du} = f_p(x, y, z, p, q)$$

$$\frac{dy}{du} = f_q(x, y, z, p, q)$$

(17)
$$\frac{dz}{du} = pf_p + qf_q$$

$$\frac{dp}{du} = -f_x - f_z p$$

$$\frac{dq}{du} = -f_y - f_z q$$

Let the solution of the system (17) which reduces to the set $x_0, y_0, z_0, p_0, q_0$ for $u = 0$ be given by:

$$x = x(u, x_0, y_0, z_0, p_0, q_0)$$
$$y = y(u, x_0, y_0, z_0, p_0, q_0)$$
$$z = z(u, x_0, y_0, z_0, p_0, q_0)$$
$$p = p(u, x_0, y_0, z_0, p_0, q_0)$$
$$q = q(u, x_0, y_0, z_0, p_0, q_0)$$

Define:

(18)
$$x = X(u, v) = x[u, \xi(v), \eta(v), \zeta(v), \pi(v), \kappa(v)]$$
$$y = Y(u, v) = y[u, \xi(v), \eta(v), \zeta(v), \pi(v), \kappa(v)]$$
$$z = Z(u, v) = z[u, \xi(v), \eta(v), \zeta(v), \pi(v), \kappa(v)]$$
$$p = P(u, v) = p[u, \xi(v), \eta(v), \zeta(v), \pi(v), \kappa(v)]$$
$$q = Q(u, v) = q[u, \xi(v), \eta(v), \zeta(v), \pi(v), \kappa(v)]$$

If the first two of these equations are solved for $u$ and $v$ in terms of $x$ and $y$ one obtains functions $u = U(x, y)$, $v = V(x, y)$. Let these be substituted into the remaining three functions of (18); one obtains:

$$z = z(x, y) = Z[U(x, y), V(x, y)]$$
$$p = p(x, y) = P[U(x, y), V(x, y)]$$
$$q = q(x, y) = Q[U(x, y), V(x, y)]$$

Then $z = z(x, y)$ is the desired solution and furthermore:

$$z_x(x, y) = p(x, y), \quad z_y(x, y) = q(x, y)$$

We shall not give the proof * of these assertions but shall con-

---

* For a proof of these results see E. J. B. Goursat, *A Course in Mathematical Analysis*, Vol. II, Pt. II, trans. by E. R. Hedrick and O. Dunkel (Boston: Ginn and Co., 1917), pp. 249 ff.

tent ourselves with an illustration of the process in the following example.

EXAMPLE. Find the solution of the equation $pq = z$ which is determined by the parabola $z = x^2$, $y = 0$.

SOLUTION. Here $f = pq - z$. The equations of the characteristic strips may be written:

$$\frac{dx}{du} = q, \quad \frac{dy}{du} = p, \quad \frac{dz}{du} = 2pq, \quad \frac{dp}{du} = p, \quad \frac{dq}{du} = q$$

From the last two equations we have $p = \pi_0 e^u$, $q = k_0 e^u$. Substituting into the remaining equations, we readily find that the solution $x = \xi(u)$, $y = \eta(u)$, $z = \zeta(u)$, $p = \pi(u)$, $q = \kappa(u)$, which for $u = 0$ has the values $\xi_0$, $\eta_0$, $\zeta_0$, $\pi_0$, $\kappa_0$, is:

(a) $\quad x = \xi_0 + \kappa_0(e^u - 1), \quad y = \eta_0 + \pi_0(e^u - 1), \quad z = \zeta_0 + \pi_0\kappa_0(e^{2u} - 1),$

$$p = \pi_0 e^u, \quad q = \kappa_0 e^u$$

The equations of the initial curve can be written in parametric form as:

$$x = \xi_0(v) = v, \quad y = \eta_0(v) = 0, \quad z = \zeta_0(v) = v^2$$

The functions $\pi_0(v)$, $\kappa_0(v)$ which determine the direction numbers of the normals to the initial curve must satisfy the equations:

$$\pi_0\kappa_0 = \zeta_0, \quad \pi_0\xi_0' + \kappa_0\eta_0' = \zeta_0'$$

The second equation reduces to $\pi_0 = 2v$, and from the first equation we then find $\kappa_0 = \dfrac{v}{2}$. If we now substitute the functions

$$\xi_0 = v, \quad \eta_0 = 0, \quad \zeta_0 = v^2, \quad \pi_0 = 2v, \quad \kappa_0 = \frac{v}{2}$$

into the equations (a) we obtain:

$$x = X(u, v) = \frac{v}{2}(e^u + 1)$$

$$y = Y(u, v) = 2v(e^u - 1)$$

(b) $\qquad z = Z(u, v) = v^2 e^{2u}$

$$p = P(u, v) = 2ve^u$$

$$q = Q(u, v) = \frac{v}{2}e^u$$

The first two equations $(b)$ are readily solved to give

$$v = \frac{4x - y}{4}, \quad e^u = \frac{4x + y}{4x - y},$$

and when these results are substituted into the third equation $(b)$ we obtain the desired solution in the form

$$z = \frac{(4x + y)^2}{16}.$$

## EXERCISE 53

1. Find the solution of the equation $xp + yq = z$ which is determined by the curve $z = 1 - x^2$, $y = 1$.
2. Find the solution of the equation $pq + z = x$ which is determined by the curve $z = x$, $y = 0$.
3. Find the solution of $xp^2 + yq^2 = 1$ passing through the curve $y = x$, $z = 0$.
4. Find the solution of $pq + xp + yq = z$ which is determined by the curve $z = 1$, $x + y = 0$.

# CHAPTER ELEVEN

# The Laplace transformation

**87. Introduction.** In this chapter we shall give a brief introduction to the theory of the Laplace transformation and its application to the solution of linear differential equations with constant coefficients. This method of solution is closely related to the method of operators described in Chapter Four. Only a brief account of the theory can be given here. For a fuller exposition, and for proofs of those theorems which are stated in this chapter without demonstration, the reader is referred to books which are devoted to the subject of the Laplace transformation.*

**88. Admissible functions and Laplace transforms.** We shall restrict attention in this discussion to a class of functions $f(x)$ defined for $0 < x < +\infty$ which have the following properties: there is a value $x_0 > 0$ such that

(a) on every finite interval $x_1 \leqq x \leqq x_2$ with $x_1 \geqq x_0$, $f(x)$

---

* R. V. Churchill, *Modern Operational Mathematics in Engineering* (New York: McGraw-Hill Book Co., Inc., 1944).

N. W. McLachlan, *Modern Operational Calculus* (London: Macmillan and Co., 1948).

G. Doetsch, *Theorie und Anwendung der Laplace-Transformation* (New York: Dover Publications, Inc., 1943).

has only a finite number of *ordinary* discontinuities, i.e., discontinuities at which $f(x)$ suffers a finite jump;

(b) $| x^k f(x) |$ is continuous and bounded on $0 < x \leqq x_0$ for some real value $k$ such that $0 \leqq k < 1$;

(c) there is a constant $\alpha$ such that $| e^{-\alpha x} f(x) |$ is bounded for $x_0 \leqq x < +\infty$.

Functions which satisfy these conditions will be called *admissible*. The conditions (a) and (b) are obviously fulfilled if $f(r)$ is continuous for $0 \leqq x < +\infty$. The condition (c) demands, in effect, that $f(x)$ should not increase more rapidly than some exponential function $e^{\alpha x}$ as $x$ becomes infinite. The function $f(x)$ is then said to be of *exponential order* $\alpha$ as $x \to +\infty$.

If now $f(x)$ is admissible and of exponential order $\alpha$, the improper integral

$$\int_0^{+\infty} e^{-px} f(x)\ dx$$

can be shown to exist for every value $p > \alpha$. In fact, the integral converges absolutely. It then defines a function

(1) $$F(p) = \int_0^\infty e^{-px} f(x)\ dx$$

for all values $p > \alpha$. The function $F(p)$ is known as the *Laplace transform* of $f(x)$, and may be designated by the notation $L[f(x)]$, so that

(2) $$L[f(x)] = \int_0^\infty e^{-px} f(x)\ dx.$$

We have here an instance of what is known as a *functional transformation*, which associates with each admissible function $f(x)$ a second function $L[f(x)]$, the Laplace transform of the first. The Laplace transformation is a *linear* functional transformation; i.e., if $f_1(x)$ and $f_2(x)$ are both admissible and of exponential order $\alpha$, then so is $c_1 f_1(x) + c_2 f_2(x)$ for any real constants $c_1$, $c_2$ and

$$L[c_1 f_1 + c_2 f_2] = c_1 L[f_1] + c_2 L[f_2]$$

as the reader may easily verify.

**251**

EXAMPLE. Discuss the admissibility of $e^{ax}$ and find its Laplace transform.

SOLUTION. The function $e^{ax}$ is continuous for $0 \leqq x < +\infty$ and is of exponential order $a$. Hence it is admissible and

(3) $$L[e^{ax}] = \int_0^\infty e^{-px} \cdot e^{ax} \, dx = \frac{e^{-(p-a)x}}{-(p-a)} \Big]_0^{+\infty}$$

$$= \frac{1}{p-a} \qquad (p > a).$$

## EXERCISE 54

Verify the admissibility of the following functions and find their Laplace transforms.

1. $k$        2. $ax + b$        3. $ax^2 + bx + c$

4. $\sin ax$        5. $\cos ax$        6. $\sinh bx$

7. $\cosh bx$        8. $(a - x)(b - x)$        9. $\dfrac{e^{-bx} - e^{-ax}}{a - b}$

10. $xe^x$        11. $x \sinh ax$        12. $x \cosh ax$

13. $x \sin ax$        14. $x \cos ax$

**89. Properties of Laplace transforms.** We note certain important properties that will be useful in the sequel.

Formally, by integration by parts, one finds

$$L[f'(x)] = \int_0^\infty e^{-px} f'(x) \, dx$$

$$= e^{-px} f(x) \Big]_0^\infty + p \int_0^\infty e^{-px} f(x) \, dx$$

$$= -f(0) + pL[f(x)] \qquad (p > \alpha)$$

if $f(x)$ is of exponential order $\alpha$. This result is a special case of the following theorem, whose rigorous proof is omitted.

*Theorem 1.* Let $f^{(n)}(x)$ exist and be continuous for $0 \leqq x < +\infty$. Then $L[f^{(n)}(x)]$ exists for $p > \alpha$, if $f(x)$ and its first $n - 1$ derivatives are continuous for $0 \leqq x < +\infty$ and are all of exponential order $\alpha$. Furthermore

(4) $$L[f^{(n)}(x)] = p^n L[f(x)] - \sum_{k=0}^{n-1} p^{n-k-1} f^{(k)}(0).$$

In the following examples, Theorem 1 is applied to yield the transforms of some simple functions.

EXAMPLE 1. Find $L[x^m]$ for any positive integer $m$.

SOLUTION. The function $f(x) = x^m$ and all its derivatives are continuous, and of exponential order $\alpha$ for any $\alpha > 0$. Also

$$f(0) = f'(0) = \cdots = f^{(m-1)}(0) = 0,$$
$$f^{(m)}(x) = m!, \quad f^{(m+1)}(x) = 0.$$

Hence

$$L[f^{(m+1)}(x)] = 0 = p^{m+1}L[x^m] - m!,$$

(5) $$L[x^m] = \frac{m!}{p^{m+1}} \qquad (p > 0).$$

EXAMPLE 2. Find $L[\sin bx]$.

SOLUTION. The function $f(x) = \sin bx$ and all its derivatives are continuous and bounded, hence of exponential order $\alpha = 0$. Therefore

$$L[f''(x)] = p^2 L[\sin bx] - pf(0) - f'(0) \qquad (p > 0).$$

Consequently

$$- b^2 L[\sin bx] = p^2 L[\sin bx] - b$$

so that

(6) $$L[\sin bx] = \frac{b}{p^2 + b^2} \qquad (p > 0).$$

Suppose now that $f(x)$ is admissible and of exponential order $\alpha$. Thus

$$L[f(x)] = F(p) = \int_0^\infty e^{-px} f(x) \, dx \qquad (p > \alpha).$$

Since this is an identity in $p$, we have

(7) $$F(p - p_0) = \int_0^\infty e^{-(p-p_0)x} f(x) \, dx$$
$$= \int_0^\infty e^{-px} \cdot e^{p_0 x} f(x) \, dx$$
$$= L[e^{p_0 x} f(x)] \qquad (p > \alpha + p_0).$$

253

This result is stated in the following theorem, and may be compared with the exponential shift discussed in Chapter Four.

*Theorem 2.* The substitution of $p - p_0$ for $p$ in the transform of $f(x)$ corresponds to the multiplication of $f(x)$ by $e^{p_0 x}$.

EXAMPLE 3. Find the transforms of $x^m e^{p_0 x}$ and $e^{-p_0 x} \sin bx$.

SOLUTION. Since $L[x^m] = \dfrac{m!}{p^{m+1}}$ for $p > 0$, we have by Theorem 2

$$(8) \qquad L[x^m e^{p_0 x}] = \frac{m!}{(p - p_0)^{m+1}} \qquad (p > p_0).$$

Also $L[\sin bx] = \dfrac{b}{p^2 + b^2}$ for $p > 0$ and hence

$$(9) \qquad L[e^{-p_0 x} \sin bx] = \frac{b}{(p + p_0)^2 + b^2} \qquad (p > -p_0).$$

If we assume that $f(x)$ is continuous and of exponential order $\alpha$, then the same is true of

$$g(x) = \int_0^x f(u)\, du.$$

Furthermore $g'(x) = f(x)$ and $g(0) = 0$. Hence

$$L[g'] = pL[g] - g(0)$$

or

$$L[f] = pL\left[\int_0^x f(u)\, du\right]$$

so that we have the following theorem:

*Theorem 3.* The division by $p$ of the transform of $f(x)$ corresponds to taking the indefinite integral of $f(x)$:

$$L\left[\int_0^x f(u)\, du\right] = \frac{1}{p} L[f(x)]$$

EXAMPLE 4. Find the transform of $1 - \cos bx$.
SOLUTION. We note that

$$\int_0^x \sin bu\, du = \frac{1}{b}(1 - \cos bx)$$

and hence

$$L[1 - \cos bx] = L\left[b\int_0^x \sin bu\, du\right]$$

$$= bL\left[\int_0^x \sin bu\, du\right]$$

$$= \frac{b^2}{p(p^2 + b^2)}.$$

The same result, of course, can be obtained from previously derived results.

## 90. Derivatives and integrals of transforms.

Suppose that $f(x)$ is admissible and of exponential order $\alpha$. Then its transform

$$F(p) = L[f(x)] = \int_0^\infty e^{-px}f(x)\, dx$$

is a function defined for $p > \alpha$, whose derivative may be calculated by taking the partial derivative with respect to $p$ under the integral sign: *

$$F'(p) = \int_0^\infty e^{-px}(-x)f(x)\, dx.$$

Consequently, it appears that differentiation of the transform of a function corresponds to multiplication of the function by $-x$. This result may be generalized as follows:

*Theorem 4.* If $f(x)$ is admissible and of exponential order $\alpha$, then

$$F^{(n)}(p) = L[(-x)^n f(x)] \qquad (p > \alpha; \; n = 1, 2, \ldots).$$

EXAMPLE 1. Find the transform of $x \sin bx$.
SOLUTION. Since $L[\sin bx] = b/(p^2 + b^2)$, it follows from Theorem 4 that

$$L[-x \sin bx] = \frac{d}{dp}\left[\frac{b}{p^2 + b^2}\right] = \frac{-2pb}{(p^2 + b^2)^2};$$

$$L[x \sin bx] = \frac{2pb}{(p^2 + b^2)^2} \qquad (p > 0).$$

* For a proof of the validity of this, see Churchill, *op. cit.*, pp. 28–30.

Again, when $f(x)$ is admissible and of exponential order $\alpha$, if $b > p > \alpha$,

$$\int_p^b F(u)\,du = \int_p^b \int_0^\infty e^{-ux} f(x)\,dx\,du.$$

It can be shown that the order of the integrations on the right can be interchanged, so that

$$\int_p^b F(u)\,du = \int_0^\infty f(x) \int_p^b e^{-ux}\,du\,dx$$

$$= \int_0^\infty \frac{f(x)}{x} \left[ e^{-px} - e^{-bx} \right] dx.$$

If we assume further that $\lim_{x \to 0^+} f(x)/x$ exists, then $f(x)/x$ is admissible and of exponential order $\alpha$. It then follows * that

$$\int_p^b F(u)\,du = \lim_{b \to \infty} \int_p^b F(u)\,du$$

$$= \int_0^\infty \frac{f(x)}{x} \lim_{b \to \infty} \left[ e^{-px} - e^{-bx} \right] dx$$

$$= \int_0^\infty \frac{f(x)}{x} e^{-px}\,dx = L\left[ \frac{f(x)}{x} \right].$$

We thus have the following result.

*Theorem 5.* If $f(x)$ is admissible and of exponential order $\alpha$, and if $\lim_{x \to 0^+} f(x)/x$ exists and

$$F(p) = L[f(x)] = \int_0^\infty e^{-px} f(x)\,dx,$$

then

$$\int_p^\infty F(u)\,du = L\left[ \frac{f(x)}{x} \right] = \int_0^\infty e^{-px} \frac{f(x)}{x}\,dx.$$

EXAMPLE 2. Find the transform of $(e^{-ax} - e^{-bx})/x$.

SOLUTION. Put $f(x) = e^{-ax} - e^{-bx}$. Then

$$F(p) = L[f(x)] = L[e^{-ax}] - L[e^{-bx}] = \frac{1}{p+a} - \frac{1}{p+b}.$$

$$L\left[ \frac{e^{-ax} - e^{-bx}}{x} \right] = \int_p^\infty \left( \frac{1}{u+a} - \frac{1}{u+b} \right) du$$

$$= \ln \frac{p+b}{p+a} \qquad \left( \begin{array}{c} p > -a \\ p > -b \end{array} \right).$$

---

* The justifications for the steps here taken can be found in R. C. Buck, *Advanced Calculus* (New York: McGraw-Hill Book Co., Inc., 1956), pp. 149 ff.

1–9. Use Theorem 1 to find the transforms for Problems 1–9 of Exercise 54.

Use Theorem 2 to find the transforms in each of the following.

10. $e^{-ax} \cos bx$        11. $e^{ax} \sinh bx$        12. $e^{-ax} \cosh bx$

13. Find the transform of $x^2 \cos bx$ by means of Theorem 4.

14. Find the transform of $2(1 - \cos bx)/x$ by an application of Theorem 5.

## 91. Inverse transforms.

We may now inquire whether, given a function $F(p)$, it is possible to find a function $f(x)$ such that $L[f(x)] = F(p)$. Such a function need not exist unless $f(x)$ satisfies certain conditions, and when it exists it need not be unique. There can, however, be not more than one such function $f(x)$ which is continuous for $x > 0$. When such a function exists, it will be designated by the notation $L^{-1}[F(p)]$ and called the *inverse transform* of $F(p)$.

Suppose $L^{-1}[F_1(p)] = f_1(x)$ and $L^{-1}[F_2(p)] = f_2(x)$, so that $L[f_1(x)] = F_1(p)$ and $L[f_2(x)] = F_2(p)$. Since $L[c_1 f_1(x) + c_2 f_2(x)] = c_1 F_1(p) + c_2 F_2(p)$, we have

$$L^{-1}[c_1 F_1(p) + c_2 F_2(p)] = c_1 f_1(x) + c_2 f_2(x)$$
$$= c_1 L^{-1}[F_1(p)] + c_2 L^{-1}[F_2(p)]$$

so that the inverse transformation is also linear.

EXAMPLE.   Find $L^{-1}\left[\dfrac{p+2}{p^2(p+1)}\right]$.

SOLUTION.   Decomposition into partial fractions gives

$$\frac{p+2}{p^2(p+1)} = \frac{2}{p^2} - \frac{1}{p} + \frac{1}{p+1};$$

$$L^{-1}\left[\frac{p+2}{p^2(p+1)}\right] = 2L^{-1}\left[\frac{1}{p^2}\right] - L^{-1}\left[\frac{1}{p}\right] + L^{-1}\left[\frac{1}{p+1}\right]$$

$$= 2x - 1 + e^{-x}.$$

The last step in the solution takes advantage of results obtained in previous illustrative examples in this chapter.

The results so far obtained may usefully be assembled in the following table.

### Table of Transforms

| $f(x)$ | $L[f(x)]$ | $\alpha$ |
|---|---|---|
| $x^m$ | $m!/p^{m+1}$ | 0 |
| $(m = 0, 1, 2, \ldots)$ | | |
| $x^{\frac{1}{2}}$ | $\frac{1}{2}(\pi/p^3)^{\frac{1}{2}}$ | 0 |
| $x^{-\frac{1}{2}}$ | $(\pi/p)^{\frac{1}{2}}$ | 0 |
| $e^{ax}$ | $1/(p - a)$ | $a$ |
| $x^m e^{ax}$ | $m!/(p - a)^{m+1}$ | $a$ |
| $(m = 0, 1, 2, \ldots)$ | | |
| $\sin bx$ | $b/(p^2 + b^2)$ | 0 |
| $\cos bx$ | $p/(p^2 + b^2)$ | 0 |
| $e^{-ax} \sin bx$ | $b/[(p + a)^2 + b^2]$ | $-a$ |
| $e^{-ax} \cos bx$ | $(p + a)/[(p + a)^2 + b^2]$ | $-a$ |
| $\sinh bx$ | $b/(p^2 - b^2)$ | $\lvert b \rvert$ |
| $\cosh bx$ | $p/(p^2 - b^2)$ | $\lvert b \rvert$ |
| $(\sinh bx)/x$ | $\frac{1}{2}\ln[(p - b)/(p + b)]$ | $\lvert b \rvert$ |

**EXERCISE 56**

Find the inverse transforms of the following functions.

1. $\dfrac{p}{p^2 + 4p - 5}$

2. $\dfrac{1}{p(p + 1)^2}$

3. $\dfrac{p}{(p + 1)(p + 2)(p + 3)}$

4. $\dfrac{1 - p}{p^2 + 4p + 3}$

5. $\dfrac{p - 1}{(p - 2)^2}$

6. $\dfrac{p^2}{(1 - p^2)^2}$

7. $\dfrac{p^2}{(p^2 + 5p + 6)(p + 1)^2}$

8. $\dfrac{p}{(p - 1)^2(p^2 + 1)}$

9. $\dfrac{2}{(p + 1)(p^2 + 2p + 3)}$

10. $\dfrac{p + 2}{p^2 + 2p + 3}$

11. $\dfrac{2p - 1}{(p - 1)(p^2 + p + 1)}$

12. $\dfrac{3p^2 + p - 8}{(p + 1)(p^2 + p - 2)}$

**92. Application to linear differential equations.** It is now possible, with the theory thus far developed, to show how the Laplace transformation may be used in the solution of ordinary linear differential equations with constant coefficients. Applications to other kinds of linear differential equations, including partial differential equations, involve development of the theory beyond that which can be presented in this chaptor. For such developments the reader is referred to the books mentioned earlier.

Let it be required to find a solution $y(x)$ of the equation

$$(10) \qquad A_0 y^{(n)} + A_1 y^{(n-1)} + \cdots + A_{n-1} y' + A_n y = Q(x),$$

in which the coefficients $A_i$ are constants, subject to the initial conditions

$$(11) \qquad \begin{aligned} y(0) &= y_0, \quad y'(0) = y_0', \quad \ldots, \\ y^{(n-1)}(0) &= y_0^{(n-1)}. \end{aligned}$$

Taking the Laplace transform of each side of (10), one has

$$(12) \qquad \begin{aligned} A_0 L[y^{(n)}] + A_1 L[y^{(n-1)}] + \cdots \\ + A_{n-1} L[y'] + A_n L[y] = L[Q(x)]. \end{aligned}$$

By an application of Theorem 1, the transform of each derivative of $y$ may be expressed algebraically in terms of $L[y]$ and the initial conditions (11). When these expressions are substituted into (12), it is possible to solve the resulting equation for the transform of $y$:

$$(13) \qquad L[y] = Y(p),$$

where $Y(p)$ is a known function of $p$. The required solution is then found by taking the inverse transform of $Y(p)$:

$$y = L^{-1}[Y(p)]$$

The last step is made easier by referral to the table on page 258 or to more extensive tables of this kind.

The process will be more readily understood after consideration of an example.

EXAMPLE. Find the solution $y(x)$ of the equation

(a)
$$y'' + y' = x^2 + 2x$$

for which $y(0) = 4$, $y'(0) = -2$.

SOLUTION. Upon taking the Laplace transform of each side of equation (a), one has

(b)
$$L[y''] + L[y'] = L[x^2] + L[2x].$$

By Theorem 1,

$$L[y'] = pL[y] - y(0) = pL[y] - 4$$

$$L[y''] = p^2 L[y] - py(0) - y'(0) = p^2 L[y] - 4p + 2$$

and, from the table of transforms,

$$L[x^2] = \frac{2}{p^3}, \quad L[2x] = \frac{2}{p^2}.$$

After substitution of these expressions into (b), one has

$$p(p+1)L[y] = \frac{2(1 + p + p^3 + 2p^4)}{p^3}$$

so that

$$L[y] = \frac{2(1 + p + p^3 + 2p^4)}{p^4(p+1)}.$$

By decomposition into partial fractions this may be written

$$L[y] = 2\left(\frac{1}{p^4} + \frac{1}{p} + \frac{1}{p+1}\right)$$

so that

$$y = L^{-1}\left[2\left(\frac{1}{p^4} + \frac{1}{p} + \frac{1}{p+1}\right)\right]$$

$$= 2\left(L^{-1}\left[\frac{1}{p^4}\right] + L^{-1}\left[\frac{1}{p}\right] + L^{-1}\left[\frac{1}{p+1}\right]\right).$$

Reference to the table of transforms yields

$$y = 2(\tfrac{1}{6}x^3 + 1 + e^{-x})$$

$$= \tfrac{1}{3}x^3 + 2 + 2e^{-x},$$

which is the desired solution.

260

## EXERCISE 57

1-7. Use the Laplace transformation to solve Problems 1-7 of Exercise 19, with the initial conditions $y(0) = y'(0) = 1$.

8-11. Solve Problems 9-12 of Exercise 19 by means of the Laplace transformation, with the initial conditions $y(0) = 1$, $y'(0) = -1$.

12-14. Solve Problems 9, 19, and 25 of Exercise 23, using the Laplace transformation, with the initial conditions $y(0) = y'(0) = 0$, $y''(0) = 1$.


**93. Convolution.** As we observed in Article 88, the Laplace transformation is a linear functional transformation. Hence it follows that for two admissible functions

$$f_1(x), \quad f_2(x)$$

of the same exponential order $\alpha$, if we let

$$(14) \quad \begin{cases} F_1(p) = L[f_1] = \int_0^\infty e^{-px} f_1(x) \, dx, \\ F_2(p) = L[f_2] = \int_0^\infty e^{-py} f_2(y) \, dy, \end{cases}$$

for $p > \alpha$, then for such values of $p$

$$F_1(p) + F_2(p) = L[f_1] + L[f_2]$$
$$= L[f_1 + f_2].$$

We now wish to inquire what may be said of the product

$$(15) \quad F_1(p) \cdot F_2(p) = L[f_1] \cdot L[f_2]$$
$$= \int_0^\infty e^{-px} f_1(x) \, dx \cdot \int_0^\infty e^{-py} f_2(y) \, dy.$$

Because of the absolute convergence of the integrals involved, we may write the following equations, which will be justified shortly.

(16) $\displaystyle\int_0^\infty e^{-px}f_1(x)\,dx \cdot \int_0^\infty e^{-py}f_2(y)\,dy$

$$= \iint\limits_G e^{-p(x+y)}f_1(x)f_2(y)\,dx\,dy$$

$$= \iint\limits_H e^{-pu}f_1(u-v)f_2(v)\,du\,dv$$

$$= \int_0^\infty e^{-pu}\left[\int_0^u f_1(u-v)f_2(v)\,dv\right]du.$$

Here the region $G$ consists of the first quadrant of the $xy$-plane, for which $0 < x < +\infty,\ 0 < y < +\infty$. The region $H$ is that portion of the $uv$-plane into which $G$ is mapped by the change of variables

(17) $$x = u - v, \quad y = v,$$

namely the points $(u, v)$ for which $0 < v < u < +\infty$.

If we take the equalities in (16) as valid, then (15) may be written

$$F_1(p) \cdot F_2(p) = L[f_1] \cdot L[f_2]$$

$$= \int_0^\infty e^{-pu}\left[\int_0^u f_1(u-v)f_2(v)\,dv\right]du$$

$$= L[f_1 * f_2].$$

Here we have introduced a new operation, $f_1 * f_2$, upon the functions $f_1$ and $f_2$, known as the *convolution* of $f_1$ and $f_2$ and defined by the equation

(18) $$(f_1 * f_2)(u) = \int_0^u f_1(u-v)f_2(v)\,dv.$$

The answer to our inquiry can now be stated in the following theorem.

*Theorem 5.* If $f_1(x)$, $f_2(x)$ are admissible functions, each of exponential order $\alpha$, then for $p > \alpha$ the product of their Laplace transforms is equal to the Laplace transform of their convolution:

(19) $\quad F_1(p) \cdot F_2(p) = L[f_1] \cdot L[f_2] = L[f_1 * f_2] \qquad (p > \alpha).$

We return now to a justification of (16).* Let $I[R]$ stand for the integral

$$I[R] = \iint_R e^{-p(x+y)} f_1(x) f_2(y) \, dx \, dy$$

calculated over any region $R$, and let $K[R]$ be the integral

$$K[R] = \iint_R e^{-p(x+y)} \mid f_1(x) \mid \cdot \mid f_2(y) \mid dx \, dy.$$

Since $f_1$ and $f_2$ are admissible functions, both of exponential order $\alpha$, the limits

$$\lim_{a \to \infty} \int_0^a e^{-px} \mid f_1(x) \mid dx, \qquad \lim_{a \to \infty} \int_0^a e^{-py} \mid f_2(y) \mid dy$$

exist, and therefore also the limits

$$\lim_{a \to \infty} \int_0^a e^{-px} f_1(x) \, dx, \qquad \lim_{a \to \infty} \int_0^a e^{-py} f_2(y) \, dy$$

for all values $p > \alpha$. Consequently

$$\lim_{a \to \infty} \left[ \int_0^a e^{-px} \mid f_1(x) \mid dx \cdot \int_0^a e^{-py} \mid f_2(y) \mid dy \right]$$

$$= \lim_{a \to \infty} \int_0^a \int_0^a e^{-p(x+y)} \mid f_1(x) \mid \cdot \mid f_2(y) \mid dx \, dy$$

$$= \lim_{a \to \infty} \int_0^{\frac{1}{2}a} \int_0^{\frac{1}{2}a} e^{-p(x+y)} \mid f_1(x) \mid \cdot \mid f_2(y) \mid dx \, dy;$$

that is,

$$\lim_{a \to \infty} \left[ \int_0^a e^{-px} \mid f_1(x) \mid dx \cdot \int_0^a e^{-py} \mid f_2(y) \mid dy \right]$$

$$= \lim_{a \to \infty} K[B_a] = \lim_{a \to \infty} K[B_{\frac{1}{2}a}],$$

where $B_a$ is the square whose vertices are $(0, 0)$, $(a, 0)$, $(0, a)$, and $(a, a)$, while $B_{\frac{1}{2}a}$ is the square with vertices $(0, 0)$, $(\frac{1}{2}a, 0)$, $(0, \frac{1}{2}a)$, and $(\frac{1}{2}a, \frac{1}{2}a)$. Therefore,

$$\lim_{a \to \infty} \{K[B_a] - K[B_{\frac{1}{2}a}]\} = \lim_{a \to \infty} \{K[C_{1a}] + K[C_{2a}] + K[C_{3a}]\} = 0,$$

where $C_{1a}$ is the triangle with vertices $(\frac{1}{2}a, 0)$, $(a, 0)$, $(\frac{1}{2}a, \frac{1}{2}a)$, $C_{2a}$ is the triangle with vertices $(0, \frac{1}{2}a)$, $(0, a)$, $(\frac{1}{2}a, \frac{1}{2}a)$, and $C_{3a}$ is the triangle with vertices $(0, a)$, $(a, 0)$, $(a, a)$.

* Cf. Churchill, *op. cit.*, pp. 36–7.

Since $K[C_{1a}]$, $K[C_{2a}]$, and $K[C_{3a}]$ are positive, it follows that

$$\lim_{a \to \infty} K[C_{1a}] = \lim_{a \to \infty} K[C_{2a}] = 0$$

and hence also

$$\lim_{a \to \infty} I[C_{1a}] = \lim_{a \to \infty} I[C_{2a}] = 0.$$

We may therefore write

$$(20) \quad F_1(p) \cdot F_2(p) = \lim_{a \to \infty} \left[ \int_0^{\frac{1}{2}a} e^{-px} f_1(x)\, dx \cdot \int_0^{\frac{1}{2}a} e^{-py} f_2(y)\, dy \right]$$

$$= \lim_{a \to \infty} \int_0^{\frac{1}{2}a} \int_0^{\frac{1}{2}a} e^{-p(x+y)} f_1(x) f_2(y)\, dx\, dy$$

$$= \lim_{a \to \infty} I[B_{\frac{1}{2}a}]$$

$$= \lim_{a \to \infty} \{ I[B_{\frac{1}{2}a}] + I[C_{1a}] + I[C_{2a}] \}$$

$$= \lim_{a \to \infty} I[C_a],$$

where $C_a$ is the triangle whose vertices are $(0, 0)$, $(a, 0)$, $(0, a)$, i.e., the region in the $xy$-plane for which $x > 0$, $y > 0$, and $x + y < a$.

Let us introduce the new variables $u$, $v$ by the equations

$$u = x + y, \quad v = y.$$

The Jacobian of this transformation is

$$\begin{vmatrix} \dfrac{\partial x}{\partial u} & \dfrac{\partial x}{\partial v} \\[2mm] \dfrac{\partial y}{\partial u} & \dfrac{\partial y}{\partial v} \end{vmatrix} = \begin{vmatrix} 1 & -1 \\ 0 & 1 \end{vmatrix} = 1,$$

and hence

$$(21) \qquad I[C_a] = \iint_{D_a} e^{-pu} f_1(u - v) f_2(v)\, du\, dv,$$

where $D_a$ is the region in the $uv$-plane for which $u - v > 0$, $v > 0$, and $u < a$.

The integral in (21) may be written as an iterated integral:

$$\iint_{D_a} e^{-pu} f_1(u - v) f_2(v) \, du \, dv$$
$$= \int_0^a e^{-pu} \left[ \int_0^u f_1(u - v) f_2(v) \, dv \right] du$$

and hence (20) becomes

$$F_1(p) \cdot F_2(p) = \lim_{a \to \infty} \int_0^a e^{-pu} \left[ \int_0^u f_1(u - v) f_2(v) \, dv \right] du$$
$$= \int_0^\infty e^{-pu} \left[ \int_0^u f_1(u - v) f_2(v) \, dv \right] du$$
$$= L[f_1 * f_2],$$

and thus the proof of Theorem 5 is completed.

The convolution operation is a commutative one; i.e., for any two admissible functions $f_1$ and $f_2$,

(22) $$f_1 * f_2 = f_2 * f_1.$$

The proof is simple. We have for any $u > 0$,

$$(f_1 * f_2)(u) = \int_0^u f_1(u - v) f_2(v) \, dv.$$

Now introduce the new variable $v_1 = u - v$. Then

$$dv_1 = - \, dv;$$

when $v = 0$, $v_1 = u$, and when $v = u$, $v_1 = 0$. Hence

$$\int_0^u f_1(u - v) f_2(v) \, dv = - \int_a^0 f_1(v_1) f_2(u - v_1) \, dv_1$$
$$= \int_0^a f_2(u - v_1) f_1(v_1) \, dv_1$$

and therefore $f_1 * f_2 = f_2 * f_1$.

For admissible functions $f_1$, $f_2$, the convolution $f_1 * f_2$ is continuous and therefore the inverse transform of the product

$$F_1(p) \cdot F_2(p) = L[f_1 * f_2]$$

must be the convolution $f_1 * f_2$:

(23) $$f_1 * f_2 = L^{-1}[F_1 \cdot F_2].$$

265

We can now also show that the convolution operation is associative; for

$$L[(f_1 * f_2) * f_3] = L[f_1 * f_2] \cdot L[f_3]$$
$$= \{L[f_1] \cdot L[f_2]\} \cdot L[f_3]$$
$$= L[f_1] \cdot \{L[f_2] \cdot L[f_3]\}$$
$$= L[f_1] \cdot L[f_2 * f_3]$$
$$= L[f_1 * (f_2 * f_3)].$$

If we take the inverse transform of each side, we find

$$(24) \qquad (f_1 * f_2) * f_3 = f_1 * (f_2 * f_3).$$

Formula (23) can be useful in helping us find the inverse transforms of functions $F(p)$ which can be expressed as products of other, simpler functions, as the following example illustrates.

EXAMPLE. Find the inverse transform of

$$F(p) = \frac{1}{p^2(p^2 + a^2)}.$$

SOLUTION. $F(p)$ can be written as the product

$$\frac{1}{p^2} \cdot \frac{1}{p^2 + a^2}.$$

Hence

$$L^{-1}\left[\frac{1}{p^2(p^2 + a^2)}\right] = L^{-1}\left[\frac{1}{p^2}\right] * L^{-1}\left[\frac{1}{p^2 + a^2}\right].$$

According to the Table of Transforms in Article 91,

$$L^{-1}\left[\frac{1}{p^2}\right] = x,$$

$$L^{-1}\left[\frac{1}{p^2 + a^2}\right] = \frac{1}{a} \sin ax,$$

and therefore

$$L^{-1}\left[\frac{1}{p^2(p^2 + a^2)}\right] = x * \frac{1}{a} \sin ax.$$

$$x * \frac{1}{a} \sin ax$$

$$= \int_0^x (x - y) \cdot \frac{1}{a} \sin ay \, dy$$

$$= \frac{1}{a} \int_0^x (x \sin ay - y \sin ay) \, dy$$

$$= \frac{1}{a} \left[ -\frac{x \cos ay}{a} - \frac{1}{a^2} (\sin ay - ay \cos ay) \right]_0^x$$

$$= \frac{1}{a} \left[ -\frac{1}{a} x \cos ax - \frac{1}{a^2} (\sin ax - ax \cos ax) + \frac{x}{a} \right]$$

$$= \frac{1}{a} 3(ax - \sin ax).$$

Thus,

$$L^{-1} \left[ \frac{1}{p^2(p^2 + a^2)} \right] = \frac{1}{a^3} (ax - \sin ax).$$

## EXERCISE 58

Find an inverse transform of each of the following functions.

1. $F(p) = \dfrac{1}{p(p - a)}$

2. $F(p) = \dfrac{1}{p(p + a)}$

3. $F(p) = \dfrac{1}{p^{\frac{3}{2}}}$

4. $F(p) = \dfrac{1}{p^{\frac{5}{2}}}$

5. $F(p) = \dfrac{1}{p(p + a)^{n+1}}$

6. $F(p) = \dfrac{1}{p(p^2 + k^2)}$

7. $F(p) = \dfrac{1}{p(p^2 - k^2)}$

8. $F(p) = \dfrac{2}{p(p^2 + k^2)^2}$

9. $F(p) = \dfrac{1}{p^2(p^2 + k^2)}$

10. $F(p) = \dfrac{1}{p^2(p^2 - k^2)}$

11. $F(p) = \dfrac{1}{p^2(p^2 + k^2)^2}$

12. $F(p) = \dfrac{1}{(p^2 + 1)(p^2 + 4)}$

13. $F(p) = \dfrac{p}{(p^2 + 1)(p^2 + 4)}$

14. $F(p) = \dfrac{p^2}{(p^2 + 1)(p^2 + 4)}$

**94. Periodic functions.** Let $f(x)$, defined for $0 \leqq x < +\infty$, be a periodic function with period $2a$ $(a > 0)$. That is,

$$f(x + 2a) = f(x)$$

for every $x \geqq 0$. Suppose also that $f(x)$ has only ordinary discontinuities on the interval $0 \leqq x < 2a$.* Then $f(x)$ is an admissible function of exponential order $\alpha = 0$ and has a Laplace transform

$$F(p) = \int_0^\infty e^{-px} f(x) \, dx \qquad (p > 0).$$

Because of the periodicity of $f(x)$, this integral may be written

$$(25) \qquad F(p) = \sum_{h=0}^\infty \int_{2na}^{2(n+1)a} e^{-px} f(x) \, dx;$$

and if for each $n$ we make the substitution $u = x - 2na$, then again taking advantage of the periodicity of $f(x)$, we may write

$$\int_{2na}^{2(n+1)a} e^{-px} f(x) \, dx = \int_0^{2a} e^{-p(u+2na)} f(u + 2na) \, du$$

$$= e^{-2npa} \int_0^{2a} e^{-pu} f(u) \, du.$$

Hence (25) becomes

$$(26) \qquad F(p) = \int_0^{2a} e^{-pu} f(u) \, du \cdot \sum_{h=0}^\infty e^{-2npa}$$

$$= (1 - e^{-2pa})^{-1} \int_0^{2a} e^{-pu} f(u) \, du,$$

since the infinite series in (26) is a geometric series, whose common ratio has an absolute value $e^{-2pa} < 1$ for $p > 0$. We may therefore state the following theorem.

*Theorem 6.* Let $f(x)$ be defined for $0 \leqq x < +\infty$ and be periodic with period $2a$. Suppose also that $f(x)$ has at most ordinary discontinuities for $0 \leqq x < 2a$ and hence for any $x$. Then the Laplace transform of $f(x)$ is given by

$$F(p) = (1 - e^{-2pa})^{-1} \int_0^{2a} e^{-pu} f(u) \, du \text{ for every } p > 0.$$

* Cf. Article 88, (a).

We may apply Theorem 6 to several periodic functions which are of particular importance in applications. Consider first the function known as the *square-wave function*, defined by

$$M(x, 2a) = \begin{cases} 1, & 0 \leq x < a, \\ -1, & a \leq x < 2a, \end{cases}$$

$$M(x + 2a, 2a) = M(x, 2a).$$

The transform of this periodic function is

$$L[M(x, 2a)] = (1 - e^{-2pa})^{-1} \int_0^{2a} e^{-px} M(x, 2a)\, dx$$

$$\doteq (1 - e^{-2pa})^{-1} \left[ \int_0^a e^{-px}\, dx - \int_a^{2a} e^{-px}\, dx \right]$$

$$= \frac{1 - e^{-pa}}{p(1 + e^{-pa})}$$

$$= \frac{1}{p} \tanh \frac{ap}{2} \qquad (p > 0).$$

The preceding discussion can be easily generalized so as to apply to any function $f(x)$ which, like the square-wave function $M(x, 2a)$, is antiperiodic with period $a$, i.e., for which

$$f(x + a) = -f(x) \qquad (x \geq 0).$$

Such a function is clearly periodic with period $2a$, since

$$f(x + 2a) = -f(x + a) = f(x) \qquad (x \geq 0).$$

With each such antiperiodic function $f(x)$ we may associate its *half-wave rectification* $g(x)$, defined by

$$g(x) = \begin{cases} f(x), & 0 \leq x < a, \\ 0, & a \leq x < 2a, \end{cases}$$

on the interval $0 \leq x < 2a$ and then defined for all other positive $x$ so as to be periodic:

$$g(x + 2a) = g(x) \qquad (x \geq 0).$$

The Laplace transforms of $f(x)$ and $g(x)$ are related by

$$L[F(x)] = (1 - e^{-pa}) L[g(x)]$$

269

as may be shown as follows, by making use of Theorem 6:

$$L[f(x)] = (1 - e^{-2pa})^{-1} \int_0^{2a} e^{-pu}f(u)\ du$$

$$= (1 - e^{-2pa})^{-1} \left[ \int_0^a e^{-pu}f(u)\ du + \int_a^{2a} e^{-pv}f(v)\ dv \right]$$

$$= (1 - e^{-2pa})^{-1} \left[ \int_0^a e^{-pu}f(u)\ du \right.$$

$$\left. + \int_0^a e^{-p(u+a)}f(u+a)\ du \right]$$

$$= \frac{1 - e^{-pa}}{1 - e^{-2pa}} \cdot \int_0^a e^{-pu}f(u)\ du$$

$$= \frac{1 - e^{-pa}}{1 - e^{-2pa}} \cdot \int_0^{2a} e^{-pu}g(u)\ du$$

$$= (1 - e^{-pa})L[g(x)].$$

In other words, the transform of the half-wave rectification is equal to the transform of the function divided by $1 - e^{-pa}$, where $2a$ is the period of the function.

EXAMPLE 1. Find the transform of the half-wave rectification of $\sin bx$.

SOLUTION. We take $f(x) = \sin bx$; the period is $2\pi/b$. The half-wave rectification is

$$g(x) = \tfrac{1}{2}[|\sin bx| + \sin bx]$$

$$= \begin{cases} \sin bx, & 0 \leqq x < \pi/b \\ 0, & \pi/b \leqq x < 2\pi/b \end{cases}$$

so that

$$L[g(x)] = (1 - e^{-\pi p/b})L[\sin bx]$$

$$= \frac{b}{p^2 + b^2} \cdot \frac{1}{1 - e^{-\pi p/b}}.$$

EXAMPLE 2. Find the transform of $|\sin bx|$.

SOLUTION. By Example 1,

$$L[|\sin bx| + \sin bx] = \frac{2b}{(p^2 + b^2)(1 - e^{-\pi p/b})}.$$

But $L[\sin bx] = b/p^2 + b^2$. Hence

$$L[|\sin bx|] = \frac{2b}{(p^2 + b^2)(1 - e^{-\pi p/b})} - \frac{b}{p^2 + b^2}$$

$$= \frac{b}{p^2 + b^2} \cdot \frac{1 + e^{-\pi p/b}}{1 - e^{-\pi p/b}} = \frac{b}{p^2 + b^2} \cdot \coth \frac{\pi p}{2b}.$$

The function $|\sin bx|$ is known as the *full-wave* rectification of $\sin bx$.

Find the Laplace transform of each of the periodic functions in Problems 1–8.

1. $\cos bx$ 

2. $\sin bx$

3. $f(x) = \begin{cases} \cos 2x, & 0 \leqq x < \dfrac{\pi}{2} \\ 0, & \dfrac{\pi}{2} \leqq x < \pi \end{cases}$

$f(x + \pi) = f(x), \quad x \geqq 0$

4. $f(x) = \begin{cases} 2, & 0 \leqq x < 3 \\ 0, & 3 \leqq x < 6 \end{cases}$

$f(x + 6) = f(x), \quad x \geqq 0$

5. $f(x) = x, \quad 0 \leqq x < 2a$

$f(x + 2a) = f(x), \quad x \geqq 0$

6. $f(x) = \sin^2 2x, \quad 0 \leqq x < \dfrac{\pi}{2}$

$\quad = \cos^2 2x, \quad \dfrac{\pi}{2} \leqq x < \pi$

$f(x + \pi) = f(x), \quad x \geqq 0$

7. $\sin^2 kx \cos^2 kx$

8. $f(x) = \begin{cases} x, & 0 \leqq x < \frac{1}{2} \\ 1 - x, & \frac{1}{2} \leqq x < \frac{3}{2} \\ x - 2, & \frac{3}{2} \leqq x < 2 \end{cases}$

$f(x + 2) = f(x), \quad x \geqq 0$

9. Find the transforms of the half-wave and full-wave rectifications of the function in Problem 8.

10. Find the transforms of the function $f(x)$ and of its half-wave and full-wave rectifications in case

$f(x) = \begin{cases} x, & 0 \leqq x < \frac{1}{2}, \\ x - 1, & \frac{1}{2} \leqq x < 1, \end{cases}$

$f(x + 1) = f(x), \quad x \geqq 0.$

## 95. Systems of differential equations.

In Article 92 we examined the application of the Laplace transformation to the problem of solving a linear differential equation with constant coefficients. The method there employed is also useful in obtaining the solution of a system of such equations involving several unknown functions. The formula given in Theorem 1 of Article 89 permits us to transform the given system of differential equations into a system of algebraic equations involving the Laplace transforms of the unknown functions. These latter equations may then be solved by algebraic means for the transforms, and the inverses of these provide the desired solution. The following examples illustrate the method.

EXAMPLE 1. Solve the system of equations

(a) $$x'(t) + 4x(t) - y(t) = t,$$
(b) $$x'(t) + y'(t) + 3y(t) = -2,$$

obtaining solutions $x(t)$, $y(t)$ which satisfy the initial conditions $x(0) = y(0) = 0$.

SOLUTION. Let $u(p) = L[x(t)]$ and $v(p) = L[y(t)]$. Then by Theorem 1 of Article 89,

$$L[x'(t)] = pu(p) - x(0) = pu(p),$$
$$L[y'(t)] = pv(p) - y(0) = pv(p).$$

If we apply the Laplace transformation to both members of equations (a) and (b), we obtain

$$L[x'(t)] + 4L[x(t)] - L[y(t)] = L[t] = \frac{1}{p^2},$$

$$L[x'(t)] + L[y'(t)] + 3L[y(t)] = L[-2] = \frac{-2}{p},$$

and substitution of the above values for the Laplace transforms yields the linear algebraic equations

(c) $$(p + 4)u(p) - v(p) = \frac{1}{p^2},$$

(d) $$pu(p) + (p + 3)v(p) = \frac{-2}{p},$$

whose solutions are readily found to be

$$u(p) = (3 - p)/p^2(p + 6)(p + 2)$$
$$= \frac{1}{4p^2} - \frac{1}{4p} - \frac{1}{16(p + 6)} + \frac{5}{16(p + 2)},$$

$$v(p) = (-9 - 2p)/p(p + 6)(p + 2)$$
$$= \frac{-3}{4p} + \frac{1}{8(p + 6)} + \frac{5}{8(p + 2)}.$$

The desired functions $x(t)$ and $y(t)$ are the inverse transforms of $u(p)$ and $v(p)$. Hence

$$x(t) = \tfrac{1}{4}t - \tfrac{1}{4} - \tfrac{1}{16}e^{-6t} + \tfrac{5}{16}e^{-2t},$$
$$y(t) = -\tfrac{3}{4} + \tfrac{1}{8}e^{-6t} + \tfrac{5}{8}e^{-2t}.$$

EXAMPLE 2. Solve the system of second-order equations

(a) $\qquad\qquad y''(t) - x''(t) - x'(t) = -3,$

(b) $\qquad\qquad x''(t) + x'(t) - y'(t) = 2t + 1$

with the initial conditions $x(0) = 1$, $y(0) = 2$, $x'(0) = 2$, $y'(0) = 2$. SOLUTION. Applying the Laplace transformation to both members of (a) and (b), we find:

$$L[y''(t)] - L[x''(t)] - L[x'(t)] = L[-3] = -3/p,$$
$$L[x''(t)] + L[x'(t)] - L[y'(t)] = L[2t + 1] = (p + 2)/p^2.$$

Again setting $u(p) = L[x(t)]$, $v(p) = L[y(t)]$, we find from Theorem 1 and the given initial conditions:

$$L[x'] = pu - x(0) = pu - 1,$$
$$L[y'] = pv - y(0) = pv - 2,$$
$$L[x''] = p^2u - px(0) - x'(0) = p^2u - p - 2,$$
$$L[y''] = p^2v - py(0) - y'(0) = p^2v - 2p - 2,$$

and substitution produces the linear algebraic equations

(c) $\qquad\qquad -(p^2 + p)u + p^2v = \dfrac{p^2 - p - 3}{p},$

(d) $\qquad\qquad (p^2 + p)u - pv = \dfrac{p^3 + p^2 + p + 2}{p^2}.$

The solutions of equations (c) and (d) are

$$u(p) = \frac{p^2 + p - 1}{p^2(p - 1)} = \frac{1}{p^2} + \frac{1}{p - 1},$$
$$v(p) = \frac{2p^3 - 2p + 2}{p^3(p - 1)} = \frac{-2}{p^3} + \frac{2}{p - 1},$$

and the inverse transforms of these give the solution:

$$x(t) = e^t + t, \quad y(t) = 2e^t - t^2.$$

273

Use the Laplace transformation to solve the following systems of differential equations with given initial conditions.

1. $x'(t) + y'(t) - x(t) = 6 - t$
   $x'(t) + y'(t) + y(t) = 3 + \frac{1}{3}t^3$
   $x(0) = -5, \quad y(0) = 2$

2. $y'(t) + y(t) - 2x'(t) = -2$
   $y'(t) + y(t) - 2x(t) = -2t$
   $x(0) = 1, \quad y(0) = 0$

3. $y'(t) + x(t) = t^2 + 1$
   $y(t) - x'(t) = -t - 1$
   $x(0) = y(0) = 0$

4. $3x'(t) + y'(t) = 6 \cos 2t - 2 \sin 2t$
   $y'(t) - x'(t) + 2x(t) + 2y(t) = 6e^{2t}$
   $x(0) = 1, \quad y(0) = 4$

5. $x'(t) - y'(t) = 1 + \sin t - \cos t$
   $x'(t) - 2y'(t) + y(t) = 3 - 2 \sin t$
   $x(0) = 1, \quad y(0) = 2$

6. $x''(t) + y''(t) - y'(t) = 6$
   $x''(t) + 3y(t) = 9t^2 - 2$
   $x(0) = y(0) = 0, \quad x'(0) = 0, \quad y'(0) = -2$

7. $y''(t) + 5x''(t) - 10 = 0$
   $x''(t) + 3x'(t) + y'(t) = 6t + 1$
   $x(0) = 1, \quad y(0) = 0, \quad x'(0) = 2, \quad y'(0) = -11$

8. $x''(t) + y''(t) + x(t) + y(t) = 2 - 6t + t^2 - t^3$
   $x''(t) - y'(t) = 2 + 3t^2$
   $x(0) = 0, \quad y(0) = 1, \quad x'(0) = 1, \quad y'(0) = 0$

9. $x''(t) - y'(t) = e^t + 2t,$
   $y''(t) + 4y(t) = -4t^2 - 10$
   $x(0) = y(0) = 0, \quad x'(0) = 3, \quad y'(0) = 0$

10. $4x''(t) - 3y''(t) - 25y(t) = 0$
    $x''(t) + 3x'(t) - 10y(t) = 0$
    $x(0) = 0, \quad y(0) = 1, \quad x'(0) = 2, \quad y'(0) = 1$

# CHAPTER TWELVE

# Fourier series

**96. Introduction.** In an attempt to solve a problem which arose in his researches on the conduction of heat, Fourier* was led to the discovery that a function may be represented by an infinite series whose terms are sines and cosines. We shall discuss this type of series briefly in the present chapter and show how such series can be utilized to solve certain boundary value problems which arise in connection with partial differential equations.

**97. Fourier series.** A series of the form

$$(1) \qquad \tfrac{1}{2}a_0 + \sum_{n=1}^{\infty} (a_n \cos nx + b_n \sin nx),$$

where the coefficients $a_0$, $a_n$, $b_n$ $(n = 1, 2, \ldots)$ are constants, is called a *trigonometric series*. When these coefficients are related to a given well-behaved function $f(x)$ in a special manner, about to be described, the series (1) is then called the *Fourier series representation* of $f(x)$.

To find the relation between the function $f(x)$ and the coefficients of the series (1), we may proceed formally as follows.

* Joseph Fourier (1768–1830), French mathematical physicist and author of *The Analytical Theory of Heat* (1822).

Let us assume that the function is defined on the interval $-\pi \leqq x < \pi$ and that the series (1) converges to $f(x)$ at each point of this interval. Multiplying $f(x)$ by $\cos mx$, where $m$ is any *positive* integer, and integrating from $-\pi$ to $\pi$, we obtain

$$\int_{-\pi}^{\pi} f(x) \cos mx \, dx = \int_{-\pi}^{\pi} \left[ \tfrac{1}{2} a_0 \cos mx + \sum_{n=1}^{\infty} (a_n \cos nx \cos mx \right.$$
$$\left. + b_n \sin nx \cos mx) \right] dx.$$

If we assume that term-by-term integration of the series is possible, we find

$$(2) \quad \int_{-\pi}^{\pi} f(x) \cos mx \, dx = \frac{a_0}{2} \int_{-\pi}^{\pi} \cos mx \, dx$$
$$+ \sum_{n=1}^{\infty} \left[ a_n \int_{-\pi}^{\pi} \cos nx \cos mx \, dx \right.$$
$$\left. + b_n \int_{-\pi}^{\pi} \sin nx \cos mx \, dx \right].$$

The integrals on the right are readily evaluated. In the first place,

$$\int_{-\pi}^{\pi} \cos mx \, dx = \frac{1}{m} \sin mx \bigg]_{-\pi}^{\pi} = 0.$$

Next, if $m \neq n$,

$$\int_{-\pi}^{\pi} \cos nx \cos mx \, dx = \tfrac{1}{2} \int_{-\pi}^{\pi} \left[ \cos (n+m)x + \cos (n-m)x \right] dx$$
$$= \frac{1}{2} \left[ \frac{\sin (n+m)x}{n+m} + \frac{\sin (n-m)x}{n-m} \right]_{-\pi}^{\pi}$$
$$= 0;$$

while, if $m = n$,

$$\int_{-\pi}^{\pi} \cos nx \cos mx \, dx = \int_{-\pi}^{\pi} \cos^2 nx \, dx$$
$$= \tfrac{1}{2} \int_{-\pi}^{\pi} (1 + \cos 2nx) \, dx$$
$$= \frac{1}{2} \left[ x + \frac{1}{2n} \sin 2nx \right]_{-\pi}^{\pi}$$
$$= \pi.$$

Similarly we find, for $m \neq n$,

$$\int_{-\pi}^{\pi} \sin nx \cos mx \, dx = \tfrac{1}{2} \int_{-\pi}^{\pi} \left[\sin (n+m)x + \sin (n-m)x\right] dx$$
$$= -\frac{1}{2} \left[\frac{\cos (n+m)x}{n+m} + \frac{\cos (n-m)x}{n-m}\right]_{-\pi}^{\pi}$$
$$= 0,$$

and the same is true for $m = n$, since in that case

$$\int_{-\pi}^{\pi} \sin nx \cos mx \, dx = \int_{-\pi}^{\pi} \sin nx \cos nx \, dx$$
$$= \tfrac{1}{2} \int_{-\pi}^{\pi} \sin 2nx \, dx$$
$$= 0.$$

Hence, when $m$ is a positive integer, all terms in the right member of (2) vanish except the one for which $m = n$, and the value of that term is $\pi a_m$; therefore we find

(3) $$a_m = \frac{1}{\pi} \int_{-\pi}^{\pi} f(x) \cos mx \, dx, \quad m = 1, 2, \ldots .$$

Actually, (3) is also valid for $m = 0$, i.e.,

$$a_0 = \frac{1}{\pi} \int_{-\pi}^{\pi} f(x) \, dx;$$

for, since $\cos 0 \cdot x = 1$, the equation (2) becomes when $m = 0$:

$$\int_{-\pi}^{\pi} f(x) \, dx = \frac{a_0}{2} \int_{-\pi}^{\pi} dx + \sum_{n=1}^{\infty} \left[a_n \int_{-\pi}^{\pi} \cos nx \, dx \right.$$
$$\left. + b_n \int_{-\pi}^{\pi} \sin nx \, dx\right].$$

All the terms on the right vanish except the first, whose value is $\pi a_0$.

The values of the coefficients $b_m$ $(m = 1, 2, \ldots)$ can be found analogously by using $\sin mx$ as the multiplier, with the result that

$$b_m = \frac{1}{\pi} \int_{-\pi}^{\pi} f(x) \sin mx \, dx, \quad m = 1, 2, \ldots .$$

We may therefore conclude that, under the hypotheses we have made, the Fourier series representation for a function $f(x)$ on the interval $-\pi \leq x < \pi$ is given by the formula

$$f(x) = \tfrac{1}{2}a_0 + \sum_{n=1}^{\infty} (a_n \cos nx + b_n \sin nx),$$

where

(4)
$$\begin{cases} a_0 = \dfrac{1}{\pi} \int_{-\pi}^{\pi} f(x)\, dx, \\[2mm] a_n = \dfrac{1}{\pi} \int_{-\pi}^{\pi} f(x) \cos nx\, dx, \\[2mm] b_n = \dfrac{1}{\pi} \int_{-\pi}^{\pi} f(x) \sin nx\, dx, \quad n = 1, 2, \ldots \end{cases}$$

EXAMPLE 1. Expand $f(x) = x$, $-\pi \leq x < \pi$, in a Fourier series.
SOLUTION. From the formulas (4) we obtain

$$a_0 = \frac{1}{\pi} \int_{-\pi}^{\pi} x\, dx = 0,$$

$$a_n = \frac{1}{\pi} \int_{-\pi}^{\pi} x \cos nx\, dx = \frac{1}{\pi} \left[ \int_{-\pi}^{0} x \cos nx\, dx + \int_{0}^{\pi} x \cos nx\, dx \right]$$
$$= \frac{1}{\pi} \left[ -\int_{0}^{\pi} x \cos nx\, dx + \int_{0}^{\pi} x \cos nx\, dx \right]$$
$$= 0, \quad n = 1, 2, \ldots,$$

$$b_n = \frac{1}{\pi} \int_{-\pi}^{\pi} x \sin nx\, dx = \frac{1}{\pi} \left[ \int_{-\pi}^{0} x \sin nx\, dx + \int_{0}^{\pi} x \sin nx\, dx \right]$$
$$= \frac{2}{\pi} \int_{0}^{\pi} x \sin nx\, dx = \frac{2}{\pi} \left[ -\frac{\pi}{n} \cos n\pi \right]$$
$$= \begin{cases} \dfrac{2}{n} & \text{if } n = 1, 3, 5, \ldots \\[2mm] -\dfrac{2}{n} & \text{if } n = 2, 4, 6, \ldots \end{cases}$$
$$= (-1)^{n+1}\frac{2}{n}, \quad n = 1, 2, 3, \ldots.$$

We conclude that

$$x = 2 \sum_{n=1}^{\infty} (-1)^{n+1} \frac{\sin nx}{n}.$$

If we put $x = \dfrac{\pi}{2}$, we then find

$$\frac{\pi}{2} = 2 \sum_{n=1}^{\infty} (-1)^{n+1} \frac{\sin (n\pi/2)}{n}$$

$$= 2 \sum_{m=1}^{\infty} \frac{(-1)^{m+1}}{2m - 1},$$

so that we then have the otherwise familiar formula

$$\frac{\pi}{4} = 1 - \frac{1}{3} + \frac{1}{5} - \frac{1}{7} + \cdots.$$

EXAMPLE 2. Find the Fourier series expansion for

$$f(x) = \begin{cases} 0, & -\pi \leqq x < -\dfrac{\pi}{2}, \\[2mm] \cos x, & -\dfrac{\pi}{2} \leqq x < \dfrac{\pi}{2}, \\[2mm] 0, & \dfrac{\pi}{2} \leqq x < \pi. \end{cases}$$

SOLUTION. The formulas (4) yield the values

$$a_0 = \frac{1}{\pi} \int_{-\frac{\pi}{2}}^{\frac{\pi}{2}} \cos x \, dx = \frac{2}{\pi},$$

$$a_n = \frac{1}{\pi} \int_{-\frac{\pi}{2}}^{\frac{\pi}{2}} \cos x \cos nx \, dx$$

$$= \begin{cases} 0, & n \text{ odd}, \\[2mm] \dfrac{1}{\pi} (-1)^{n/2} \left[ \dfrac{1}{n+1} - \dfrac{1}{n-1} \right] = \dfrac{2(-1)^{n/2}}{\pi(1 - n^2)}, & n \text{ even}, \end{cases}$$

$$b_n = \frac{1}{\pi} \int_{-\frac{\pi}{2}}^{\frac{\pi}{2}} \cos x \sin nx \, dx$$

$$= 0, \quad n = 1, 2, \ldots.$$

Hence

$$f(x) = \frac{1}{\pi} + \frac{2}{\pi} \sum_{m=1}^{\infty} \frac{(-1)^m}{1 - m^2} \cos 2mx.$$

Obtain the Fourier series representation for each of the following functions.

1. $f(x) = \sin 5x, \quad -\pi \leqq x < \pi$

2. $f(x) = |\cos x|, \quad -\pi \leqq x < \pi$

3. $f(x) = \cos^2 x, \quad -\pi \leqq x < \pi$

4. $f(x) = x^2, \quad -\pi \leqq x < \pi$

5. $f(x) = x \cos x, \quad -\pi \leqq x < \pi$

6. $f(x) = \begin{cases} -x, & -\pi \leqq x < 0 \\ 0, & 0 \leqq x < \pi \end{cases}$

7. $f(x) = \begin{cases} 0, & -\pi \leqq x < -\dfrac{\pi}{2} \\ \sin x, & -\dfrac{\pi}{2} \leqq x < \dfrac{\pi}{2} \\ 0, & \dfrac{\pi}{2} \leqq x < \pi \end{cases}$

8. $f(x) = \begin{cases} x, & -\pi \leqq x < 0 \\ -x, & 0 \leqq x < \pi \end{cases}$

9. $f(x) = \begin{cases} -1, & -\pi \leqq x < 0 \\ 0, & 0 \leqq x < \dfrac{\pi}{2} \\ 1, & \dfrac{\pi}{2} \leqq x < \pi \end{cases}$

10. $f(x) = \begin{cases} -2 - \dfrac{x}{\pi}, & -\pi \leqq x < 0 \\ 0, & x = 0 \\ 2 - \dfrac{x}{\pi}, & 0 < x < \pi \end{cases}$

**98. The hypotheses.** In deriving the formulas (4) which relate the coefficients of a trigonometric series to the function $f(x)$ of which that series is the Fourier expansion, we proceeded quite formally. We assumed that the trigonometric series converged at each point of the interval $-\pi \leqq x < \pi$, and that the value to which it converged was the same as the value of $f(x)$ at that point. We assumed further that the various integrations we performed were possible and that the integration of the series could be obtained by term-wise integration.

280

We now wish to consider the matter more rigorously. Given a function $f(x)$ defined on $-\pi \leq x < \pi$, we may associate with it the Fourier series representation

$$\tfrac{1}{2}a_0 + \sum_{n=1}^{\infty} (a_n \cos nx + b_n \sin nx),$$

where

$$a_0 = \frac{1}{\pi} \int_{-\pi}^{\pi} f(x) \, dx,$$

$$a_n = \frac{1}{\pi} \int_{-\pi}^{\pi} f(x) \cos nx \, dx,$$

$$b_n = \frac{1}{\pi} \int_{-\pi}^{\pi} f(x) \sin nx \, dx, \quad n = 1, 2, \ldots.$$

We can then raise several questions: For what functions $f(x)$ is the Fourier series well defined? For what functions does the series converge and to what values? We shall settle these questions by defining a class of functions which satisfy the following four hypotheses:

(a) $f(x)$ is a single-valued function defined on the interval $-\pi \leq x < \pi$;

(b) $f(x)$ is bounded on the interval $-\pi \leq x < \pi$;

(c) $f(x)$ is continuous, except possibly for a finite number of discontinuities, on $-\pi \leq x < \pi$;

(d) $f(x)$ has only a finite number of maxima and minima on $-\pi \leq x < \pi$.

It is then possible to prove the following statement.* *Any function $f(x)$ which satisfies the hypotheses (a)–(d) has a Fourier series representation which converges to $f(x)$ if $x$ is a point of continuity for $f(x)$ on $-\pi \leq x < \pi$, but converges to*

$$\tfrac{1}{2} \lim_{h \to 0^+} \{f(x + h) + f(x - h)\}$$

*if $x$ is a point of discontinuity for $f(x)$ on $-\pi \leq x < \pi$.*

The class of functions for which analogous statements are true can be made much larger, but the class defined above will suffice for our purposes.

* Cf. H. S. Carslaw, *Introduction to the Theory of Fourier's Series and Integrals*, 3d ed. (New York: Dover Publications, Inc., 1930).

We have thus far restricted ourselves to functions $f(x)$ defined only on the interval $-\pi \leq x < \pi$. However, we can extend the definition of $f(x)$ to the whole domain of real numbers $-\infty < x < +\infty$ by the relation

$$f(x + 2n\pi) = f(x), \quad n = \pm 1, \pm 2, \ldots$$

The resulting function will be periodic on $-\infty < x < \infty$ with period $2\pi$. Since each term of the Fourier series for $f(x)$ has period $2\pi$, the same is true of the series, and the representation of $f(x)$ will be valid not merely on $-\pi \leq x < \pi$ but also on $-\infty < x < \infty$.

**99. Other periods.** The restriction thus far made to functions defined on the interval $-\pi \leq x < \pi$ and their periodic extensions to $-\infty < x < \infty$ is not essential. Suppose that $f(x)$ is defined on the interval $x_1 \leq x < x_2$ and has the properties which result from the hypotheses (a)–(d) of Article 98 when the interval $-\pi \leq x < \pi$ is replaced by $x_1 \leq x < x_2$. If we let $2a = x_2 - x_1$, then we may define the periodic extension of $f(x)$ to the interval $-\infty < x < \infty$ by the formula

$$f(x + 2na) = f(x), \quad n = \pm 1, \pm 2, \ldots$$

The substitution $x = at/\pi$ transforms $f(x)$ into a function $g(t) = f(at/\pi)$ which has period $2\pi$, since

$$g(t + 2\pi) = f\left[\frac{a}{\pi}(t + 2\pi)\right] = f\left[\frac{at}{\pi} + 2a\right] = f\left[\frac{at}{\pi}\right] = g(t).$$

The function $g(t)$ satisfies the hypotheses (a)–(d) of Article 98 and has the Fourier series representation

$$(5) \quad \tfrac{1}{2}\lim_{h\to 0^+}\left[g(t + h) + g(t - h)\right] = \tfrac{1}{2}a_0 + \sum_{n=1}^{\infty}(a_n \cos nt + b_n \sin nt),$$

where

$$(6) \quad \begin{cases} a_0 = \dfrac{1}{\pi}\displaystyle\int_{-\pi}^{\pi} g(t)\,dt, \\[2mm] a_n = \dfrac{1}{\pi}\displaystyle\int_{-\pi}^{\pi} g(t)\cos nt\,dt, \\[2mm] b_n = \dfrac{1}{\pi}\displaystyle\int_{-\pi}^{\pi} g(t)\sin nt\,dt, \quad n = 1, 2, \ldots. \end{cases}$$

Observe that the left member of (5) reduces to $g(t)$ if $t$ is a point at which $g(t)$ is continuous. If we now replace $t$ by $\pi x/a$, we obtain

$$\tfrac{1}{2} \lim_{h \to 0^+} \left[ f(x+h) + f(x-h) \right]$$

$$= \frac{1}{2} a_0 + \sum_{n=1}^{\infty} \left[ a_n \cos\left( \frac{n\pi x}{a} \right) + b_n \sin\left( \frac{n\pi x}{a} \right) \right]$$

and furthermore

$$(6') \quad \begin{cases} a_0 = \dfrac{1}{a} \displaystyle\int_{-a}^{a} f(x)\, dx \\[2mm] \quad = \dfrac{2}{x_2 - x_1} \displaystyle\int_{x_1}^{x_2} f(x)\, dx, \\[2mm] a_n = \dfrac{1}{a} \displaystyle\int_{-a}^{a} f(x) \cos\left( \dfrac{n\pi x}{a} \right) dx \\[2mm] \quad = \dfrac{2}{x_2 - x_1} \displaystyle\int_{x_1}^{x_2} f(x) \cos\left( \dfrac{2n\pi x}{x_2 - x_1} \right) dx, \\[2mm] b_n = \dfrac{1}{a} \displaystyle\int_{-a}^{a} f(x) \sin\left( \dfrac{n\pi x}{a} \right) dx \\[2mm] \quad = \dfrac{2}{x_2 - x_1} \displaystyle\int_{x_1}^{x_2} f(x) \sin\left( \dfrac{2n\pi x}{x_2 - x_1} \right) dx, \quad n = 1, 2, \ldots. \end{cases}$$

The fact that the integrals in (6') may be taken over the interval $x_1 \leqq x < x_2$ rather than $-a \leqq x < a$ results from the periodicity of $f(x)$.

EXAMPLE. Expand $f(x) = 3x + 2$ in a Fourier series on the interval $2 \leqq x < 4$.

SOLUTION. Here $2a = 4 - 2 = 2$. From the formulas (6') we find

$$a_0 = \int_2^4 (3x + 2)\, dx = 22,$$

$$a_n = \int_2^4 (3x + 2) \cos(n\pi x)\, dx = 0,$$

$$b_n = \int_2^4 (3x + 2) \sin(n\pi x)\, dx = -\frac{6}{n\pi}, \quad n = 1, 2, \ldots,$$

and hence

$$f(x) = 11 - \frac{6}{\pi} \sum_{n=1}^{\infty} \frac{\sin(n\pi x)}{n}.$$

283

The coefficients $a_0$, $a_n$, $b_n$ can of course also be computed, though not so simply, from (6). We have $t = \pi x$ and

$$f(x) = 3x + 2 = \frac{3t}{\pi} + 2 = g(t).$$

The function $g(t)$ is then defined on the interval $2\pi \leqq t < 4\pi$. We may then consider the periodic extension of $g(t)$ to the interval $-\infty < t < \infty$, and hence we find:

$$g(t) = \begin{cases} \dfrac{3t}{\pi} + 14, & -\pi \leqq t < 0, \\[2mm] \dfrac{3t}{\pi} + 8, & 0 \leqq t < \pi. \end{cases}$$

Hence by (6),

$$a_0 = \frac{1}{\pi} \left[ \int_{-\pi}^0 \left( \frac{3t}{\pi} + 14 \right) dt + \int_0^\pi \left( \frac{3t}{\pi} + 8 \right) dt \right],$$

$$a_n = \frac{1}{\pi} \left[ \int_{-\pi}^0 \left( \frac{3t}{\pi} + 14 \right) \cos nt\, dt + \int_0^\pi \left( \frac{3t}{\pi} + 8 \right) \cos nt\, dt \right],$$

$$b_n = \frac{1}{\pi} \left[ \int_{-\pi}^0 \left( \frac{3t}{\pi} + 14 \right) \sin nt\, dt + \int_0^\pi \left( \frac{3t}{\pi} + 8 \right) \sin nt\, dt \right],$$

and these yield the same values for $a_0$, $a_n$, $b_n$ as before.

### EXERCISE 62

Obtain the Fourier series for each of the following functions.

1. $f(x) = x^2, \quad 1 \leqq x < 3$
2. $f(x) = x, \quad 0 \leqq x < 2$
3. $f(x) = 2x + 3, \quad 0 \leqq x < \pi$
4. $f(x) = x^2 - 1, \quad -\pi \leqq x < 0$

5. $f(x) = \begin{cases} 2x, & 0 \leqq x < 5 \\ 2(10 - x), & 5 \leqq x \leqq 10 \end{cases}$

6. $f(x) = \begin{cases} 1, & -1 \leqq x < 0 \\ x, & 0 \leqq x < 1 \end{cases}$

7. $f(x) = \begin{cases} 2, & 0 \leqq x < 2 \\ 4, & 2 \leqq x < 4 \end{cases}$

8. $f(x) = \begin{cases} x, & -1 \leqq x < 0 \\ x^2, & 0 \leqq x < 1 \end{cases}$

**100. Sine and cosine series.** Consider a function $f(x)$ defined on $-\pi \leq x < \pi$, which satisfies the hypotheses $(a)$–$(d)$ of Article 98. If $f(x) = f(-x)$ for each $x$ on the interval, then $f(x)$ is called an *even* function. When we take the periodic extension of $f(x)$ to the interval $-\infty < x < \infty$, this extension will also be an even function.

For the coefficients of the Fourier series for such an even function we have the following calculation:

$$
\begin{aligned}
a_0 &= \frac{1}{\pi} \int_{-\pi}^{\pi} f(x)\, dx \\
&= \frac{1}{\pi} \left[ \int_{-\pi}^{0} f(y)\, dy + \int_{0}^{\pi} f(x)\, dx \right] \\
&= \frac{1}{\pi} \left[ \int_{-\pi}^{0} f(-y)\, dy + \int_{0}^{\pi} f(x)\, dx \right] \\
&= \frac{1}{\pi} \left[ \int_{0}^{\pi} f(y)\, dy + \int_{0}^{\pi} f(x)\, dx \right] = \frac{2}{\pi} \int_{0}^{\pi} f(x)\, dx,
\end{aligned}
$$

$$
\begin{aligned}
a_n &= \frac{1}{\pi} \int_{-\pi}^{\pi} f(x) \cos nx\, dx \\
&= \frac{1}{\pi} \left[ \int_{-\pi}^{0} f(y) \cos ny\, dy + \int_{0}^{\pi} f(x) \cos nx\, dx \right] \\
&= \frac{1}{\pi} \left[ \int_{-\pi}^{0} f(-y) \cos(-ny)\, dy + \int_{0}^{\pi} f(x) \cos nx\, dx \right] \\
&= \frac{1}{\pi} \left[ \int_{0}^{\pi} f(y) \cos ny\, dy + \int_{0}^{\pi} f(x) \cos nx\, dx \right] \\
&= \frac{2}{\pi} \int_{0}^{\pi} f(x) \cos nx\, dx,
\end{aligned}
$$

$$
\begin{aligned}
b_n &= \frac{1}{\pi} \int_{-\pi}^{\pi} f(x) \sin nx\, dx \\
&= \frac{1}{\pi} \left[ \int_{-\pi}^{0} f(y) \sin ny\, dy + \int_{0}^{\pi} f(x) \sin nx\, dx \right] \\
&= \frac{1}{\pi} \left[ -\int_{-\pi}^{0} f(-y) \sin(-ny)\, dy + \int_{0}^{\pi} f(x) \sin nx\, dx \right] \\
&= \frac{1}{\pi} \left[ -\int_{0}^{\pi} f(y) \sin ny\, dy + \int_{0}^{\pi} f(x) \sin nx\, dx \right] \\
&= 0, \quad n = 1, 2, \ldots.
\end{aligned}
$$

Thus the Fourier series for the even function $f(x)$ reduces to a series in cosines only:

(7) $$f(x) = \tfrac{1}{2}a_0 + \sum_{n=1}^{\infty} a_n \cos nx,$$

where

(8) $$\begin{cases} a_0 = \dfrac{2}{\pi} \displaystyle\int_0^{\pi} f(x)\, dx, \\[2mm] a_n = \dfrac{2}{\pi} \displaystyle\int_0^{\pi} f(x) \cos nx\, dx, \quad n = 1, 2, \ldots. \end{cases}$$

Suppose now that we have a function $g(x)$ defined on the interval $0 \leqq x < \pi$ but in all other respects satisfying the hypotheses $(a)$–$(d)$ of Article 98. We may define the even function $f(x)$ on the interval $-\pi < x < \pi$ as follows:

$$f(x) = \begin{cases} g(x), & 0 \leqq x < \pi, \\ g(-x), & -\pi < x \leqq 0, \end{cases}$$

and it then follows from (7) and (8) that the Fourier series representation of $g(x)$ on the interval $0 \leqq x < \pi$ is

(7′) $$g(x) = f(x) = \tfrac{1}{2}a_0 + \sum_{n=1}^{\infty} a_n \cos nx,$$

where

(8′) $$\begin{cases} a_0 = \dfrac{2}{\pi} \displaystyle\int_0^{\pi} f(x)\, dx = \dfrac{2}{\pi} \displaystyle\int_0^{\pi} g(x)\, dx, \\[2mm] a_n = \dfrac{2}{\pi} \displaystyle\int_0^{\pi} f(x) \cos nx\, dx = \dfrac{2}{\pi} \displaystyle\int_0^{\pi} g(x) \cos nx\, dx, \\[2mm] \qquad\qquad\qquad\qquad\qquad\qquad n = 1, 2, \ldots. \end{cases}$$

The series (7′) with coefficients given by (8′) is known as the *Fourier cosine series* representation for $g(x)$.

Analogous considerations apply to a function $F(x)$, defined on $-\pi \leqq x < \pi$, which is *odd*, i.e., for which $F(-x) = -F(x)$ for every $x$ on $-\pi \leqq x < \pi$. Calculations like those above show that in this case $a_0 = a_n = 0$, $n = 1, 2, \ldots$, while

$$b_n = \frac{2}{\pi} \int_0^{\pi} F(x) \sin nx\, dx, \quad n = 1, 2, \ldots,$$

286

so that the Fourier series representation for the odd function $F(x)$ reduces to a series in sines only:

$$(9) \qquad F(x) = \sum_{n=1}^{\infty} b_n \sin nx,$$

where

$$(10) \qquad b_n = \frac{2}{\pi} \int_0^{\pi} F(x) \sin nx \, dx, \quad n = 1, 2, \ldots .$$

If now, starting with the function $g(x)$ defined on the interval $0 \leqq x < \pi$, we define the odd function $F(x)$ on the interval $-\pi < x < \pi$ as follows:

$$F(x) = \begin{cases} g(x), & 0 \leqq x < \pi, \\ -g(-x), & -\pi < x < 0, \end{cases}$$

then from (9) and (10) we obtain the Fourier series representation of $g(x)$ on the interval $0 \leqq x < \pi$ in the form

$$(9') \qquad g(x) = F(x) = \sum_{n=1}^{\infty} b_n \sin nx,$$

where

$$(10') \qquad b_n = \frac{2}{\pi} \int_0^{\pi} F(x) \sin nx \, dx = \frac{2}{\pi} \int_0^{\pi} g(x) \sin nx \, dx,$$
$$n = 1, 2, \ldots .$$

The series (9') with coefficients given by (10') is known as the *Fourier sine series* representation for $g(x)$.

The case of a function $g(x)$ which is defined on an interval $x_1 \leqq x < x_2$ rather than $0 \leqq x < \pi$ can be treated as in Article 99. The result is that $g(x)$ can be represented either by a Fourier cosine series on the interval $x_1 \leqq x < x_2$ of the form

$$(7'') \qquad g(x) = \frac{1}{2} a_0 + \sum_{n=1}^{\infty} a_n \cos \frac{n\pi x}{x_2 - x_1},$$

where

$$(8'') \qquad \begin{cases} a_0 = \dfrac{2}{x_2 - x_1} \displaystyle\int_{x_1}^{x_2} g(x) \, dx, \\[2ex] a_n = \dfrac{2}{x_2 - x_1} \displaystyle\int_{x_1}^{x_2} g(x) \cos \frac{n\pi x}{x_2 - x_1} \, dx, \quad n = 1, 2, \ldots, \end{cases}$$

287

or by a Fourier sine series of the form

$$(9'') \qquad g(x) = \sum_{n=1}^{\infty} b_n \sin \frac{n\pi x}{x_2 - x_1},$$

where

$$(10'') \quad b_n = \frac{2}{x_2 - x_1} \int_{x_1}^{x_2} g(x) \sin \frac{n\pi x}{x_2 - x_1}\, dx, \quad n = 1, 2, \ldots.$$

EXAMPLE. Obtain the sine and cosine series for the function

$$g(x) = x^2, \quad 0 \leqq x < \pi.$$

SOLUTION. We have

$$b_n = \frac{2}{\pi} \int_0^{\pi} x^2 \sin nx\, dx$$

$$= \frac{2}{\pi} \left[ -\frac{x^2 \cos nx}{n} + \frac{2x \sin nx}{n^2} + \frac{2 \cos nx}{n^3} \right]_0^{\pi}$$

$$= \frac{4(-1)^n}{\pi} \left\{ \frac{1 - (-1)^n}{n^3} - \frac{\pi^2}{2n} \right\}, \quad n = 1, 2, \ldots.$$

Thus the sine series is

$$x^2 = \frac{4}{\pi} \left\{ \left( \frac{\pi^2}{2} - 2 \right) \sin x - \frac{\pi^2}{4} \sin 2x + \left( \frac{\pi^2}{9} - \frac{2}{27} \right) \sin 3x + \cdots \right\}.$$

Further,

$$a_0 = \frac{2}{\pi} \int_0^{\pi} x^2\, dx$$

$$= \frac{2\pi^2}{3},$$

$$a_n = \frac{2}{\pi} \int_0^{\pi} x^2 \cos nx\, dx$$

$$= \frac{2}{\pi} \left[ \frac{x^2 \sin nx}{n} + \frac{2x \cos nx}{n^2} - \frac{2 \sin nx}{n^3} \right]_0^{\pi}$$

$$= (-1)^n \frac{4}{n^2}, \quad n = 1, 2, \ldots,$$

and hence the cosine series is

$$x^2 = \frac{2\pi^2}{3} + \sum_{n=1}^{\infty} (-1)^n \frac{4}{n^2} \cos nx.$$

## EXERCISE 63

Obtain the Fourier sine series for each of the following functions.

1. $f(x) = 2, \quad 0 \leqq x < \pi$
2. $f(x) = \sin^2 x, \quad 0 \leqq x < \pi$
3. $f(x) = x \sin x, \quad 0 \leqq x < \pi$
4. $f(x) = |\sin x|, \quad 0 \leqq x < \pi$
5. $f(x) = \begin{cases} x, & 0 \leqq x < 2 \\ 4 - x, & 2 \leqq x < 4 \end{cases}$

Obtain the Fourier cosine series for each of the following functions.

6. $f(x) = \begin{cases} 0, & 0 \leqq x \leqq \dfrac{\pi}{2} \\ x, & \dfrac{\pi}{2} < x < \pi \end{cases}$

7. $f(x) = \sin 3x, \quad 0 \leqq x < \pi$
8. $f(x) = e^{-x}, \quad 0 \leqq x < \pi$
9. $f(x) = \begin{cases} x, & 0 \leqq x < 2 \\ 4 - x, & 2 \leqq x < 4 \end{cases}$
10. $f(x) = (x + 1)^2, \quad -2 \leqq x < 0$

**101. Applications.** Fourier series are naturally useful in the study of periodic phenomena and in connection with the problem of solving boundary value problems concerning partial differential equations that arise in such studies. We shall give two examples of such boundary value problems.

(a) *One-dimensional heat flow.* Suppose that heat flows through an infinite slab of heat-conducting material, bounded by two parallel planes. Let us denote by $x$ the distance, from one of these planes, of any plane parallel to it, so that the two bounding planes are given by $x = 0$ and $x = 2a$. If we assume that at each instant of time $t$, the temperature on any plane parallel to the faces is the same at all of its points and depends only upon the time $t$ and the distance $x$ of that plane from the first bounding face, then it can be shown that the temperature is a function $u(x, t)$ which satisfies the following partial differential equation:

(11) $$\frac{\partial u}{\partial t} = k \frac{\partial^2 u}{\partial x^2}.$$

Here $k$ is a constant which depends on the physical properties of the material.

Suppose now that at all times the temperature on the bounding planes is kept at zero, while on each interior plane the temperature at time $t = 0$ is a constant $K \neq 0$. We seek to find the temperature at points of the body at all later times $t > 0$.

The physical conditions described in the preceding paragraph are translatable into the following conditions on the function $u(x, t)$:

(12) $$\begin{cases} u(0, t) = 0, & 0 \leq t < \infty, \\ u(2a, t) = 0, & 0 \leq t < \infty, \\ u(x, 0) = K \neq 0, & 0 < x < 2a. \end{cases}$$

The problem then is to find a solution $u(x, t)$ of the partial differential equation (11) subject to the boundary conditions (12).

We shall first seek a solution of the differential equation (11) of a particularly simple form, namely, a solution $u(x, t)$ of the form $X(x) \cdot T(t)$, $X$ depending only on $x$ and $T$ being a function of $t$ alone. While we cannot hope that in general so simple a solution of (11) can be made also to satisfy the boundary conditions (12), it may be that some combination of such solutions will prove successful.

Substitution of $u(x, t) = X(x) \cdot T(t)$ into (11) yields the equation

$$X \frac{dT}{dt} = kT \frac{d^2 X}{dx^2},$$

which can be written

(13) $$\left(\frac{1}{kT}\right)\frac{dT}{dt} = \left(\frac{1}{X}\right)\frac{d^2 X}{dx^2}$$

and which must be satisfied identically for $t > 0$, $0 < x < 2a$.

290

Since the left member of (13) is a function of $t$ alone and the right member of $x$ alone, this requires that both members have a constant value $c$, independent of both $x$ and $t$. We are thus led to the two ordinary differential equations

(14) $$\frac{dT}{dt} = ckT, \quad \frac{d^2X}{dx^2} = cX.$$

The nature of the general solution of the second of these depends upon whether the constant $c$ is positive or negative. If $c$ is positive or zero, the general solution of the second equation is a combination of real exponential functions of $x$; and it would then be impossible to satisfy the first two boundary conditions of (12), which require that

(15) $$X(0) = X(2a) = 0.$$

Hence we may assume that $c$ is negative and define $\alpha$ so that $c = -\alpha^2 < 0$. The equations (14) now become

$$\frac{dT}{dt} = -k\alpha^2 T, \quad \frac{d^2X}{dx^2} = -\alpha^2 X,$$

whose general solutions are

(16) $$T = C_1 e^{-k\alpha^2 t}, \quad X = A_1 \cos \alpha x + B_1 \sin \alpha x.$$

The conditions (15) require that

$$X(0) = A_1 = 0,$$
$$X(2a) = B_1 \sin 2\alpha a = 0.$$

If we were to satisfy the second of these by taking $B_1 = 0$, then the resulting function $u(x, t) = XT$ would be identically zero and hence incapable of satisfying the third condition of (12). Consequently, we require instead that $\sin 2\alpha a = 0$, so that $2\alpha a$ must be some integral multiple of $\pi$, say, $n\pi$. Hence we find that $\alpha = n\pi/2a$, so that our particular solution, which we now designate as $u_n(x, t)$, has the form

(17) $$u_n(x, t) = b_n e^{-kn^2\pi^2 t/4a^2} \sin \left( \frac{n\pi x}{2a} \right).$$

The particular solution (17) still does not satisfy the third condition of (12). But we note that, because the differential equation (11) is linear, any linear combination of particular

291

solutions, with constant coefficients, is also a solution; and even a linear combination of infinitely many such solutions, provided the resulting series is convergent and has other needed properties.

We may therefore formally construct an infinite series

$$\sum_{n=1}^{\infty} u_n(x, t) = \sum_{n=1}^{\infty} b_n e^{-kn^2\pi^2 t/4a^2} \sin\left(\frac{n\pi x}{2a}\right)$$

and attempt to determine the coefficients $b_n$ so that for $t = 0$

$$K = \sum_{n=1}^{\infty} u_n(x, 0) = \sum_{n=1}^{\infty} b_n \sin\left(\frac{n\pi x}{2a}\right)$$

on the interval $0 < x < 2a$. But this is the same thing as representing $K$ by a Fourier sine series on that interval. The values of the coefficients $b_n$ are therefore given by

$$b_n = \frac{1}{a} \int_0^{2a} K \sin\left(\frac{n\pi x}{2a}\right) dx = \frac{2K}{n\pi} (1 - \cos n\pi).$$

Hence

$$(18) \quad u(x, t) = \frac{4K}{\pi}\left[ e^{-k\pi^2/4a^2} \sin\frac{\pi x}{2a} + \frac{1}{3} e^{-9k\pi^2/4a^2} \sin\frac{3\pi x}{2a} + \cdots \right].$$

It remains to be established that the function $u(x, t)$ given by (18) has the properties required of a solution of the boundary value problem, but we shall not attempt this.

(b) *The vibrating string.* When an elastic string, stretched between two fixed points $x = 0$ and $x = L$, is displaced from its position of equilibrium and then released, it undergoes vibrations about that position which can be described by giving the displacement $Y(x, t)$ at each instant $t$ of the point whose distance from the initial end of the stretched string is $x$. It can be shown that, for small displacements, $Y(x, t)$ must satisfy the partial differential equation

$$(19) \qquad \frac{\partial^2 Y}{\partial t^2} = C^2 \frac{\partial^2 Y}{\partial x^2},$$

where $C^2 = T/\rho$ and $T$ is the tension in the string while $\rho$ is the density (mass per unit length) of the string.

Consider a string which weighs 0.5 lb. and which is stretched between two points 3 ft. apart by a force of 1 lb. The mid-point of the string is then lifted above its position of equilibrium a distance of 3 inches and then released from rest. Find the displacement function $Y(x, t)$.

Since the weight of the string is 0.5 lb., the mass is $0.5/g$, where $g$ is the acceleration due to gravity, and hence the density $\rho$ is $0.5/3g - 1/6g$ Consequently, $C^2 = T/\rho = 6g$.

The differential equation which $Y(x, t)$ must satisfy is therefore

(20)
$$\frac{\partial^2 Y}{\partial t^2} = 6g\, \frac{\partial^2 Y}{\partial x^2}.$$

Furthermore, the boundary conditions for $Y(x, t)$ are

(21)
$$\begin{cases} Y(0, t) = 0, \quad t \geq 0, \\ Y(3, t) = 0, \quad t \geq 0, \\ \dfrac{\partial Y}{\partial t}\,(x, 0) = 0, \quad 0 \leq x \leq 3, \\ Y(x, 0) = \begin{cases} \frac{1}{6}x, & 0 \leq x < 1.5, \\ \frac{1}{6}(x - 3), & 1.5 \leq x \leq 3. \end{cases} \end{cases}$$

The first two of these conditions express the fact that the end points of the string are always fixed; the third condition states that the string, in its initial displacement, is at rest; and the last condition describes the initial displacement.

We shall employ a technique similar to that used in section $(a)$. We shall seek a particular solution $Y(x, t)$ of the form $X(x) \cdot T(t)$ for the differential equation (20). Substitution yields

$$X\,\frac{\partial^2 T}{\partial t^2} = 6gT\,\frac{\partial^2 X}{\partial x^2},$$

or

(22)
$$\frac{1}{6gT}\,\frac{\partial^2 T}{\partial t^2} = \frac{1}{X}\,\frac{\partial^2 X}{\partial x^2},$$

and as before both the left and right members of (22) must be equal to a negative constant $-\alpha^2$. When we set each member

293

of equation (22) equal to $-\alpha^2$, we are led to the equations

$$\frac{\partial^2 T}{\partial t^2} = -6g\alpha^2 T, \quad \frac{\partial^2 X}{\partial x^2} = -\alpha^2 X.$$

The general solutions of these equations are

$$X = A_1 \cos \alpha x + B_1 \sin \alpha x,$$
$$T = C_1 \cos \alpha t\sqrt{6g} + D_1 \sin \alpha t\sqrt{6g},$$

so that

$$Y(x, t) = (A_1 \cos \alpha x + B_1 \sin \alpha x)(C_1 \cos \alpha t\sqrt{6g} + D_1 \sin \alpha t\sqrt{6g}).$$

The first condition of (21) requires that for all $t \geq 0$

$$Y(0, t) = A_1(C_1 \cos \alpha t\sqrt{6g} + D_1 \sin \alpha t\sqrt{6g}) = 0,$$

so that $A_1 = 0$ and hence

$$Y(x, t) = (\sin \alpha x)(A \cos \alpha t\sqrt{6g} + B \sin \alpha t\sqrt{6g}),$$

where we have set $A = B_1 C_1$, $B = B_1 D_1$.

The second condition of (21) demands that

$$Y(3, t) = (\sin 3\alpha)(A \cos \alpha t\sqrt{6g} + B \sin \alpha t\sqrt{6g}) = 0$$

identically for $t \geq 0$, and hence $\sin 3\alpha = 0$. Therefore $3\alpha = n\pi$ for some integer $n$, so that $\alpha = n\pi/3$. We thus have a particular solution

$$(23) \quad Y_n(x, t) = \left(\sin \frac{n\pi x}{3}\right)\left(A \cos \frac{n\pi t\sqrt{6g}}{3} + B \sin \frac{n\pi t\sqrt{6g}}{3}\right),$$

which satisfies the first two conditions of (21).

Differentiating (23) with respect to $t$, we find

$$\frac{\partial Y_n(x, t)}{\partial t} = \left(\frac{n\pi\sqrt{6g}}{3} \sin \frac{n\pi x}{3}\right)\left(-A \sin \frac{n\pi t\sqrt{6g}}{3} + B \cos \frac{n\pi t\sqrt{6g}}{3}\right).$$

The third condition of (21) requires that

$$\frac{\partial Y_n(x, 0)}{\partial t} = B \frac{n\pi\sqrt{6g}}{3} \sin \frac{n\pi x}{3} = 0$$

identically for $0 \leqq x \leqq 3$, so that $B = 0$ and therefore

$$Y_n(x, t) = a_n \sin \frac{n\pi x}{3} \cos \frac{n\pi t \sqrt{6g}}{3}$$

is a particular solution which satisfies the first three conditions of (21).

In an attempt to satisfy the fourth of the conditions (21) we shall form the series

$$Y(x, t) = \sum_{n=1}^{\infty} Y_n(x, t)$$

$$= \sum_{n=1}^{\infty} b_n \sin \frac{n\pi x}{3} \cos \frac{n\pi t \sqrt{6g}}{3}$$

and determine the coefficients $b_n$ so that

$$Y(x, 0) = \sum_{n=1}^{\infty} b_n \sin \frac{n\pi x}{3}$$
$$= g(x)$$

on the interval $0 \leqq x \leqq 3$, where we have written $g(x)$ for the function

$$g(x) = \begin{cases} \frac{1}{6}x, & 0 \leqq x < 1.5, \\ \frac{1}{6}(x - 3), & 1.5 \leqq x \leqq 3. \end{cases}$$

But this means to represent the function $g(x)$ by its Fourier sine series on the interval $0 \leqq x \leqq 3$, and hence the coefficients $b_n$ have the values

$$b_n = \frac{2}{3} \int_0^3 g(x) \sin \frac{n\pi x}{3} \, dx$$

$$= \frac{2}{3} \left[ \int_0^{\frac{3}{2}} \frac{1}{6} x \sin \frac{n\pi x}{3} \, dx + \int_{\frac{3}{2}}^3 \frac{1}{6} (x - 3) \sin \frac{n\pi x}{3} \, dx \right]$$

$$= -\frac{1}{n\pi} \cos \frac{n\pi}{2}, \quad n = 1, 2, \ldots.$$

Hence

$$Y(x, t) = \frac{1}{\pi} \left( \frac{1}{2} \sin \frac{2\pi x}{3} \cos \frac{2\pi t \sqrt{6g}}{3} - \frac{1}{4} \sin \frac{4\pi x}{3} \cos \frac{4\pi t \sqrt{6g}}{3} + \cdots \right).$$

295

A string 6 feet long weighs 0.6 lb. and is stretched by a 3-lb. force. Assume that the string lies along the $x$-axis with one end fixed at $(0, 0)$ and the other at $(6, 0)$. At time $t = 0$ the string is given a shape of the graph of $f(x)$ and then released from rest. Determine the subsequent displacement $Y(x, t)$, assuming values of $f(x)$ as given in Problems 1–5.

1. $f(x) = 0.5 \left( \cos \dfrac{\pi x}{3} - 1 \right)$

2. $f(x) = \begin{cases} e^x - 1, & 0 \leqq x < 3 \\ e^{6-x} - 1, & 3 \leqq x \leqq 6 \end{cases}$

3. $f(x) = \dfrac{1}{2} \sin \dfrac{\pi x}{6}$

4. $f(x) = \begin{cases} 0.2x, & 0 \leqq x < 3 \\ 0.2(6 - x), & 3 \leqq x \leqq 6 \end{cases}$

5. $f(x) = \begin{cases} 0.5 \sin \dfrac{\pi x}{3}, & 0 \leqq x < 3 \\ -0.5(\cos \pi x - 1), & 3 \leqq x \leqq 6 \end{cases}$

| Number | Square | Square Root | Number | Square | Square Root | Number | Square | Square Root |
|---|---|---|---|---|---|---|---|---|
| 1 | 1 | 1.000 | 51 | 2,601 | 7.141 | 101 | 10,201 | 10.050 |
| 2 | 4 | 1.414 | 52 | 2,704 | 7.211 | 102 | 10,404 | 10.100 |
| 3 | 9 | 1.732 | 53 | 2,809 | 7.280 | 103 | 10,609 | 10.149 |
| 4 | 16 | 2.000 | 54 | 2,916 | 7.348 | 104 | 10,816 | 10.198 |
| 5 | 25 | 2.236 | 55 | 3,025 | 7.416 | 105 | 11,025 | 10.247 |
| 6 | 36 | 2.449 | 56 | 3,136 | 7.483 | 106 | 11,236 | 10.296 |
| 7 | 49 | 2.646 | 57 | 3,249 | 7.550 | 107 | 11,449 | 10.344 |
| 8 | 64 | 2.828 | 58 | 3,364 | 7.616 | 108 | 11,664 | 10.392 |
| 9 | 81 | 0.000 | 59 | 3,481 | 7.681 | 109 | 11,881 | 10.440 |
| 10 | 100 | 3.162 | 60 | 3,600 | 7.746 | 110 | 12,100 | 10.488 |
| 11 | 121 | 3.317 | 61 | 3,721 | 7.810 | 111 | 12,321 | 10.536 |
| 12 | 144 | 3.464 | 62 | 3,844 | 7.874 | 112 | 12,544 | 10.583 |
| 13 | 169 | 3.606 | 63 | 3,969 | 7.937 | 113 | 12,769 | 10.630 |
| 14 | 196 | 3.742 | 64 | 4,096 | 8.000 | 114 | 12,996 | 10.677 |
| 15 | 225 | 3.873 | 65 | 4,225 | 8.062 | 115 | 13,225 | 10.724 |
| 16 | 256 | 4.000 | 66 | 4,356 | 8.124 | 116 | 13,456 | 10.770 |
| 17 | 289 | 4.123 | 67 | 4,489 | 8.185 | 117 | 13,689 | 10.817 |
| 18 | 324 | 4.243 | 68 | 4,624 | 8.246 | 118 | 13,924 | 10.863 |
| 19 | 361 | 4.359 | 69 | 4,761 | 8.307 | 119 | 14,161 | 10.909 |
| 20 | 400 | 4.472 | 70 | 4,900 | 8.367 | 120 | 14,400 | 10.954 |
| 21 | 441 | 4.583 | 71 | 5,041 | 8.426 | 121 | 14,641 | 11.000 |
| 22 | 484 | 4.690 | 72 | 5,184 | 8.485 | 122 | 14,884 | 11.045 |
| 23 | 529 | 4.796 | 73 | 5,329 | 8.544 | 123 | 15,129 | 11.091 |
| 24 | 576 | 4.899 | 74 | 5,476 | 8.602 | 124 | 15,376 | 11.136 |
| 25 | 625 | 5.000 | 75 | 5,625 | 8.660 | 125 | 15,625 | 11.180 |
| 26 | 676 | 5.099 | 76 | 5,776 | 8.718 | 126 | 15,876 | 11.225 |
| 27 | 729 | 5.196 | 77 | 5,929 | 8.775 | 127 | 16,129 | 11.269 |
| 28 | 784 | 5.292 | 78 | 6,084 | 8.832 | 128 | 16,384 | 11.314 |
| 29 | 841 | 5.385 | 79 | 6,241 | 8.888 | 129 | 16,641 | 11.358 |
| 30 | 900 | 5.477 | 80 | 6,400 | 8.944 | 130 | 16,900 | 11.402 |
| 31 | 961 | 5.568 | 81 | 6,561 | 9.000 | 131 | 17,161 | 11.446 |
| 32 | 1,024 | 5.657 | 82 | 6,724 | 9.055 | 132 | 17,424 | 11.489 |
| 33 | 1,089 | 5.745 | 83 | 6,889 | 9.110 | 133 | 17,689 | 11.533 |
| 34 | 1,156 | 5.831 | 84 | 7,056 | 9.165 | 134 | 17,956 | 11.576 |
| 35 | 1,225 | 5.916 | 85 | 7,225 | 9.220 | 135 | 18,225 | 11.619 |
| 36 | 1,296 | 6.000 | 86 | 7,396 | 9.274 | 136 | 18,496 | 11.662 |
| 37 | 1,369 | 6.083 | 87 | 7,569 | 9.327 | 137 | 18,769 | 11.705 |
| 38 | 1,444 | 6.164 | 88 | 7,744 | 9.381 | 138 | 19,044 | 11.747 |
| 39 | 1,521 | 6.245 | 89 | 7,921 | 9.434 | 139 | 19,321 | 11.790 |
| 40 | 1,600 | 6.325 | 90 | 8,100 | 9.487 | 140 | 19,600 | 11.832 |
| 41 | 1,681 | 6.403 | 91 | 8,281 | 9.539 | 141 | 19,881 | 11.874 |
| 42 | 1,764 | 6.481 | 92 | 8,464 | 9.592 | 142 | 20,164 | 11.916 |
| 43 | 1,849 | 6.557 | 93 | 8,649 | 9.644 | 143 | 20,449 | 11.958 |
| 44 | 1,936 | 6.633 | 94 | 8,836 | 9.695 | 144 | 20,736 | 12.000 |
| 45 | 2,025 | 6.708 | 95 | 9,025 | 9.747 | 145 | 21,025 | 12.042 |
| 46 | 2,116 | 6.782 | 96 | 9,216 | 9.798 | 146 | 21,316 | 12.083 |
| 47 | 2,209 | 6.856 | 97 | 9,409 | 9.849 | 147 | 21,609 | 12.124 |
| 48 | 2,304 | 6.928 | 98 | 9,604 | 9.899 | 148 | 21,904 | 12.166 |
| 49 | 2,401 | 7.000 | 99 | 9,801 | 9.950 | 149 | 22,201 | 12.207 |
| 50 | 2,500 | 7.071 | 100 | 10,000 | 10.000 | 150 | 22,500 | 12.247 |

| Degrees | Radians | Sin | Cos | Tan | Cot | Sec | Csc | | |
|---|---|---|---|---|---|---|---|---|---|
| 0° 00' | .0000 | .0000 | 1.0000 | .0000 | —— | 1.000 | —— | 1.5708 | 90° 00' |
| 10 | 029 | 029 | 000 | 029 | 343.8 | 000 | 343.8 | 679 | 50 |
| 20 | 058 | 058 | 000 | 058 | 171.9 | 000 | 171.9 | 650 | 40 |
| 30 | .0087 | .0087 | 1.0000 | .0087 | 114.6 | 1.000 | 114.6 | 1.5621 | 30 |
| 40 | 116 | 116 | .9999 | 116 | 85.94 | 000 | 85.95 | 592 | 20 |
| 50 | 145 | 145 | 999 | 145 | 68.75 | 000 | 68.76 | 563 | 10 |
| 1° 00' | .0175 | .0175 | .9998 | .0175 | 57.29 | 1.000 | 57.30 | 1.5533 | 89° 00' |
| 10 | 204 | 204 | 998 | 204 | 49.10 | 000 | 49.11 | 504 | 50 |
| 20 | 233 | 233 | 997 | 233 | 42.96 | 000 | 42.98 | 475 | 40 |
| 30 | .0262 | .0262 | .9997 | .0262 | 38.19 | 1.000 | 38.20 | 1.5446 | 30 |
| 40 | 291 | 291 | 996 | 291 | 34.37 | 000 | 34.38 | 417 | 20 |
| 50 | 320 | 320 | 995 | 320 | 31.24 | 001 | 31.26 | 388 | 10 |
| 2° 00' | .0349 | .0349 | .9994 | .0349 | 28.64 | 1.001 | 28.65 | 1.5359 | 88° 00' |
| 10 | 378 | 378 | 993 | 378 | 26.43 | 001 | 26.45 | 330 | 50 |
| 20 | 407 | 407 | 992 | 407 | 24.54 | 001 | 24.56 | 301 | 40 |
| 30 | .0436 | .0436 | .9990 | .0437 | 22.90 | 1.001 | 22.93 | 1.5272 | 30 |
| 40 | 465 | 465 | 989 | 466 | 21.47 | 001 | 21.49 | 243 | 20 |
| 50 | 495 | 494 | 988 | 495 | 20.21 | 001 | 20.23 | 213 | 10 |
| 3° 00' | .0524 | .0523 | .9986 | .0524 | 19.08 | 1.001 | 19.11 | 1.5184 | 87° 00' |
| 10 | 553 | 552 | 985 | 553 | 18.07 | 002 | 18.10 | 155 | 50 |
| 20 | 582 | 581 | 983 | 582 | 17.17 | 002 | 17.20 | 126 | 40 |
| 30 | .0611 | .0610 | .9981 | .0612 | 16.35 | 1.002 | 16.38 | 1.5097 | 30 |
| 40 | 640 | 640 | 980 | 641 | 15.60 | 002 | 15.64 | 068 | 20 |
| 50 | 669 | 669 | 978 | 670 | 14.92 | 002 | 14.96 | 039 | 10 |
| 4° 00' | .0698 | .0698 | .9976 | .0699 | 14.30 | 1.002 | 14.34 | 1.5010 | 86° 00' |
| 10 | 727 | 727 | 974 | 729 | 13.73 | 003 | 13.76 | 981 | 50 |
| 20 | 756 | 756 | 971 | 758 | 13.20 | 003 | 13.23 | 952 | 40 |
| 30 | .0785 | .0785 | .9969 | .0787 | 12.71 | 1.003 | 12.75 | 1.4923 | 30 |
| 40 | 814 | 814 | 967 | 816 | 12.25 | 003 | 12.29 | 893 | 20 |
| 50 | 844 | 843 | 964 | 846 | 11.83 | 004 | 11.87 | 864 | 10 |
| 5° 00' | .0873 | .0872 | .9962 | .0875 | 11.43 | 1.004 | 11.47 | 1.4835 | 85° 00' |
| 10 | 902 | 901 | 959 | 904 | 11.06 | 004 | 11.10 | 806 | 50 |
| 20 | 931 | 929 | 957 | 934 | 10.71 | 004 | 10.76 | 777 | 40 |
| 30 | .0960 | .0958 | .9954 | .0963 | 10.39 | 1.005 | 10.43 | 1.4748 | 30 |
| 40 | 989 | 987 | 951 | 992 | 10.08 | 005 | 10.13 | 719 | 20 |
| 50 | .1018 | .1016 | 948 | .1022 | 9.788 | 005 | 9.839 | 690 | 10 |
| 6° 00' | .1047 | .1045 | .9945 | .1051 | 9.514 | 1.006 | 9.567 | 1.4661 | 84° 00' |
| 10 | 076 | 074 | 942 | 080 | 9.255 | 006 | 9.309 | 632 | 50 |
| 20 | 105 | 103 | 939 | 110 | 9.010 | 006 | 9.065 | 603 | 40 |
| 30 | .1134 | .1132 | .9936 | .1139 | 8.777 | 1.006 | 8.834 | 1.4573 | 30 |
| 40 | 164 | 161 | 932 | 169 | 8.556 | 007 | 8.614 | 544 | 20 |
| 50 | 193 | 190 | 929 | 198 | 8.345 | 007 | 8.405 | 515 | 10 |
| 7° 00' | .1222 | .1219 | .9925 | .1228 | 8.144 | 1.008 | 8.206 | 1.4486 | 83° 00' |
| 10 | 251 | 248 | 922 | 257 | 7.953 | 008 | 8.016 | 457 | 50 |
| 20 | 280 | 276 | 918 | 287 | 7.770 | 008 | 7.834 | 428 | 40 |
| 30 | .1309 | .1305 | .9914 | .1317 | 7.596 | 1.009 | 7.661 | 1.4399 | 30 |
| 40 | 338 | 334 | 911 | 346 | 7.429 | 009 | 7.496 | 370 | 20 |
| 50 | 367 | 363 | 907 | 376 | 7.269 | 009 | 7.337 | 341 | 10 |
| 8° 00' | .1396 | .1392 | .9903 | .1405 | 7.115 | 1.010 | 7.185 | 1.4312 | 82° 00' |
| 10 | 425 | 421 | 899 | 435 | 6.968 | 010 | 7.040 | 283 | 50 |
| 20 | 454 | 449 | 894 | 465 | 6.827 | 011 | 6.900 | 254 | 40 |
| 30 | .1484 | .1478 | .9890 | .1495 | 6.691 | 1.011 | 6.765 | 1.4224 | 30 |
| 40 | 513 | 507 | 886 | 524 | 6.561 | 012 | 6.636 | 195 | 20 |
| 50 | 542 | 536 | 881 | 554 | 6.435 | 012 | 6.512 | 166 | 10 |
| 9° 00' | .1571 | .1564 | .9877 | .1584 | 6.314 | 1.012 | 6.392 | 1.4137 | 81° 00' |
| | | Cos | Sin | Cot | Tan | Csc | Sec | Radians | Degrees |

# II. FOUR-PLACE VALUES OF FUNCTIONS AND RADIANS

| Degrees | Radians | Sin | Cos | Tan | Cot | Sec | Csc | Radians | Degrees |
|---|---|---|---|---|---|---|---|---|---|
| 9° 00′ | .1571 | .1564 | .9877 | .1584 | 6.314 | 1.012 | 6.392 | 1.4137 | 81° 00′ |
| 10 | 600 | 593 | 872 | 614 | 197 | 013 | 277 | 108 | 50 |
| 20 | 629 | 622 | 868 | 644 | 084 | 013 | 166 | 079 | 40 |
| 30 | .1658 | .1650 | .9863 | .1673 | 5.976 | 1.014 | 6.059 | 1.4050 | 30 |
| 40 | 687 | 679 | 858 | 703 | 871 | 014 | 5.955 | 1.4021 | 20 |
| 50 | 716 | 708 | 853 | 733 | 769 | 015 | 855 | 992 | 10 |
| 10° 00′ | .1745 | .1736 | .9848 | .1763 | 5.671 | 1.015 | 5.759 | 1.3963 | 80° 00′ |
| 10 | 774 | 765 | 843 | 793 | 576 | 016 | 665 | 934 | 50 |
| 20 | 804 | 794 | 838 | 823 | 485 | 016 | 575 | 904 | 40 |
| 30 | .1833 | .1822 | .9833 | .1853 | 5.396 | 1.017 | 5.487 | 1.3875 | 30 |
| 40 | 862 | 851 | 827 | 883 | 309 | 018 | 403 | 846 | 20 |
| 50 | 891 | 880 | 822 | 914 | 226 | 018 | 320 | 817 | 10 |
| 11° 00′ | .1920 | .1908 | .9816 | .1944 | 5.145 | 1.019 | 5.241 | 1.3788 | 79° 00′ |
| 10 | 949 | 937 | 811 | 974 | 066 | 019 | 164 | 759 | 50 |
| 20 | 978 | 965 | 805 | .2004 | 4.989 | 020 | | 730 | 40 |
| 30 | .2007 | .1994 | .9799 | .2035 | 4.915 | 1.020 | 5.016 | 1.3701 | 30 |
| 40 | 036 | 2022 | 793 | 065 | 843 | 021 | 4.945 | 672 | 20 |
| 50 | 065 | 051 | 787 | 095 | 773 | 022 | 876 | 643 | 10 |
| 12° 00′ | .2094 | .2079 | .9781 | .2126 | 4.705 | 1.022 | 4.810 | 1.3614 | 78° 00′ |
| 10 | 123 | 108 | 775 | 156 | 638 | 023 | 745 | 584 | 50 |
| 20 | 153 | 136 | 769 | 186 | 574 | 024 | 682 | 555 | 40 |
| 30 | .2182 | .2164 | .9763 | .2217 | 4.511 | 1.024 | 4.620 | 1.3526 | 30 |
| 40 | 211 | 193 | 757 | 247 | 449 | 025 | 560 | 497 | 20 |
| 50 | 240 | 221 | 750 | 278 | 390 | 026 | 502 | 468 | 10 |
| 13° 00′ | .2269 | .2250 | .9744 | .2309 | 4.331 | 1.026 | 4.445 | 1.3439 | 77° 00′ |
| 10 | 298 | 278 | 737 | 339 | 275 | 027 | 390 | 410 | 50 |
| 20 | 327 | 306 | 730 | 370 | 219 | 028 | 336 | 381 | 40 |
| 30 | .2356 | .2334 | .9724 | .2401 | 4.165 | 1.028 | 4.284 | 1.3352 | 30 |
| 40 | 385 | 303 | 717 | 432 | 113 | 029 | 232 | 323 | 20 |
| 50 | 414 | 391 | 710 | 462 | 061 | 030 | 182 | 294 | 10 |
| 14° 00′ | .2443 | .2419 | .9703 | .2493 | 4.011 | 1.031 | 4.134 | 1.3265 | 76° 00′ |
| 10 | 473 | 447 | 696 | 524 | 3.962 | 031 | 086 | 235 | 50 |
| 20 | 502 | 476 | 689 | 555 | 914 | 032 | 039 | 206 | 40 |
| 30 | .2531 | .2504 | .9681 | .2586 | 3.867 | 1.033 | 3.994 | 1.3177 | 30 |
| 40 | 560 | 532 | 674 | 617 | 821 | 034 | 950 | 148 | 20 |
| 50 | 589 | 560 | 667 | 648 | 776 | 034 | 906 | 119 | 10 |
| 15° 00′ | .2618 | .2588 | .9659 | .2679 | 3.732 | 1.035 | 3.864 | 1.3090 | 75° 00′ |
| 10 | 647 | 616 | 652 | 711 | 689 | 036 | 822 | 061 | 50 |
| 20 | 676 | 644 | 644 | 742 | 647 | 037 | 782 | 032 | 40 |
| 30 | .2705 | .2672 | .9636 | .2773 | 3.606 | 1.038 | 3.742 | 1.3003 | 30 |
| 40 | 734 | 700 | 628 | 805 | 566 | 039 | 703 | 974 | 20 |
| 50 | 763 | 728 | 621 | 836 | 526 | 039 | 665 | 945 | 10 |
| 16° 00′ | .2793 | .2756 | .9613 | .2867 | 3.487 | 1.040 | 3.628 | 1.2915 | 74° 00′ |
| 10 | 822 | 784 | 605 | 899 | 450 | 041 | 592 | 886 | 50 |
| 20 | 851 | 812 | 596 | 931 | 412 | 042 | 556 | 857 | 40 |
| 30 | .2880 | .2840 | .9588 | .2962 | 3.376 | 1.043 | 3.521 | 1.2828 | 30 |
| 40 | 909 | 868 | 580 | 994 | 340 | 044 | 487 | 799 | 20 |
| 50 | 938 | 896 | 572 | .3026 | 305 | 045 | 453 | 770 | 10 |
| 17° 00′ | .2967 | .2924 | .9563 | .3057 | 3.271 | 1.046 | 3.420 | 1.2741 | 73° 00′ |
| 10 | 996 | 952 | 555 | 089 | 237 | 047 | 388 | 712 | 50 |
| 20 | .3025 | 979 | 546 | 121 | 204 | 048 | 356 | 683 | 40 |
| 30 | .3054 | .3007 | .9537 | .3153 | 3.172 | 1.049 | 3.326 | 1.2654 | 30 |
| 40 | 083 | 035 | 528 | 185 | 140 | 049 | 295 | 625 | 20 |
| 50 | 113 | 062 | 520 | 217 | 108 | 050 | 265 | 595 | 10 |
| 18° 00′ | .3142 | .3090 | .9511 | .3249 | 3.078 | 1.051 | 3.236 | 1.2566 | 72° 00′ |
| | | Cos | Sin | Cot | Tan | Csc | Sec | Radians | Degrees |

| Degrees | Radians | Sin | Cos | Tan | Cot | Sec | Csc | | |
|---|---|---|---|---|---|---|---|---|---|
| 18° 00′ | .3142 | .3090 | .9511 | .3249 | 3.078 | 1.051 | 3.236 | 1.2566 | 72° 00′ |
| 10 | 171 | 118 | 502 | 281 | 047 | 052 | 207 | 537 | 50 |
| 20 | 200 | 145 | 492 | 314 | 018 | 053 | 179 | 508 | 40 |
| 30 | .3229 | .3173 | .9483 | .3346 | 2.989 | 1.054 | 3.152 | 1.2479 | 30 |
| 40 | 258 | 201 | 474 | 378 | 960 | 056 | 124 | 450 | 20 |
| 50 | 287 | 228 | 465 | 411 | 932 | 057 | 098 | 421 | 10 |
| 19° 00′ | .3316 | .3256 | .9455 | .3443 | 2.904 | 1.058 | 3.072 | 1.2392 | 71° 00′ |
| 10 | 345 | 283 | 446 | 476 | 877 | 059 | 046 | 363 | 50 |
| 20 | 374 | 311 | 436 | 508 | 850 | 060 | 021 | 334 | 40 |
| 30 | .3403 | .3338 | .9426 | .3541 | 2.824 | 1.061 | 2.996 | 1.2305 | 30 |
| 40 | 432 | 365 | 417 | 574 | 798 | 062 | 971 | 275 | 20 |
| 50 | 462 | 393 | 407 | 607 | 773 | 063 | 947 | 246 | 10 |
| 20° 00′ | .3491 | .3420 | .9397 | .3640 | 2.747 | 1.064 | 2.924 | 1.2217 | 70° 00′ |
| 10 | 520 | 448 | 387 | 673 | 723 | 065 | 901 | 188 | 50 |
| 20 | 549 | 475 | 377 | 706 | 699 | 066 | 878 | 159 | 40 |
| 30 | .3578 | .3502 | .9367 | .3739 | 2.675 | 1.068 | 2.855 | 1.2130 | 30 |
| 40 | 607 | 529 | 356 | 772 | 651 | 069 | 833 | 101 | 20 |
| 50 | 636 | 557 | 346 | 805 | 628 | 070 | 812 | 072 | 10 |
| 21° 00′ | .3665 | .3584 | .9336 | .3839 | 2.605 | 1.071 | 2.790 | 1.2043 | 69° 00′ |
| 10 | 694 | 611 | 325 | 872 | 583 | 072 | 769 | 1.2014 | 50 |
| 20 | 723 | 638 | 315 | 906 | 560 | 074 | 749 | 985 | 40 |
| 30 | .3752 | .3665 | .9304 | .3939 | 2.539 | 1.075 | 2.729 | 1.1956 | 30 |
| 40 | 782 | 692 | 293 | 973 | 517 | 076 | 709 | 926 | 20 |
| 50 | 811 | 719 | 283 | .4006 | 496 | 077 | 689 | 897 | 10 |
| 22° 00′ | .3840 | .3746 | .9272 | .4040 | 2.475 | 1.079 | 2.669 | 1.1868 | 68° 00′ |
| 10 | 869 | 773 | 261 | 074 | 455 | 080 | 650 | 839 | 50 |
| 20 | 898 | 800 | 250 | 108 | 434 | 081 | 632 | 810 | 40 |
| 30 | .3927 | .3827 | .9239 | .4142 | 2.414 | 1.082 | 2.613 | 1.1781 | 30 |
| 40 | 956 | 854 | 228 | 176 | 394 | 084 | 595 | 752 | 20 |
| 50 | 985 | 881 | 216 | 210 | 375 | 085 | 577 | 723 | 10 |
| 23° 00′ | .4014 | .3907 | .9205 | .4245 | 2.356 | 1.086 | 2.559 | 1.1694 | 67° 00′ |
| 10 | 043 | 934 | 194 | 279 | 337 | 088 | 542 | 665 | 50 |
| 20 | 072 | 961 | 182 | 314 | 318 | 089 | 525 | 636 | 40 |
| 30 | .4102 | .3987 | .9171 | .4348 | 2.300 | 1.090 | 2.508 | 1.1606 | 30 |
| 40 | 131 | .4014 | 159 | 383 | 282 | 092 | 491 | 577 | 20 |
| 50 | 160 | 041 | 147 | 417 | 264 | 093 | 475 | 548 | 10 |
| 24° 00′ | .4189 | .4067 | .9135 | .4452 | 2.246 | 1.095 | 2.459 | 1.1519 | 66° 00′ |
| 10 | 218 | 094 | 124 | 487 | 229 | 096 | 443 | 490 | 50 |
| 20 | 247 | 120 | 112 | 522 | 211 | 097 | 427 | 461 | 40 |
| 30 | .4276 | .4147 | .9100 | .4557 | 2.194 | 1.099 | 2.411 | 1.1432 | 30 |
| 40 | 305 | 173 | 088 | 592 | 177 | 100 | 396 | 403 | 20 |
| 50 | 334 | 200 | 075 | 628 | 161 | 102 | 381 | 374 | 10 |
| 25° 00′ | .4363 | .4226 | .9063 | .4663 | 2.145 | 1.103 | 2.366 | 1.1345 | 65° 00′ |
| 10 | 392 | 253 | 051 | 699 | 128 | 105 | 352 | 316 | 50 |
| 20 | 422 | 279 | 038 | 734 | 112 | 106 | 337 | 286 | 40 |
| 30 | .4451 | .4305 | .9026 | .4770 | 2.097 | 1.108 | 2.323 | 1.1257 | 30 |
| 40 | 480 | 331 | 013 | 806 | 081 | 109 | 309 | 228 | 20 |
| 50 | 509 | 358 | 001 | 841 | 066 | 111 | 295 | 199 | 10 |
| 26° 00′ | .4538 | .4384 | .8988 | .4877 | 2.050 | 1.113 | 2.281 | 1.1170 | 64° 00′ |
| 10 | 567 | 410 | 975 | 913 | 035 | 114 | 268 | 141 | 50 |
| 20 | 596 | 436 | 962 | 950 | 020 | 116 | 254 | 112 | 40 |
| 30 | .4625 | .4462 | .8949 | .4986 | 2.006 | 1.117 | 2.241 | 1.1083 | 30 |
| 40 | 654 | 488 | 936 | .5022 | 1.991 | 119 | 228 | 054 | 20 |
| 50 | 683 | 514 | 923 | 059 | 977 | 121 | 215 | 1.1025 | 10 |
| 27° 00′ | .4712 | .4540 | .8910 | .5095 | 1.963 | 1.122 | 2.203 | 1.0996 | 63° 00′ |
| | | Cos | Sin | Cot | Tan | Csc | Sec | Radians | Degrees |

## II. FOUR-PLACE VALUES OF FUNCTIONS AND RADIANS

| Degrees | Radians | Sin | Cos | Tan | Cot | Sec | Csc | | |
|---|---|---|---|---|---|---|---|---|---|
| 27° 00′ | .4712 | .4540 | .8910 | .5095 | 1.963 | 1.122 | 2.203 | 1.0996 | 63° 00′ |
| 10 | 741 | 566 | 897 | 132 | 949 | 124 | 190 | 966 | 50 |
| 20 | 771 | 592 | 884 | 169 | 935 | 126 | 178 | 937 | 40 |
| 30 | .4800 | .4617 | .8870 | .5206 | 1.921 | 1.127 | 2.166 | 1.0908 | 30 |
| 40 | 829 | 643 | 857 | 243 | 907 | 129 | 154 | 879 | 20 |
| 50 | 858 | 669 | 843 | 280 | 894 | 131 | 142 | 850 | 10 |
| 28° 00′ | .4887 | .4695 | .8829 | .5317 | 1.881 | 1.133 | 2.130 | 1.0821 | 62° 00′ |
| 10 | 916 | 720 | 816 | 354 | 868 | ·134 | 118 | 792 | 50 |
| 20 | 945 | 746 | 802 | 392 | 855 | 136 | 107 | 763 | 40 |
| 30 | .4974 | .4772 | .8788 | .5430 | 1.842 | 1.138 | 2.096 | 1.0734 | 30 |
| 40 | .5003 | 797 | 774 | 467 | 829 | 140 | 085 | 705 | 20 |
| 50 | 032 | 823 | 805 | 505 | 816 | 142 | 074 | 676 | 10 |
| 29° 00′ | .5061 | .4848 | .8746 | .5543 | 1.804 | 1.143 | 2.063 | 1.0647 | 61° 00′ |
| 10 | 091 | 874 | 732 | 581 | 792 | 145 | 052 | 617 | 50 |
| 20 | 120 | 899 | 718 | 619 | 780 | 147 | 041 | 588 | 40 |
| 30 | .5149 | .4924 | .8704 | .5658 | 1.767 | 1.149 | 2.031 | 1.0559 | 30 |
| 40 | 178 | 950 | 689 | 696 | 756 | 151 | 020 | 530 | 20 |
| 50 | 207 | 975 | 675 | 735 | 744 | 153 | 010 | 501 | 10 |
| 30° 00′ | .5236 | .5000 | .8660 | .5774 | 1.732 | 1.155 | 2.000 | 1.0472 | 60° 00′ |
| 10 | 265 | 025 | 646 | 812 | 720 | 157 | 1.990 | 443 | 50 |
| 20 | 294 | 050 | 631 | 851 | 709 | 159 | 980 | 414 | 40 |
| 30 | .5323 | .5075 | .8616 | .5890 | 1.698 | 1.161 | 1.970 | 1.0385 | 30 |
| 40 | 352 | 100 | 601 | 930 | 686 | 163 | 961 | 356 | 20 |
| 50 | 381 | 125 | 587 | 969 | .678 | 165 | 951 | 327 | 10 |
| 31° 00′ | .5411 | .5150 | .8572 | .6009 | 1.664 | 1.167 | 1.942 | 1.0297 | 59° 00′ |
| 10 | 440 | 175 | 557 | 048 | 653 | ·169 | 932 | 268 | 50 |
| 20 | 469 | 200 | 542 | 088 | 643 | 171 | 923 | 239 | 40 |
| 30 | .5498 | .5225 | .8526 | .6128 | 1.632 | 1.173 | 1.914 | 1.0210 | 30 |
| 40 | 527 | 250 | 511 | 168 | 621 | 175 | 905 | 181 | 20 |
| 50 | 556 | 275 | 496 | 208 | 611 | 177 | 896 | 152 | 10 |
| 32° 00′ | .5585 | .5299 | .8480 | .6249 | 1.600 | 1.179 | 1.887 | 1.0123 | 58° 00′ |
| 10 | 614 | 324 | 465 | 289 | 590 | 181 | 878 | 094 | 50 |
| 20 | 643 | 348 | 450 | 330 | 580 | 184 | 870 | 065 | 40 |
| 30 | .5672 | .5373 | .8434 | .6371 | 1.570 | 1.186 | 1.861 | 1.0036 | 30 |
| 40 | 701 | 398 | 418 | 412 | 560 | 188 | 853 | 1.0007 | 20 |
| 50 | 730 | 422 | 403 | 453 | 550 | 190 | 844 | 977 | 10 |
| 33° 00′ | .5760 | .5446 | .8387 | .6494 | 1.540 | 1.192 | 1.836 | .9948 | 57° 00′ |
| 10 | 789 | 471 | 371 | 536 | 530 | 195 | ·828 | 919 | 50 |
| 20 | 818 | 495 | 355 | 577 | 520 | 197 | 820 | 890 | 40 |
| 30 | .5847 | .5519 | .8339 | .6619 | 1.511 | 1.199 | 1.812 | .9861 | 30 |
| 40 | 876 | 544 | 323 | 661 | 501 | 202 | 804 | 832 | 20 |
| 50 | 905 | 568 | 307 | 703 | 1.492 | 204 | 796 | 803 | 10 |
| 34° 00′ | .5934 | .5592 | .8290 | .6745 | 1.483 | 1.206 | 1.788 | .9774 | 56° 00′ |
| 10 | 963 | 616 | 274 | 787 | 473 | 209 | 781 | 745 | 50 |
| 20 | 992 | 640 | 258 | 830 | 464 | 211 | 773 | 716 | 40 |
| 30 | .6021 | .5664 | .8241 | .6873 | 1.455 | 1.213 | 1.766 | .9687 | 30 |
| 40 | 050 | 688 | 225 | 916 | 446 | 216 | 758 | 657 | 20 |
| 50 | 080 | 712 | 208 | 959 | 437 | 218 | 751 | 628 | 10 |
| 35° 00′ | .6109 | .5736 | .8192 | .7002 | 1.428 | 1.221 | 1.743 | .9599 | 55° 00′ |
| 10 | 138 | 760 | 175 | 046 | 419 | 223 | 736 | 570 | 50 |
| 20 | 167 | 783 | 158 | 089 | 411 | 226 | 729 | 541 | 40 |
| 30 | .6196 | .5807 | .8141 | .7133 | 1.402 | 1.228 | 1.722 | .9512 | 30 |
| 40 | 225 | 831 | 124 | 177 | .393 | 231 | 715 | 483 | 20 |
| 50 | 254 | 854 | 107 | 221 | 385 | 233 | 708 | 454 | 10 |
| 36° 00′ | .6283 | .5878 | .8090 | .7265 | 1.376 | 1.236 | 1.701 | .9425 | 54° 00′ |
| | | Cos | Sin | Cot | Tan | Csc | Sec | Radians | Degrees |

301

| Degrees | Radians | Sin | Cos | Tan | Cot | Sec | Csc | | |
|---|---|---|---|---|---|---|---|---|---|
| 36° 00′ | .6283 | .5878 | .8090 | .7265 | 1.376 | 1.236 | 1.701 | .9425 | 54° 00′ |
| 10 | 312 | 901 | 073 | 310 | 368 | 239 | 695 | 396 | 50 |
| 20 | 341 | 925 | 056 | 355 | 360 | 241 | 688 | 367 | 40 |
| 30 | .6370 | .5948 | .8039 | .7400 | 1.351 | 1.244 | 1.681 | .9338 | 30 |
| 40 | 400 | 972 | 021 | 445 | 343 | 247 | 675 | 308 | 20 |
| 50 | 429 | 995 | 004 | 490 | 335 | 249 | 668 | 279 | 10 |
| 37° 00′ | .6458 | .6018 | .7986 | .7536 | 1.327 | 1.252 | 1.662 | .9250 | 53° 00′ |
| 10 | 487 | 041 | 969 | 581 | 319 | 255 | 655 | 221 | 50 |
| 20 | 516 | 065 | 951 | 627 | 311 | 258 | 649 | 192 | 40 |
| 30 | .6545 | .6088 | .7934 | .7673 | 1.303 | 1.260 | 1.643 | .9163 | 30 |
| 40 | 574 | 111 | 916 | 720 | 295 | 263 | 636 | 134 | 20 |
| 50 | 603 | 134 | 898 | 766 | 288 | 266 | 630 | 105 | 10 |
| 38° 00′ | .6632 | .6157 | .7880 | .7813 | 1.280 | 1.269 | 1.624 | .9076 | 52° 00′ |
| 10 | 661 | 180 | 862 | 860 | 272 | 272 | 618 | 047 | 50 |
| 20 | 690 | 202 | 844 | 907 | 265 | 275 | 612 | .9018 | 40 |
| 30 | .6720 | .6225 | .7826 | .7954 | 1.257 | 1.278 | 1.606 | .8988 | 30 |
| 40 | 749 | 248 | 808 | .8002 | 250 | 281 | 601 | 959 | 20 |
| 50 | 778 | 271 | 790 | 050 | 242 | 284 | 595 | 930 | 10 |
| 39° 00′ | .6807 | .6293 | .7771 | .8098 | 1.235 | 1.287 | 1.589 | .8901 | 51° 00′ |
| 10 | 836 | 316 | 753 | 146 | 228 | 290 | 583 | 872 | 50 |
| 20 | 865 | 338 | 735 | 195 | 220 | 293 | 578 | 843 | 40 |
| 30 | .6894 | .6361 | .7716 | .8243 | 1.213 | 1.296 | 1.572 | .8814 | 30 |
| 40 | 923 | 383 | 698 | 292 | 206 | 299 | 567 | 785 | 20 |
| 50 | 952 | 406 | 679 | 342 | 199 | 302 | 561 | 756 | 10 |
| 40° 00′ | .6981 | .6428 | .7660 | .8391 | 1.192 | 1.305 | 1.556 | .8727 | 50° 00′ |
| 10 | .7010 | 450 | 642 | 441 | 185 | 309 | 550 | 698 | 50 |
| 20 | 039 | 472 | 623 | 491 | 178 | 312 | 545 | 668 | 40 |
| 30 | .7069 | .6494 | .7604 | .8541 | 1.171 | 1.315 | 1.540 | .8639 | 30 |
| 40 | 098 | 517 | 585 | 591 | 164 | 318 | 535 | 610 | 20 |
| 50 | 127 | 539 | 566 | 642 | 157 | 322 | 529 | 581 | 10 |
| 41° 00′ | .7156 | .6561 | .7547 | .8693 | 1.150 | 1.325 | 1.524 | .8552 | 49° 00′ |
| 10 | 185 | 583 | 528 | 744 | 144 | 328 | 519 | 523 | 50 |
| 20 | 214 | 604 | 509 | 796 | 137 | 332 | 514 | 494 | 40 |
| 30 | .7243 | .6626 | .7490 | .8847 | 1.130 | 1.335 | 1.509 | .8465 | 30 |
| 40 | 272 | 648 | 470 | 899 | 124 | 339 | 504 | 436 | 20 |
| 50 | 301 | 670 | 451 | 952 | 117 | 342 | 499 | 407 | 10 |
| 42° 00′ | .7330 | .6691 | .7431 | .9004 | 1.111 | 1.346 | 1.494 | .8378 | 48° 00′ |
| 10 | 359 | 713 | 412 | 057 | 104 | 349 | 490 | 348 | 50 |
| 20 | 389 | 734 | 392 | 110 | 098 | 353 | 485 | 319 | 40 |
| 30 | .7418 | .6756 | .7373 | .9163 | 1.091 | 1.356 | 1.480 | .8290 | 30 |
| 40 | 447 | 777 | 353 | 217 | 085 | 360 | 476 | 261 | 20 |
| 50 | 476 | 799 | 333 | 271 | 079 | 364 | 471 | 232 | 10 |
| 43° 00′ | .7505 | .6820 | .7314 | .9325 | 1.072 | 1.367 | 1.466 | .8203 | 47° 00′ |
| 10 | 534 | 841 | 294 | 380 | 066 | 371 | 462 | 174 | 50 |
| 20 | 563 | 862 | 274 | 435 | 060 | 375 | 457 | 145 | 40 |
| 30 | .7592 | .6884 | .7254 | .9490 | 1.054 | 1.379 | 1.453 | .8116 | 30 |
| 40 | 621 | 905 | 234 | 545 | 048 | 382 | 448 | 087 | 20 |
| 50 | 650 | 926 | 214 | 601 | 042 | 386 | 444 | 058 | 10 |
| 44° 00′ | .7679 | .6947 | .7193 | .9657 | 1.036 | 1.390 | 1.440 | .8029 | 46° 00′ |
| 10 | 709 | 967 | 173 | 713 | 030 | 394 | 435 | 999 | 50 |
| 20 | 738 | 988 | 153 | 770 | 024 | 398 | 431 | 970 | 40 |
| 30 | .7767 | .7009 | .7133 | .9827 | 1.018 | 1.402 | 1.427 | .7941 | 30 |
| 40 | 796 | 030 | 112 | 884 | 012 | 406 | 423 | 912 | 20 |
| 50 | 825 | 050 | 092 | 942 | 006 | 410 | 418 | 883 | 10 |
| 45° 00′ | .7854 | .7071 | .7071 | 1.000 | 1.000 | 1.414 | 1.414 | .7854 | 45° 00′ |
| | | Cos | Sin | Cot | Tan | Csc | Sec | Radians | Degrees |

302

| | .00 | .01 | .02 | .03 | .04 | .05 | .06 | .07 | .08 | .09 |
|---|---|---|---|---|---|---|---|---|---|---|
| 0.0 | | 5.3948 | 6.0880 | 6.4934 | 6.7811 | 7.0043 | 7.1866 | 7.3407 | 7.4743 | 7.5921 |
| 0.1 | 7.6974 | 7.7927 | 7.8797 | 7.9598 | 8.0339 | 8.1029 | 8.1674 | 8.2280 | 8.2852 | 8.3393 |
| 0.2 | 8.3906 | 8.4393 | 8.4859 | 8.5303 | 8.5729 | 8.6137 | 8.6529 | 8.6907 | 8.7270 | 8.7621 |
| 0.3 | 8.7960 | 8.8288 | 8.8606 | 8.8913 | 8.9212 | 8.9502 | 8.9783 | 9.0057 | 9.0324 | 9.0584 |
| 0.4 | 9.0837 | 9.1084 | 9.1325 | 9.1560 | 9.1790 | 9.2015 | 9.2235 | 9.2450 | 9.2660 | 9.2867 |
| 0.5 | 9.3069 | 9.3267 | 9.3461 | 9.3651 | 9.3838 | 9.4022 | 9.4202 | 9.4379 | 9.4553 | 9.4724 |
| 0.6 | 9.4892 | 9.5057 | 9.5220 | 9.5380 | 9.5537 | 9.5692 | 9.5845 | 9.5995 | 9.6143 | 9.6289 |
| 0.7 | 9.6433 | 9.6575 | 9.6715 | 9.6853 | 9.6989 | 9.7123 | 9.7256 | 9.7386 | 9.7515 | 9.7643 |
| 0.8 | 9.7769 | 9.7893 | 9.8015 | 9.8137 | 9.8256 | 9.8375 | 9.8492 | 9.8607 | 9.8722 | 9.8835 |
| 0.9 | 9.8946 | 9.9057 | 9.9166 | 9.9274 | 9.9381 | 9.9487 | 9.9592 | 9.9695 | 9.9798 | 9.9899 |

When using the preceding table, subtract 10 from the tabular value.

| | .00 | .01 | .02 | .03 | .04 | .05 | .06 | .07 | .08 | .09 |
|---|---|---|---|---|---|---|---|---|---|---|
| 1.0 | 0.0000 | 0.0100 | 0.0198 | 0.0296 | 0.0392 | 0.0488 | 0.0583 | 0.0677 | 0.0770 | 0.0862 |
| 1.1 | 0.0953 | 0.1044 | 0.1133 | 0.1222 | 0.1310 | 0.1398 | 0.1484 | 0.1570 | 0.1655 | 0.1740 |
| 1.2 | 0.1823 | 0.1906 | 0.1989 | 0.2070 | 0.2151 | 0.2231 | 0.2311 | 0.2390 | 0.2469 | 0.2546 |
| 1.3 | 0.2624 | 0.2700 | 0.2776 | 0.2852 | 0.2927 | 0.3001 | 0.3075 | 0.3148 | 0.3221 | 0.3293 |
| 1.4 | 0.3365 | 0.3436 | 0.3507 | 0.3577 | 0.3646 | 0.3716 | 0.3784 | 0.3853 | 0.3920 | 0.3988 |
| 1.5 | 0.4055 | 0.4121 | 0.4187 | 0.4253 | 0.4318 | 0.4383 | 0.4447 | 0.4511 | 0.4574 | 0.4637 |
| 1.6 | 0.4700 | 0.4762 | 0.4824 | 0.4886 | 0.4947 | 0.5008 | 0.5068 | 0.5128 | 0.5188 | 0.5247 |
| 1.7 | 0.5306 | 0.5365 | 0.5423 | 0.5481 | 0.5539 | 0.5596 | 0.5653 | 0.5710 | 0.5766 | 0.5822 |
| 1.8 | 0.5878 | 0.5933 | 0.5988 | 0.6043 | 0.6098 | 0.6152 | 0.6206 | 0.6259 | 0.6313 | 0.6366 |
| 1.9 | 0.6419 | 0.6471 | 0.6523 | 0.6575 | 0.6627 | 0.6678 | 0.6729 | 0.6780 | 0.6831 | 0.6881 |
| 2.0 | 0.6931 | 0.6981 | 0.7031 | 0.7080 | 0.7130 | 0.7178 | 0.7227 | 0.7275 | 0.7324 | 0.7372 |
| 2.1 | 0.7419 | 0.7467 | 0.7514 | 0.7561 | 0.7608 | 0.7655 | 0.7701 | 0.7747 | 0.7793 | 0.7839 |
| 2.2 | 0.7885 | 0.7930 | 0.7975 | 0.8020 | 0.8065 | 0.8109 | 0.8154 | 0.8198 | 0.8242 | 0.8286 |
| 2.3 | 0.8329 | 0.8372 | 0.8416 | 0.8459 | 0.8502 | 0.8544 | 0.8587 | 0.8629 | 0.8671 | 0.8713 |
| 2.4 | 0.8755 | 0.8796 | 0.8838 | 0.8879 | 0.8920 | 0.8961 | 0.9002 | 0.9042 | 0.9083 | 0.9123 |

## III. NATURAL LOGARITHMS

|  | .00 | .01 | .02 | .03 | .04 | .05 | .06 | .07 | .08 | .09 |
|---|---|---|---|---|---|---|---|---|---|---|
| **2.5** | 0.9163 | 0.9203 | 0.9243 | 0.9282 | 0.9322 | 0.9361 | 0.9400 | 0.9439 | 0.9478 | 0.9517 |
| 2.6 | 0.9555 | 0.9594 | 0.9632 | 0.9670 | 0.9708 | 0.9746 | 0.9783 | 0.9821 | 0.9858 | 0.9895 |
| 2.7 | 0.9933 | 0.9969 | 1.0006 | 1.0043 | 1.0080 | 1.0116 | 1.0152 | 1.0188 | 1.0225 | 1.0260 |
| 2.8 | 1.0296 | 1.0332 | 1.0367 | 1.0403 | 1.0438 | 1.0473 | 1.0508 | 1.0543 | 1.0578 | 1.0613 |
| 2.9 | 1.0647 | 1.0682 | 1.0716 | 1.0750 | 1.0784 | 1.0818 | 1.0852 | 1.0886 | 1.0919 | 1.0953 |
| **3.0** | 1.0986 | 1.1019 | 1.1053 | 1.1086 | 1.1119 | 1.1151 | 1.1184 | 1.1217 | 1.1249 | 1.1282 |
| 3.1 | 1.1314 | 1.1346 | 1.1378 | 1.1410 | 1.1442 | 1.1474 | 1.1506 | 1.1537 | 1.1569 | 1.1600 |
| 3.2 | 1.1632 | 1.1663 | 1.1694 | 1.1725 | 1.1756 | 1.1787 | 1.1817 | 1.1848 | 1.1878 | 1.1909 |
| 3.3 | 1.1939 | 1.1970 | 1.2000 | 1.2030 | 1.2060 | 1.2090 | 1.2119 | 1.2149 | 1.2179 | 1.2208 |
| 3.4 | 1.2238 | 1.2267 | 1.2296 | 1.2326 | 1.2355 | 1.2384 | 1.2413 | 1.2442 | 1.2470 | 1.2499 |
| **3.5** | 1.2528 | 1.2556 | 1.2585 | 1.2613 | 1.2641 | 1.2669 | 1.2698 | 1.2726 | 1.2754 | 1.2782 |
| 3.6 | 1.2809 | 1.2837 | 1.2865 | 1.2892 | 1.2920 | 1.2947 | 1.2975 | 1.3002 | 1.3029 | 1.3056 |
| 3.7 | 1.3083 | 1.3110 | 1.3137 | 1.3164 | 1.3191 | 1.3218 | 1.3244 | 1.3271 | 1.3297 | 1.3324 |
| 3.8 | 1.3350 | 1.3376 | 1.3403 | 1.3429 | 1.3455 | 1.3481 | 1.3507 | 1.3533 | 1.3558 | 1.3584 |
| 3.9 | 1.3610 | 1.3635 | 1.3661 | 1.3686 | 1.3712 | 1.3737 | 1.3762 | 1.3788 | 1.3813 | 1.3838 |
| **4.0** | 1.3863 | 1.3888 | 1.3913 | 1.3938 | 1.3962 | 1.3987 | 1.4012 | 1.4036 | 1.4061 | 1.4085 |
| 4.1 | 1.4110 | 1.4134 | 1.4159 | 1.4183 | 1.4207 | 1.4231 | 1.4255 | 1.4279 | 1.4303 | 1.4327 |
| 4.2 | 1.4351 | 1.4375 | 1.4398 | 1.4422 | 1.4446 | 1.4469 | 1.4493 | 1.4516 | 1.4540 | 1.4563 |
| 4.3 | 1.4586 | 1.4609 | 1.4633 | 1.4656 | 1.4679 | 1.4702 | 1.4725 | 1.4748 | 1.4770 | 1.4793 |
| 4.4 | 1.4816 | 1.4839 | 1.4861 | 1.4884 | 1.4907 | 1.4929 | 1.4952 | 1.4974 | 1.4996 | 1.5019 |
| **4.5** | 1.5041 | 1.5063 | 1.5085 | 1.5107 | 1.5129 | 1.5151 | 1.5173 | 1.5195 | 1.5217 | 1.5239 |
| 4.6 | 1.5261 | 1.5282 | 1.5304 | 1.5326 | 1.5347 | 1.5369 | 1.5390 | 1.5412 | 1.5433 | 1.5454 |
| 4.7 | 1.5476 | 1.5497 | 1.5518 | 1.5539 | 1.5560 | 1.5581 | 1.5602 | 1.5623 | 1.5644 | 1.5665 |
| 4.8 | 1.5686 | 1.5707 | 1.5728 | 1.5748 | 1.5769 | 1.5790 | 1.5810 | 1.5831 | 1.5851 | 1.5872 |
| 4.9 | 1.5892 | 1.5913 | 1.5933 | 1.5953 | 1.5974 | 1.5994 | 1.6014 | 1.6034 | 1.6054 | 1.6074 |
| **5.0** | 1.6094 | 1.6114 | 1.6134 | 1.6154 | 1.6174 | 1.6194 | 1.6214 | 1.6233 | 1.6253 | 1.6273 |
| 5.1 | 1.6292 | 1.6312 | 1.6332 | 1.6351 | 1.6371 | 1.6390 | 1.6409 | 1.6429 | 1.6448 | 1.6467 |
| 5.2 | 1.6487 | 1.6506 | 1.6525 | 1.6544 | 1.6563 | 1.6582 | 1.6601 | 1.6620 | 1.6639 | 1.6658 |
| 5.3 | 1.6677 | 1.6696 | 1.6715 | 1.6734 | 1.6752 | 1.6771 | 1.6790 | 1.6808 | 1.6827 | 1.6845 |
| 5.4 | 1.6864 | 1.6882 | 1.6901 | 1.6919 | 1.6938 | 1.6956 | 1.6974 | 1.6993 | 1.7011 | 1.7029 |
| **5.5** | 1.7047 | 1.7066 | 1.7084 | 1.7102 | 1.7120 | 1.7138 | 1.7156 | 1.7174 | 1.7192 | 1.7210 |
| 5.6 | 1.7228 | 1.7246 | 1.7263 | 1.7281 | 1.7299 | 1.7317 | 1.7334 | 1.7352 | 1.7370 | 1.7387 |
| 5.7 | 1.7405 | 1.7422 | 1.7440 | 1.7457 | 1.7475 | 1.7492 | 1.7509 | 1.7527 | 1.7544 | 1.7561 |
| 5.8 | 1.7579 | 1.7596 | 1.7613 | 1.7630 | 1.7647 | 1.7664 | 1.7682 | 1.7699 | 1.7716 | 1.7733 |
| 5.9 | 1.7750 | 1.7766 | 1.7783 | 1.7800 | 1.7817 | 1.7834 | 1.7851 | 1.7867 | 1.7884 | 1.7901 |
| **6.0** | 1.7918 | 1.7934 | 1.7951 | 1.7967 | 1.7984 | 1.8001 | 1.8017 | 1.8034 | 1.8050 | 1.8066 |
| 6.1 | 1.8083 | 1.8099 | 1.8116 | 1.8132 | 1.8148 | 1.8164 | 1.8181 | 1.8197 | 1.8213 | 1.8229 |
| 6.2 | 1.8245 | 1.8262 | 1.8278 | 1.8294 | 1.8310 | 1.8326 | 1.8342 | 1.8358 | 1.8374 | 1.8390 |
| 6.3 | 1.8406 | 1.8421 | 1.8437 | 1.8453 | 1.8469 | 1.8485 | 1.8500 | 1.8516 | 1.8532 | 1.8547 |
| 6.4 | 1.8563 | 1.8579 | 1.8594 | 1.8610 | 1.8625 | 1.8641 | 1.8656 | 1.8672 | 1.8687 | 1.8703 |
| **6.5** | 1.8718 | 1.8733 | 1.8749 | 1.8764 | 1.8779 | 1.8795 | 1.8810 | 1.8825 | 1.8840 | 1.8856 |
| 6.6 | 1.8871 | 1.8886 | 1.8901 | 1.8916 | 1.8931 | 1.8946 | 1.8961 | 1.8976 | 1.8991 | 1.9006 |
| 6.7 | 1.9021 | 1.9036 | 1.9051 | 1.9066 | 1.9081 | 1.9095 | 1.9110 | 1.9125 | 1.9140 | 1.9155 |
| 6.8 | 1.9169 | 1.9184 | 1.9199 | 1.9213 | 1.9228 | 1.9242 | 1.9257 | 1.9272 | 1.9286 | 1.9301 |
| 6.9 | 1.9315 | 1.9330 | 1.9344 | 1.9359 | 1.9373 | 1.9387 | 1.9402 | 1.9416 | 1.9430 | 1.9445 |

| | .00 | .01 | .02 | .03 | .04 | .05 | .06 | .07 | .08 | .09 |
|---|---|---|---|---|---|---|---|---|---|---|
| 7.0 | 1.9459 | 1.9473 | 1.9488 | 1.9502 | 1.9516 | 1.9530 | 1.9544 | 1.9559 | 1.9573 | 1.9587 |
| 7.1 | 1.9601 | 1.9615 | 1.9629 | 1.9643 | 1.9657 | 1.9671 | 1.9685 | 1.9699 | 1.9713 | 1.9727 |
| 7.2 | 1.9741 | 1.9755 | 1.9769 | 1.9782 | 1.9796 | 1.9810 | 1.9824 | 1.9838 | 1.9851 | 1.9865 |
| 7.3 | 1.9879 | 1.9892 | 1.9906 | 1.9920 | 1.9933 | 1.9947 | 1.9961 | 1.9974 | 1.9988 | 2.0001 |
| 7.4 | 2.0015 | 2.0028 | 2.0042 | 2.0055 | 2.0069 | 2.0082 | 2.0096 | 2.0109 | 2.0122 | 2.0136 |
| 7.5 | 2.0149 | 2.0162 | 2.0176 | 2.0189 | 2.0202 | 2.0215 | 2.0229 | 2.0242 | 2.0255 | 2.0268 |
| 7.6 | 2.0282 | 2.0295 | 2.0308 | 2.0321 | 2.0334 | 2.0347 | 2.0360 | 2.0373 | 2.0386 | 2.0399 |
| 7.7 | 2.0412 | 2.0425 | 2.0438 | 2.0451 | 2.0464 | 2.0477 | 2.0490 | 2.0503 | 2.0516 | 2.0528 |
| 7.8 | 2.0541 | 2.0554 | 2.0567 | 2.0580 | 2.0592 | 2.0605 | 2.0618 | 2.0631 | 2.0643 | 2.0656 |
| 7.9 | 2.0669 | 2.0681 | 2.0694 | 2.0707 | 2.0719 | 2.0732 | 2.0744 | 2.0757 | 2.0769 | 2.0782 |
| 8.0 | 2.0794 | 2.0807 | 2.0819 | 2.0832 | 2.0844 | 2.0857 | 2.0869 | 2.0882 | 2.0894 | 2.0906 |
| 8.1 | 2.0919 | 2.0931 | 2.0943 | 2.0956 | 2.0968 | 2.0980 | 2.0992 | 2.1005 | 2.1017 | 2.1029 |
| 8.2 | 2.1041 | 2.1054 | 2.1066 | 2.1078 | 2.1090 | 2.1102 | 2.1114 | 2.1126 | 2.1138 | 2.1150 |
| 8.3 | 2.1163 | 2.1175 | 2.1187 | 2.1199 | 2.1211 | 2.1223 | 2.1235 | 2.1247 | 2.1258 | 2.1270 |
| 8.4 | 2.1282 | 2.1294 | 2.1306 | 2.1318 | 2.1330 | 2.1342 | 2.1353 | 2.1365 | 2.1377 | 2.1389 |
| 8.5 | 2.1401 | 2.1412 | 2.1424 | 2.1436 | 2.1448 | 2.1459 | 2.1471 | 2.1483 | 2.1494 | 2.1500 |
| 8.6 | 2.1518 | 2.1529 | 2.1541 | 2.1552 | 2.1564 | 2.1576 | 2.1587 | 2.1599 | 2.1610 | 2.1622 |
| 8.7 | 2.1633 | 2.1645 | 2.1656 | 2.1668 | 2.1679 | 2.1691 | 2.1702 | 2.1713 | 2.1725 | 2.1736 |
| 8.8 | 2.1748 | 2.1759 | 2.1770 | 2.1782 | 2.1793 | 2.1804 | 2.1815 | 2.1827 | 2.1838 | 2.1849 |
| 8.9 | 2.1861 | 2.1872 | 2.1883 | 2.1894 | 2.1905 | 2.1917 | 2.1928 | 2.1939 | 2.1950 | 2.1961 |
| 9.0 | 2.1972 | 2.1983 | 2.1994 | 2.2006 | 2.2017 | 2.2028 | 2.2039 | 2.2050 | 2.2061 | 2.2072 |
| 9.1 | 2.2083 | 2.2094 | 2.2105 | 2.2116 | 2.2127 | 2.2138 | 2.2148 | 2.2159 | 2.2170 | 2.2181 |
| 9.2 | 2.2192 | 2.2203 | 2.2214 | 2.2225 | 2.2235 | 2.2246 | 2.2257 | 2.2268 | 2.2279 | 2.2289 |
| 9.3 | 2.2300 | 2.2311 | 2.2322 | 2.2332 | 2.2343 | 2.2354 | 2.2364 | 2.2375 | 2.2386 | 2.2396 |
| 9.4 | 2.2407 | 2.2418 | 2.2428 | 2.2439 | 2.2450 | 2.2460 | 2.2471 | 2.2481 | 2.2492 | 2.2502 |
| 9.5 | 2.2513 | 2.2523 | 2.2534 | 2.2544 | 2.2555 | 2.2565 | 2.2576 | 2.2586 | 2.2597 | 2.2607 |
| 9.6 | 2.2618 | 2.2628 | 2.2638 | 2.2649 | 2.2659 | 2.2670 | 2.2680 | 2.2690 | 2.2701 | 2.2711 |
| 9.7 | 2.2721 | 2.2732 | 2.2742 | 2.2752 | 2.2762 | 2.2773 | 2.2783 | 2.2793 | 2.2803 | 2.2814 |
| 9.8 | 2.2824 | 2.2834 | 2.2844 | 2.2854 | 2.2865 | 2.2875 | 2.2885 | 2.2895 | 2.2905 | 2.2915 |
| 9.9 | 2.2925 | 2.2935 | 2.2946 | 2.2956 | 2.2966 | 2.2976 | 2.2986 | 2.2996 | 2.3006 | 2.3016 |

| | 0 | 1 | 2 | 3 | 4 | 5 | 6 | 7 | 8 | 9 |
|---|---|---|---|---|---|---|---|---|---|---|
| 1 | 2.3026 | 2.3979 | 2.4849 | 2.5649 | 2.6391 | 2.7080 | 2.7726 | 2.8332 | 2.8904 | 2.9444 |
| 2 | 2.9957 | 3.0445 | 3.0910 | 3.1355 | 3.1780 | 3.2189 | 3.2581 | 3.2958 | 3.3322 | 3.3673 |
| 3 | 3.4012 | 3.4340 | 3.4657 | 3.4965 | 3.5264 | 3.5553 | 3.5835 | 3.6109 | 3.6376 | 3.6636 |
| 4 | 3.6889 | 3.7136 | 3.7377 | 3.7612 | 3.7842 | 3.8067 | 3.8286 | 3.8501 | 3.8712 | 3.8918 |
| 5 | 3.9120 | 3.9318 | 3.9512 | 3.9703 | 3.9890 | 4.0073 | 4.0253 | 4.0430 | 4.0604 | 4.0775 |
| 6 | 4.0943 | 4.1109 | 4.1271 | 4.1431 | 4.1589 | 4.1744 | 4.1896 | 4.2047 | 4.2195 | 4.2341 |
| 7 | 4.2485 | 4.2627 | 4.2767 | 4.2905 | 4.3041 | 4.3175 | 4.3307 | 4.3438 | 4.3567 | 4.3694 |
| 8 | 4.3820 | 4.3944 | 4.4067 | 4.4188 | 4.4308 | 4.4426 | 4.4543 | 4.4659 | 4.4773 | 4.4886 |
| 9 | 4.4998 | 4.5109 | 4.5218 | 4.5326 | 4.5433 | 4.5539 | 4.5643 | 4.5747 | 4.5850 | 4.5951 |
| 10 | 4.6052 | 4.6151 | 4.6250 | 4.6347 | 4.6444 | 4.6540 | 4.6634 | 4.6728 | 4.6821 | 4.6913 |

| $x$ | $e^{-x}$ | $e^x$ | sinh $x$ | cosh $x$ |
|------|----------|---------|-----------|-----------|
| **0.00** | 1.0000 | 1.0000 | 0.0000 | 1.0000 |
| .01 | 0.9900 | 1.0101 | 0.0100 | 1.0001 |
| .02 | .9802 | 1.0202 | 0.0200 | 1.0002 |
| .03 | .9704 | 1.0305 | 0.0300 | 1.0005 |
| .04 | .9608 | 1.0408 | 0.0400 | 1.0008 |
| **.05** | .9512 | 1.0513 | 0.0500 | 1.0013 |
| .06 | .9418 | 1.0618 | 0.0600 | 1.0018 |
| .07 | .9324 | 1.0725 | 0.0701 | 1.0025 |
| .08 | .9231 | 1.0833 | 0.0801 | 1.0032 |
| .09 | .9139 | 1.0942 | 0.0901 | 1.0041 |
| **.10** | .9048 | 1.1052 | 0.1002 | 1.0050 |
| .11 | .8958 | 1.1163 | 0.1102 | 1.0061 |
| .12 | .8869 | 1.1275 | 0.1203 | 1.0072 |
| .13 | .8781 | 1.1388 | 0.1304 | 1.0085 |
| .14 | .8694 | 1.1503 | 0.1405 | 1.0098 |
| **.15** | .8607 | 1.1618 | 0.1506 | 1.0113 |
| .16 | .8521 | 1.1735 | 0.1607 | 1.0128 |
| .17 | .8437 | 1.1853 | 0.1708 | 1.0145 |
| .18 | .8353 | 1.1972 | 0.1810 | 1.0162 |
| .19 | .8270 | 1.2092 | 0.1911 | 1.0181 |
| **.20** | .8187 | 1.2214 | 0.2013 | 1.0201 |
| .21 | .8106 | 1.2337 | 0.2115 | 1.0221 |
| .22 | .8025 | 1.2461 | 0.2218 | 1.0243 |
| .23 | .7945 | 1.2586 | 0.2320 | 1.0266 |
| .24 | .7866 | 1.2712 | 0.2423 | 1.0289 |
| **.25** | .7788 | 1.2840 | 0.2526 | 1.0314 |
| .26 | .7711 | 1.2969 | 0.2629 | 1.0340 |
| .27 | .7634 | 1.3100 | 0.2733 | 1.0367 |
| .28 | .7558 | 1.3231 | 0.2837 | 1.0395 |
| .29 | .7483 | 1.3364 | 0.2941 | 1.0423 |

| $x$ | $e^{-x}$ | $e^x$ | sinh $x$ | cosh $x$ |
|---|---|---|---|---|
| **.30** | .7408 | 1.3499 | 0.3045 | 1.0453 |
| .31 | .7334 | 1.3634 | 0.3150 | 1.0484 |
| .32 | .7261 | 1.3771 | 0.3255 | 1.0516 |
| .33 | .7189 | 1.3910 | 0.3360 | 1.0549 |
| .34 | .7118 | 1.4049 | 0.3466 | 1.0584 |
| **.35** | .7047 | 1.4191 | 0.3572 | 1.0619 |
| .36 | .6977 | 1.4333 | 0.3678 | 1.0655 |
| .37 | .6907 | 1.4477 | 0.3785 | 1.0692 |
| .38 | .6839 | 1.4623 | 0.3892 | 1.0731 |
| .39 | .6771 | 1.4770 | 0.4000 | 1.0770 |
| **.40** | .6703 | 1.4918 | 0.4108 | 1.0811 |
| .41 | .6636 | 1.5068 | 0.4216 | 1.0852 |
| .42 | .6570 | 1.5220 | 0.4325 | 1.0895 |
| .43 | .6505 | 1.5373 | 0.4434 | 1.0939 |
| .44 | .6440 | 1.5527 | 0.4543 | 1.0984 |
| **.45** | .6376 | 1.5683 | 0.4653 | 1.1030 |
| .46 | .6313 | 1.5841 | 0.4764 | 1.1077 |
| .47 | .6250 | 1.6000 | 0.4875 | 1.1125 |
| .48 | .6188 | 1.6161 | 0.4986 | 1.1174 |
| .49 | .6126 | 1.6323 | 0.5098 | 1.1225 |
| **.50** | .6065 | 1.6487 | 0.5211 | 1.1276 |
| .51 | .6005 | 1.6653 | 0.5324 | 1.1329 |
| .52 | .5945 | 1.6820 | 0.5438 | 1.1383 |
| .53 | .5886 | 1.6989 | 0.5552 | 1.1438 |
| .54 | .5827 | 1.7160 | 0.5666 | 1.1494 |
| **.55** | .5770 | 1.7333 | 0.5782 | 1.1551 |
| .56 | .5712 | 1.7507 | 0.5897 | 1.1609 |
| .57 | .5655 | 1.7683 | 0.6014 | 1.1669 |
| .58 | .5599 | 1.7860 | 0.6131 | 1.1730 |
| .59 | .5543 | 1.8040 | 0.6248 | 1.1792 |
| **.60** | .5488 | 1.8221 | 0.6367 | 1.1855 |
| .61 | .5433 | 1.8404 | 0.6485 | 1.1919 |
| .62 | .5379 | 1.8589 | 0.6605 | 1.1984 |
| .63 | .5326 | 1.8776 | 0.6725 | 1.2051 |
| .64 | .5273 | 1.8965 | 0.6846 | 1.2119 |
| **.65** | .5220 | 1.9155 | 0.6967 | 1.2188 |
| .66 | .5169 | 1.9348 | 0.7090 | 1.2258 |
| .67 | .5117 | 1.9542 | 0.7213 | 1.2330 |
| .68 | .5066 | 1.9739 | 0.7336 | 1.2402 |
| .69 | .5016 | 1.9937 | 0.7461 | 1.2476 |
| **.70** | .4966 | 2.0138 | 0.7586 | 1.2552 |
| .71 | .4916 | 2.0340 | 0.7712 | 1.2628 |
| .72 | .4867 | 2.0544 | 0.7838 | 1.2706 |
| .73 | .4819 | 2.0751 | 0.7966 | 1.2785 |
| .74 | .4771 | 2.0959 | 0.8094 | 1.2865 |
| **.75** | .4724 | 2.1170 | 0.8223 | 1.2947 |
| .76 | .4677 | 2.1383 | 0.8353 | 1.3030 |
| .77 | .4630 | 2.1598 | 0.8484 | 1.3114 |
| .78 | .4584 | 2.1815 | 0.8615 | 1.3199 |
| .79 | .4538 | 2.2034 | 0.8748 | 1.3286 |

| $x$ | $e^{-x}$ | $e^x$ | sinh $x$ | cosh $x$ |
|---|---|---|---|---|
| **.80** | .4493 | 2.2255 | 0.8881 | 1.3374 |
| .81 | .4449 | 2.2479 | 0.9015 | 1.3464 |
| .82 | .4404 | 2.2705 | 0.9150 | 1.3555 |
| .83 | .4360 | 2.2933 | 0.9286 | 1.3647 |
| .84 | .4317 | 2.3164 | 0.9423 | 1.3740 |
| **.85** | .4274 | 2.3396 | 0.9561 | 1.3835 |
| .86 | .4232 | 2.3632 | 0.9700 | 1.3932 |
| .87 | .4190 | 2.3869 | 0.9840 | 1.4029 |
| .88 | .4148 | 2.4109 | 0.9981 | 1.4128 |
| .89 | .4107 | 2.4351 | 1.0122 | 1.4229 |
| **.90** | .4066 | 2.4596 | 1.0265 | 1.4331 |
| .91 | .4025 | 2.4843 | 1.0409 | 1.4434 |
| .92 | .3985 | 2.5093 | 1.0554 | 1.4539 |
| .93 | .3946 | 2.5345 | 1.0700 | 1.4645 |
| .94 | .3906 | 2.5600 | 1.0847 | 1.4753 |
| **.95** | .3867 | 2.5857 | 1.0995 | 1.4862 |
| .96 | .3829 | 2.6117 | 1.1144 | 1.4973 |
| .97 | .3791 | 2.6379 | 1.1294 | 1.5085 |
| .98 | .3753 | 2.6645 | 1.1446 | 1.5199 |
| .99 | .3716 | 2.6912 | 1.1598 | 1.5314 |
| **1.00** | .3679 | 2.7183 | 1.1752 | 1.5431 |
| 1.05 | .3499 | 2.8577 | 1.2539 | 1.6038 |
| 1.10 | .3329 | 3.0042 | 1.3356 | 1.6685 |
| 1.15 | .3166 | 3.1582 | 1.4208 | 1.7374 |
| 1.20 | .3012 | 3.3201 | 1.5095 | 1.8107 |
| **1.25** | .2865 | 3.4903 | 1.6019 | 1.8884 |
| 1.30 | .2725 | 3.6693 | 1.6984 | 1.9709 |
| 1.35 | .2592 | 3.8574 | 1.7991 | 2.0583 |
| 1.40 | .2466 | 4.0552 | 1.9043 | 2.1509 |
| 1.45 | .2346 | 4.2631 | 2.0143 | 2.2488 |
| **1.50** | .2231 | 4.4817 | 2.1293 | 2.3524 |
| 1.55 | .2122 | 4.7115 | 2.2496 | 2.4619 |
| 1.60 | .2019 | 4.9530 | 2.3756 | 2.5775 |
| 1.65 | .1920 | 5.2070 | 2.5075 | 2.6995 |
| 1.70 | .1827 | 5.4739 | 2.6456 | 2.8283 |
| **1.75** | .1738 | 5.7546 | 2.7904 | 2.9642 |
| 1.80 | .1653 | 6.0496 | 2.9422 | 3.1075 |
| 1.85 | .1572 | 6.3598 | 3.1013 | 3.2585 |
| 1.90 | .1496 | 6.6859 | 3.2682 | 3.4177 |
| 1.95 | .1423 | 7.0287 | 3.4432 | 3.5855 |
| **2.00** | .1353 | 7.3891 | 3.6269 | 3.7622 |
| 2.05 | .1287 | 7.7679 | 3.8196 | 3.9483 |
| 2.10 | .1225 | 8.1662 | 4.0219 | 4.1443 |
| 2.15 | .1165 | 8.5849 | 4.2342 | 4.3507 |
| 2.20 | .1108 | 9.0250 | 4.4571 | 4.5679 |
| **2.25** | .1054 | 9.4877 | 4.6912 | 4.7966 |
| 2.30 | .1003 | 9.9742 | 4.9370 | 5.0372 |
| 2.35 | .0954 | 10.486 | 5.1951 | 5.2905 |
| 2.40 | .0907 | 11.023 | 5.4662 | 5.5569 |
| 2.45 | .0863 | 11.588 | 5.7510 | 5.8373 |

## IV. EXPONENTIAL AND HYPERBOLIC FUNCTIONS

| $x$ | $e^{-x}$ | $e^x$ | sinh $x$ | cosh $x$ |
|---|---|---|---|---|
| **2.50** | .0821 | 12.182 | 6.0502 | 6.1323 |
| 2.55 | .0781 | 12.807 | 6.3645 | 6.4426 |
| 2.60 | .0743 | 13.464 | 6.6947 | 6.7690 |
| 2.65 | .0706 | 14.154 | 7.0417 | 7.1123 |
| 2.70 | .0672 | 14.880 | 7.4063 | 7.4735 |
| **2.75** | .0639 | 15.643 | 7.7894 | 7.8533 |
| 2.80 | .0608 | 16.445 | 8.1919 | 8.2527 |
| 2.85 | .0578 | 17.288 | 8.6150 | 8.6728 |
| 2.90 | .0550 | 18.174 | 9.0596 | 9.1146 |
| 2.95 | .0523 | 19.106 | 9.5268 | 9.5791 |
| **3.00** | .0498 | 20.086 | 10.018 | 10.068 |
| 3.05 | .0474 | 21.115 | 10.534 | 10.581 |
| 3.10 | .0450 | 22.198 | 11.076 | 11.122 |
| 3.15 | .0428 | 23.336 | 11.647 | 11.689 |
| 3.20 | .0408 | 24.533 | 12.246 | 12.287 |
| **3.25** | .0388 | 25.790 | 12.876 | 12.915 |
| 3.30 | .0369 | 27.113 | 13.538 | 13.575 |
| 3.35 | .0351 | 28.503 | 14.234 | 14.269 |
| 3.40 | .0334 | 29.964 | 14.965 | 14.999 |
| 3.45 | .0317 | 31.500 | 15.734 | 15.766 |
| **3.50** | .0302 | 33.115 | 16.543 | 16.573 |
| 3.55 | .0287 | 34.813 | 17.392 | 17.421 |
| 3.60 | .0273 | 36.598 | 18.286 | 18.313 |
| 3.65 | .0260 | 38.475 | 19.224 | 19.250 |
| 3.70 | .0247 | 40.447 | 20.211 | 20.236 |
| **3.75** | .0235 | 42.521 | 21.249 | 21.272 |
| 3.80 | .0224 | 44.701 | 22.339 | 22.362 |
| 3.85 | .0213 | 46.993 | 23.486 | 23.507 |
| 3.90 | .0202 | 49.402 | 24.691 | 24.711 |
| 3.95 | .0192 | 51.935 | 25.958 | 25.977 |
| **4.00** | .0183 | 54.598 | 27.290 | 27.308 |
| 4.10 | .0166 | 60.340 | 30.162 | 30.178 |
| 4.20 | .0150 | 66.686 | 33.336 | 33.351 |
| 4.30 | .0136 | 73.700 | 36.843 | 36.857 |
| 4.40 | .0123 | 81.451 | 40.719 | 40.732 |
| **4.50** | .0111 | 90.017 | 45.003 | 45.014 |
| 4.60 | .0100 | 99.484 | 49.737 | 49.747 |
| 4.70 | .0091 | 109.95 | 54.969 | 54.978 |
| 4.80 | .0082 | 121.51 | 60.751 | 60.759 |
| 4.90 | .0074 | 134.29 | 67.141 | 67.149 |
| **5.00** | .0067 | 148.41 | 74.203 | 74.210 |
| 5.20 | .0055 | 181.27 | 90.633 | 90.639 |
| 5.40 | .0045 | 221.41 | 110.70 | 110.71 |
| 5.60 | .0037 | 270.43 | 135.21 | 135.22 |
| 5.80 | .0030 | 330.30 | 165.15 | 165.15 |
| **6.00** | .0025 | 403.43 | 201.71 | 201.72 |
| 7.00 | .0009 | 1096.6 | 548.32 | 548.32 |
| 8.00 | .0003 | 2981.0 | 1490.5 | 1490.5 |
| 9.00 | .0001 | 8103.1 | 4051.5 | 4051.5 |
| 10.00 | .00005 | 22026. | 11013. | 11013. |

# V. A TABLE OF INTEGRALS

## Forms Involving $ax + b$

1. $\displaystyle\int \frac{x\,dx}{ax+b} = \frac{1}{a^2}[ax+b-b\ln(ax+b)]$

2. $\displaystyle\int \frac{x\,dx}{(ax+b)^2} = \frac{1}{a^2}\left[\frac{b}{ax+b} + \ln(ax+b)\right]$

3. $\displaystyle\int \frac{x\,dx}{(ax+b)^3} = \frac{1}{a^2}\left[\frac{-1}{ax+b} + \frac{b}{2(ax+b)^2}\right]$

4. $\displaystyle\int \frac{x\,dx}{(ax+b)^4} = \frac{1}{a^2}\left[\frac{-1}{2(ax+b)^2} + \frac{b}{3(ax+b)^3}\right]$

5. $\displaystyle\int \frac{x\,dx}{(ax+b)^n} = \frac{1}{a^2}\left[\frac{-1}{(n-2)(ax+b)^{n-2}} + \frac{b}{(n-1)(ax+b)^{n-1}}\right],\ n \neq 1, 2$

6. $\displaystyle\int \frac{x^2\,dx}{ax+b} = \frac{1}{a^3}\left[\frac{(ax+b)^2}{2} - 2b(ax+b) + b^2\ln(ax+b)\right]$

7. $\displaystyle\int \frac{x^2\,dx}{(ax+b)^2} = \frac{1}{a^3}\left[ax+b - \frac{b^2}{ax+b} - 2b\ln(ax+b)\right]$

8. $\displaystyle\int \frac{x^2\,dx}{(ax+b)^3} = \frac{1}{a^3}\left[\frac{2b}{ax+b} - \frac{b^2}{2(ax+b)^2} + \ln(ax+b)\right]$

9. $\displaystyle\int \frac{x^2\,dx}{(ax+b)^4} = \frac{1}{a^3}\left[\frac{-1}{ax+b} + \frac{b}{(ax+b)^2} - \frac{b^2}{3(ax+b)^3}\right]$

10. $\displaystyle\int \frac{x^2\,dx}{(ax+b)^n}$

$\displaystyle = \frac{1}{a^3}\left[\frac{-1}{(n-3)(ax+b)^{n-3}} + \frac{2b}{(n-2)(ax+b)^{n-2}} - \frac{b^2}{(n-1)(ax+b)^{n-1}}\right],$
$$n \neq 1, 2, 3$$

11. $\displaystyle\int x^m(ax+b)^n\,dx$

$\displaystyle = \frac{1}{m+n+1}\left[x^{m+1}(ax+b)^n + bn\int x^m(ax+b)^{n-1}\,dx\right],\ m+n \neq -1$

12. $\displaystyle\int x^m(ax+b)^n\,dx$

$\displaystyle = \frac{1}{b(n+1)}\left[-x^{m+1}(ax+b)^{n+1} + (m+n+2)\int x^m(ax+b)^{n+1}\,dx\right]$
$$b \neq 0,\ n \neq -1$$

## Forms Involving $ax^2 + bx + c$

13. $\displaystyle\int \frac{dx}{ax^2+bx+c} = \frac{2}{\sqrt{4ac-b^2}}\arctan\frac{2ax+b}{\sqrt{4ac-b^2}},\quad b^2-4ac < 0$

310

14. $\displaystyle\int \frac{dx}{ax^2 + bx + c} = \frac{1}{\sqrt{b^2 - 4ac}} \ln \frac{2ax + b - \sqrt{b^2 - 4ac}}{2ax + b + \sqrt{b^2 - 4ac}}, \quad b^2 - 4ac > 0$

15. $\displaystyle\int \frac{dx}{(ax^2 + bx + c)^2} = \frac{1}{(4ac - b^2)}\left[\frac{2ax + b}{ax^2 + bx + c} + 2a\int \frac{dx}{ax^2 + bx + c}\right],$

$$b^2 - 4ac \neq 0$$

16. $\displaystyle\int \frac{dx}{(ax^2 + bx + c)^3}$

$$= \frac{1}{(4ac - b^2)^2}\left[\frac{(4ac - b^2)(2ax + b)}{2(ax^2 + bx + c)^2} + \frac{3a(2ax + b)}{ax^2 + bx + c} + 6a^2\int \frac{dx}{ax^2 + bx + c}\right],$$

$$b^2 - 4ac \neq 0$$

17. $\displaystyle\int \frac{dx}{(ax^2 + bx + c)^n}$

$$= \frac{1}{(n - 1)(4ac - b^2)}\left[\frac{2ax + b}{(ax^2 + bx + c)^{n-1}} + 2a(2n - 3)\int \frac{dx}{(ax^2 + bx + c)^{n-1}}\right],$$

$$n \neq 1, \, b^2 - 4ac \neq 0$$

## Forms Involving $\sqrt{ax + b}$

18. $\displaystyle\int x\sqrt{ax + b}\, dx = \frac{2(3ax - 2b)(ax + b)^{\frac{3}{2}}}{15a^2}$

19. $\displaystyle\int x^2\sqrt{ax + b}\, dx = \frac{2(15a^2x^2 - 12abx + 8b^2)(ax + b)^{\frac{3}{2}}}{105a^3}$

20. $\displaystyle\int \frac{\sqrt{ax + b}}{x}\, dx = 2\sqrt{ax + b} + 2\sqrt{b}\ln \frac{\sqrt{ax + b} - \sqrt{b}}{\sqrt{x}}, \quad b > 0$

21. $\displaystyle\int \frac{\sqrt{ax + b}}{x}\, dx = 2\sqrt{ax + b} - 2\sqrt{-b}\arctan \frac{\sqrt{ax + b}}{\sqrt{-b}}, \quad b < 0$

22. $\displaystyle\int \frac{\sqrt{ax + b}}{x^2}\, dx = -\frac{\sqrt{ax + b}}{x} + \frac{a}{\sqrt{b}}\ln \frac{\sqrt{ax + b} - \sqrt{b}}{\sqrt{x}}, \quad b > 0$

23. $\displaystyle\int \frac{\sqrt{ax + b}}{x^2}\, dx = -\frac{\sqrt{ax + b}}{x} + \frac{a}{\sqrt{-b}}\arctan \frac{\sqrt{ax + b}}{\sqrt{-b}}, \quad b < 0$

24. $\displaystyle\int \frac{dx}{x\sqrt{ax + b}} = \frac{2}{\sqrt{b}}\ln \frac{\sqrt{ax + b} - \sqrt{b}}{\sqrt{x}}, \quad b > 0$

25. $\displaystyle\int \frac{dx}{x\sqrt{ax + b}} = \frac{2}{\sqrt{-b}}\arctan \frac{\sqrt{ax + b}}{\sqrt{-b}}, \quad b < 0$

26. $\displaystyle\int \frac{dx}{x^2\sqrt{ax + b}} = -\frac{\sqrt{ax + b}}{bx} - \frac{a}{b^{\frac{3}{2}}}\ln \frac{\sqrt{ax + b} - \sqrt{b}}{\sqrt{x}}, \quad b > 0$

27. $\displaystyle\int \frac{dx}{x^2\sqrt{ax + b}} = -\frac{\sqrt{ax + b}}{bx} + \frac{a}{(-b)^{\frac{3}{2}}}\arctan \frac{\sqrt{ax + b}}{\sqrt{-b}}, \quad b < 0$

28. $\displaystyle\int \frac{x\,dx}{\sqrt{ax+b}} = \frac{2(ax-2b)\sqrt{ax+b}}{3a^2}$

29. $\displaystyle\int \frac{x^2\,dx}{\sqrt{ax+b}} = \frac{2(3a^2x^2 - 4abx + 8b^2)\sqrt{ax+b}}{15a^3}$

30. $\displaystyle\int \frac{x^n\,dx}{\sqrt{ax+b}} = \frac{2x^n\sqrt{ax+b}}{(2n+1)a} - \frac{2nb}{(2n+1)a}\int \frac{x^{n-1}\,dx}{\sqrt{ax+b}}, \quad n \neq -\tfrac{1}{2}$

31. $\displaystyle\int \frac{dx}{x^n\sqrt{ax+b}} = \frac{-\sqrt{ax+b}}{(n-1)bx^{n-1}} - \frac{(2n-3)a}{2(n-1)b}\int \frac{dx}{x^{n-1}\sqrt{ax+b}},$
$$b \neq 0, \; n \neq 1$$

32. $\displaystyle\int x^n\sqrt{ax+b}\,dx = \frac{2}{(2n+3)a}\left[x^n(ax+b)^{\frac{3}{2}} - bn\int x^{n-1}\sqrt{ax+b}\,dx\right],$
$$n \neq -\tfrac{3}{2}$$

33. $\displaystyle\int \frac{\sqrt{ax+b}}{x^n}\,dx = \frac{1}{n-1}\left[-\frac{\sqrt{ax+b}}{x^{n-1}} + \frac{a}{2}\int \frac{dx}{x^{n-1}\sqrt{ax+b}}\right], \quad n \neq 1$

## Forms Involving $\sqrt{x^2 \pm a^2}$

34. $\displaystyle\int \sqrt{x^2 \pm a^2}\,dx = \frac{x}{2}\sqrt{x^2 \pm a^2} \pm \frac{a^2}{2}\ln(x + \sqrt{x^2 \pm a^2})$

35. $\displaystyle\int x^2\sqrt{x^2 \pm a^2}\,dx = \frac{x}{8}(2x^2 \pm a^2)\sqrt{x^2 \pm a^2} - \frac{a^4}{8}\ln(x + \sqrt{x^2 \pm a^2})$

36. $\displaystyle\int (x^2 \pm a^2)^{\frac{3}{2}}\,dx = \frac{x}{8}(2x^2 \pm 5a^2)\sqrt{x^2 \pm a^2} + \frac{3a^4}{8}\ln(x + \sqrt{x^2 \pm a^2})$

37. $\displaystyle\int x^2(x^2 \pm a^2)^{\frac{3}{2}}\,dx = \frac{x}{48}(8x^4 \pm 14a^2x^2 + 3a^4)\sqrt{x^2 \pm a^2}$
$$\mp \frac{a^6}{16}\ln(x + \sqrt{x^2 \pm a^2})$$

38. $\displaystyle\int (x^2 \pm a^2)^{\frac{5}{2}}\,dx = \frac{x}{48}(8x^4 \pm 26a^2x^2 + 33a^4)\sqrt{x^2 \pm a^2}$
$$\pm \frac{5a^6}{16}\ln(x + \sqrt{x^2 \pm a^2})$$

39. $\displaystyle\int x^2(x^2 \pm a^2)^{\frac{5}{2}}\,dx = \frac{x}{384}(48x^6 \pm 136a^2x^4 + 118a^4x^2 \pm 15a^6)\sqrt{x^2 \pm a^2}$
$$- \frac{5a^8}{128}\ln(x + \sqrt{x^2 \pm a^2})$$

40. $\displaystyle\int \frac{\sqrt{x^2 + a^2}}{x}\,dx = \sqrt{x^2 + a^2} - a\ln\frac{a + \sqrt{x^2 + a^2}}{x}$

41. $\displaystyle\int \frac{\sqrt{x^2 - a^2}}{x}\,dx = \sqrt{x^2 - a^2} + a\arcsin\frac{a}{x}$

42. $\int \dfrac{\sqrt{x^2 \pm a^2}}{x^2}\, dx = -\dfrac{\sqrt{x^2 \pm a^2}}{x} + \ln(x + \sqrt{x^2 \pm a^2})$

43. $\int \dfrac{(x^2 + a^2)^{\frac{3}{2}}}{x}\, dx = \dfrac{1}{3}(x^2 + 4a^2)\sqrt{x^2 + a^2} - a^3 \ln \dfrac{a + \sqrt{x^2 + a^2}}{x}$

44. $\int \dfrac{(x^2 - a^2)^{\frac{3}{2}}}{x}\, dx = \dfrac{1}{3}(x^2 - 4a^2)\sqrt{x^2 - a^2} - a^3 \arcsin \dfrac{a}{x}$

45. $\int \dfrac{(x^2 \pm a^2)^{\frac{3}{2}}}{x^2}\, dx = \dfrac{1}{2x}(x^2 \mp 2a^2)\sqrt{x^2 \pm a^2} \pm \dfrac{3a^2}{2}\ln(x + \sqrt{x^2 \pm a^2})$

46. $\int \dfrac{(x^2 + a^2)^{\frac{5}{2}}}{x}\, dx = \dfrac{1}{15}(3x^4 + 11a^2x^2 + 23a^4)\sqrt{x^2 + a^2}$
$$- a^5 \ln \dfrac{a + \sqrt{x^2 + a^2}}{x}$$

47. $\int \dfrac{(x^2 - a^2)^{\frac{5}{2}}}{x}\, dx = \dfrac{1}{15}(3x^4 - 11a^2x^2 + 23a^4)\sqrt{x^2 - a^2} + a^5 \arcsin \dfrac{a}{x}$

48. $\int \dfrac{(x^2 \pm a^2)^{\frac{5}{2}}}{x^2}\, dx = \dfrac{1}{8x}(2x^4 \pm 9a^2x^2 - 8a^4)\sqrt{x^2 \pm a^2}$
$$+ \dfrac{15a^4}{8}\ln(x + \sqrt{x^2 \pm a^2})$$

49. $\int \dfrac{dx}{\sqrt{x^2 \pm a^2}} = \ln(x + \sqrt{x^2 \pm a^2})$

50. $\int \dfrac{x^2\, dx}{\sqrt{x^2 \pm a^2}} = \dfrac{x}{2}\sqrt{x^2 \pm a^2} \mp \dfrac{a^2}{2}\ln(x + \sqrt{x^2 \pm a^2})$

51. $\int \dfrac{dx}{(x^2 \pm a^2)^{\frac{3}{2}}} = \pm \dfrac{x}{a^2\sqrt{x^2 \pm a^2}}$

52. $\int \dfrac{x^2\, dx}{(x^2 \pm a^2)^{\frac{3}{2}}} = -\dfrac{x}{\sqrt{x^2 \pm a^2}} + \ln(x + \sqrt{x^2 \pm a^2})$

53. $\int \dfrac{dx}{(x^2 \pm a^2)^{\frac{5}{2}}} = \dfrac{x(2x^2 \pm 3a^2)}{3a^4(x^2 \pm a^2)^{\frac{3}{2}}}$

54. $\int \dfrac{x^2\, dx}{(x^2 \pm a^2)^{\frac{5}{2}}} = \pm \dfrac{x^3}{3a^2(x^2 \pm a^2)^{\frac{3}{2}}}$

55. $\int \dfrac{dx}{x\sqrt{x^2 + a^2}} = -\dfrac{1}{a}\ln \dfrac{a + \sqrt{x^2 + a^2}}{x}$

56. $\int \dfrac{dx}{x\sqrt{x^2 - a^2}} = -\dfrac{1}{a}\arcsin \dfrac{a}{x}$

57. $\int \dfrac{dx}{x^2\sqrt{x^2 \pm a^2}} = \mp \dfrac{1}{a^2 x}\sqrt{x^2 \pm a^2}$

58. $\int \dfrac{dx}{x(x^2 + a^2)^{\frac{3}{2}}} = \dfrac{1}{a^2\sqrt{x^2 + a^2}} - \dfrac{1}{a^3}\ln \dfrac{a + \sqrt{x^2 + a^2}}{x}$

59. $\displaystyle\int \frac{dx}{x(x^2 - a^2)^{\frac{3}{2}}} = -\frac{1}{a^2\sqrt{x^2 - a^2}} + \frac{1}{a^3} \text{ arc sin } \frac{a}{x}$

60. $\displaystyle\int \frac{dx}{x^2(x^2 + a^2)^{\frac{3}{2}}} = -\frac{(2x^2 \pm a^2)}{a^4 x\sqrt{x^2 \pm a^2}}$

61. $\displaystyle\int \frac{dx}{x(x^2 + a^2)^{\frac{5}{2}}} = \frac{3x^2 + 4a^2}{3a^4(x^2 + a^2)^{\frac{3}{2}}} - \frac{1}{a^5} \ln \frac{a + \sqrt{x^2 + a^2}}{x}$

62. $\displaystyle\int \frac{dx}{x(x^2 - a^2)^{\frac{5}{2}}} = \frac{3x^2 - 4a^2}{3a^4(x^2 - a^2)^{\frac{3}{2}}} - \frac{1}{a^5} \text{ arc sin } \frac{a}{x}$

63. $\displaystyle\int \frac{dx}{x^2(x^2 \pm a^2)^{\frac{5}{2}}} = \mp \frac{8x^4 \pm 12a^2x^2 + 3a_4}{3a^6 x(x^2 \pm a^2)^{\frac{3}{2}}}$

## Forms Involving $\sqrt{a^2 - x^2}$

64. $\displaystyle\int \sqrt{a^2 - x^2}\, dx = \frac{x}{2}\sqrt{a^2 - x^2} + \frac{a^2}{2} \text{ arc sin } \frac{x}{a}$

65. $\displaystyle\int x^2\sqrt{a^2 - x^2}\, dx = \frac{x}{8}(2x^2 - a^2)\sqrt{a^2 - x^2} + \frac{a^4}{8} \text{ arc sin } \frac{x}{a}$

66. $\displaystyle\int (a^2 - x^2)^{\frac{3}{2}}\, dx = \frac{x}{8}(5a^2 - 2x^2)\sqrt{a^2 - x^2} + \frac{3a^4}{8} \text{ arc sin } \frac{x}{a}$

67. $\displaystyle\int x^2(a^2 - x^2)^{\frac{3}{2}}\, dx = -\frac{x}{48}(3a^4 - 14a^2x^2 + 8x^4)\sqrt{a^2 - x^2} + \frac{a^6}{16} \text{ arc sin } \frac{x}{a}$

68. $\displaystyle\int (a^2 - x^2)^{\frac{5}{2}}\, dx = \frac{x}{48}(33a^4 - 26a^2x^2 + 8x^4)\sqrt{a^2 - x^2} + \frac{5a^6}{16} \text{ arc sin } \frac{x}{a}$

69. $\displaystyle\int x^2(a^2 - x^2)^{\frac{5}{2}}\, dx = -\frac{x}{384}(15a^6 - 118a^4x^2 + 136a^2x^4 - 48x^6)\sqrt{a^2 - x^2}$
$$+ \frac{5a^8}{128} \text{ arc sin } \frac{x}{a}$$

70. $\displaystyle\int \frac{\sqrt{a^2 - x^2}}{x}\, dx = \sqrt{a^2 - x^2} - a \ln \frac{a + \sqrt{a^2 - x^2}}{x}$

71. $\displaystyle\int \frac{\sqrt{a^2 - x^2}}{x^2}\, dx = -\frac{\sqrt{a^2 - x^2}}{x} - \text{arc sin } \frac{x}{a}$

72. $\displaystyle\int \frac{(a^2 - x^2)^{\frac{3}{2}}}{x}\, dx = \frac{1}{3}(4a^2 - x^2)\sqrt{a^2 - x^2} + a^3 \ln \frac{a - \sqrt{a^2 - x^2}}{x}$

73. $\displaystyle\int \frac{(a^2 - x^2)^{\frac{3}{2}}}{x^2}\, dx = -\frac{1}{2x}(2a^2 + x^2)\sqrt{a^2 - x^2} - \frac{3a^2}{2} \text{ arc sin } \frac{x}{a}$

74. $\displaystyle\int \frac{(a^2 - x^2)^{\frac{5}{2}}}{x}\, dx = \frac{1}{15}(23a^4 - 11a^2x^2 + 3x^4)\sqrt{a^2 - x^2}$
$$- a^5 \ln \frac{a + \sqrt{a^2 - x^2}}{x}$$

75. $\int \dfrac{(a^2 - x^2)^{\frac{5}{2}}}{x^2}\, dx = -\dfrac{1}{8x}(8a^4 + 9a^2x^2 - 2x^4)\sqrt{a^2 - x^2} - \dfrac{15a^4}{8}\arcsin\dfrac{x}{a}$

76. $\int \dfrac{x^2}{\sqrt{a^2 - x^2}}\, dx = -\dfrac{x}{2}\sqrt{a^2 - x^2} + \dfrac{a^2}{2}\arcsin\dfrac{x}{a}$

77. $\int \dfrac{dx}{(a^2 - x^2)^{\frac{3}{2}}} = \dfrac{x}{a^2\sqrt{a^2 - x^2}}$

78. $\int \dfrac{x^2}{(a^2 - x^2)^{\frac{3}{2}}}\, dx = \dfrac{x}{\sqrt{a^2 - x^2}} - \arcsin\dfrac{x}{a}$

79. $\int \dfrac{dx}{(a^2 - x^2)^{\frac{5}{2}}} = \dfrac{x(3a^2 - 2x^2)}{3a^4(a^2 - x^2)^{\frac{3}{2}}}$

80. $\int \dfrac{x^2}{(a^2 - x^2)^{\frac{5}{2}}}\, dx = \dfrac{x^3}{3a^2(a^2 - x^2)^{\frac{3}{2}}}$

81. $\int \dfrac{dx}{x\sqrt{a^2 - x^2}} = \dfrac{1}{a}\ln\dfrac{a - \sqrt{a^2 - x^2}}{x}$

82. $\int \dfrac{dx}{x^2\sqrt{a^2 - x^2}} = -\dfrac{\sqrt{a^2 - x^2}}{a^2x}$

83. $\int \dfrac{dx}{x(a^2 - x^2)^{\frac{3}{2}}} = \dfrac{1}{a^2\sqrt{a^2 - x^2}} + \dfrac{1}{a^3}\ln\dfrac{a - \sqrt{a^2 - x^2}}{x}$

84. $\int \dfrac{dx}{x^2(a^2 - x^2)^{\frac{3}{2}}} = \dfrac{2x^2 - a^2}{a^4x\sqrt{a^2 - x^2}}$

85. $\int \dfrac{dx}{x(a^2 - x^2)^{\frac{5}{2}}} = \dfrac{4a^2 - 3x^2}{3a^4(a^2 - x^2)^{\frac{3}{2}}} - \dfrac{1}{a^5}\ln\dfrac{a + \sqrt{a^2 - x^2}}{x}$

86. $\int \dfrac{dx}{x^2(a^2 - x^2)^{\frac{5}{2}}} = -\dfrac{3a^4 - 12a^2x^2 + 8x^4}{3a^6x(a^2 - x^2)^{\frac{3}{2}}}$

## Powers of Trigonometric Functions

87. $\int \sin^2 x\, dx = \dfrac{x}{2} - \dfrac{\sin 2x}{4}$

88. $\int \sin^3 x\, dx = \dfrac{\cos 3x}{12} - \dfrac{3\cos x}{4}$

89. $\int \sin^4 x\, dx = \dfrac{3x}{8} - \dfrac{\sin 2x}{4} + \dfrac{\sin 4x}{32}$

90. $\int \sin^5 x\, dx = -\dfrac{5\cos x}{8} + \dfrac{5\cos 3x}{48} - \dfrac{\cos 5x}{80}$

91. $\int \sin^6 x\, dx = \dfrac{5x}{16} - \dfrac{15\sin 2x}{64} + \dfrac{3\sin 4x}{64} - \dfrac{\sin 6x}{192}$

92. $\displaystyle\int \sin^7 x\, dx = -\frac{35 \cos x}{64} + \frac{7 \cos 3x}{64} - \frac{7 \cos 5x}{320} + \frac{\cos 7x}{448}$

93. $\displaystyle\int \cos^2 x\, dx = \frac{x}{2} + \frac{\sin 2x}{4}$

94. $\displaystyle\int \cos^3 x\, dx = \frac{3 \sin x}{4} + \frac{\sin 3x}{12}$

95. $\displaystyle\int \cos^4 x\, dx = \frac{3x}{8} + \frac{\sin 2x}{4} + \frac{\sin 4x}{32}$

96. $\displaystyle\int \cos^5 x\, dx = \frac{5 \sin x}{8} + \frac{5 \sin 3x}{48} + \frac{\sin 5x}{80}$

97. $\displaystyle\int \cos^6 x\, dx = \frac{5x}{16} + \frac{15 \sin 2x}{64} + \frac{3 \sin 4x}{64} + \frac{\sin 6x}{192}$

98. $\displaystyle\int \cos^7 x\, dx = \frac{35 \sin x}{64} + \frac{7 \sin 3x}{64} + \frac{7 \sin 5x}{320} + \frac{\sin 7x}{448}$

99. $\displaystyle\int \tan^2 x\, dx = \tan x - x$

100. $\displaystyle\int \tan^3 x\, dx = \frac{\tan^2 x}{2} + \ln \cos x$

101. $\displaystyle\int \tan^4 x\, dx = \frac{\tan^3 x}{3} - \tan x + x$

102. $\displaystyle\int \tan^5 x\, dx = \frac{\tan^4 x}{4} - \frac{\tan^2 x}{2} - \ln \cos x$

103. $\displaystyle\int \tan^6 x\, dx = \frac{\tan^5 x}{5} - \frac{\tan^3 x}{3} + \tan x - x$

104. $\displaystyle\int \tan^7 x\, dx = \frac{\tan^6 x}{6} - \frac{\tan^4 x}{4} + \frac{\tan^2 x}{2} + \ln \cos x$

105. $\displaystyle\int \cot^2 x\, dx = -\cot x - x$

106. $\displaystyle\int \cot^3 x\, dx = -\frac{\cot^2 x}{2} - \ln \sin x$

107. $\displaystyle\int \cot^4 x\, dx = -\frac{\cot^3 x}{3} + \cot x + x$

108. $\displaystyle\int \cot^5 x\, dx = -\frac{\cot^4 x}{4} + \frac{\cot^2 x}{2} + \ln \sin x$

109. $\displaystyle\int \cot^6 x\, dx = -\frac{\cot^5 x}{5} + \frac{\cot^3 x}{3} - \cot x - x$

110. $\displaystyle\int \cot^7 x\, dx = -\frac{\cot^6 x}{6} + \frac{\cot^4 x}{4} - \frac{\cot^2 x}{2} - \ln \sin x$

111. $\int \sec^3 x\, dx = \frac{1}{2} \sec x \tan x + \frac{1}{2} \ln (\sec x + \tan x)$

112. $\int \sec^4 x\, dx = \tan x + \frac{1}{3} \tan^3 x$

113. $\int \sec^5 x\, dx = \frac{3}{8} \sec x \tan x + \frac{1}{4} \sec^3 x \tan x + \frac{3}{8} \ln (\sec x + \tan x)$

114. $\int \sec^6 x\, dx = \tan x + \frac{2}{3} \tan^3 x + \frac{1}{5} \tan^5 x$

115. $\int \sec^7 x\, dx = \frac{5}{16} \sec x \tan x + \frac{5}{24} \sec^3 x \tan x + \frac{1}{6} \sec^5 x \tan x$
$$+ \tfrac{5}{16} \ln (\sec x + \tan x)$$

116. $\int \csc^3 x\, dx = -\frac{1}{2} \cot x \csc x + \frac{1}{2} \ln (\csc x - \cot x)$

117. $\int \csc^4 x\, dx = -\cot x - \frac{1}{3} \cot^3 x$

118. $\int \csc^5 x\, dx = -\frac{3}{8} \cot x \csc x - \frac{1}{4} \cot x \csc^3 x + \frac{3}{8} \ln (\csc x - \cot x)$

119. $\int \csc^6 x\, dx = -\cot x - \frac{2}{3} \cot^3 x - \frac{1}{5} \cot^5 x$

120. $\int \csc^7 x\, dx = -\frac{5}{16} \cot x \csc x - \frac{5}{24} \cot x \csc^3 x - \frac{1}{6} \cot x \csc^5 x$
$$+ \tfrac{5}{16} \ln (\csc x - \cot x)$$

## Products of Powers of $x$ and of $\sin x$ or $\cos x$

121. $\int x \sin x\, dx = \sin x - x \cos x$

122. $\int x^2 \sin x\, dx = 2x \sin x - (x^2 - 2) \cos x$

123. $\int x^3 \sin x\, dx = 3(x^2 - 2) \sin x - (x^3 - 6x) \cos x$

124. $\int x^4 \sin x\, dx = 4(x^3 - 6x) \sin x - (x^4 - 12x^2 + 24) \cos x$

125. $\int x^n \sin x\, dx = -x^n \cos x + n \int x^{n-1} \cos x\, dx$

126. $\int x \cos x\, dx = \cos x + x \sin x$

127. $\int x^2 \cos x\, dx = 2x \cos x + (x^2 - 2) \sin x$

128. $\int x^3 \cos x\, dx = 3(x^2 - 2) \cos x + (x^3 - 6x) \sin x$

**317**

129. $\int x^4 \cos x \, dx = 4(x^3 - 6x) \cos x + (x^4 - 12x^2 + 24) \sin x$

130. $\int x^n \cos x \, dx = x^n \sin x - n \int x^{n-1} \sin x \, dx$

131. $\int x \sin^2 x \, dx = \frac{1}{4}x^2 - \frac{1}{4}x \sin 2x - \frac{1}{8} \cos 2x$

132. $\int x^2 \sin^2 x \, dx = \frac{1}{6}x^3 - \frac{1}{8}(2x^2 - 1) \sin 2x - \frac{1}{4}x \cos 2x$

133. $\int x^3 \sin^2 x \, dx = \frac{1}{8}x^4 - \frac{1}{8}(2x^3 - 3x) \sin 2x - \frac{3}{16}(2x^2 - 1) \cos 2x$

134. $\int x \cos^2 x \, dx = \frac{1}{4}x^2 + \frac{1}{4}x \sin 2x + \frac{1}{8} \cos 2x$

135. $\int x^2 \cos^2 x \, dx = \frac{1}{6}x^3 + \frac{1}{8}(2x^2 - 1) \sin 2x + \frac{1}{4}x \cos 2x$

136. $\int x^3 \cos^2 x \, dx = \frac{1}{8}x^4 + \frac{1}{8}(2x^3 - 3x) \sin 2x + \frac{3}{16}(2x^2 - 1) \cos 2x$

## Miscellaneous Forms Involving sin $x$, cos $x$

137. $\int \frac{dx}{1 + \sin x} = \frac{\sin x - 1}{\cos x}$

138. $\int \frac{dx}{1 - \sin x} = \frac{1 + \sin x}{\cos x}$

139. $\int \frac{dx}{(1 + \sin x)^2} = -\frac{(1 - \sin x)(2 + \sin x)}{3 \cos x(1 + \sin x)}$

140. $\int \frac{dx}{(1 - \sin x)^2} = \frac{(1 + \sin x)(2 - \sin x)}{3 \cos x(1 - \sin x)}$

141. $\int \frac{dx}{1 + \cos x} = \frac{1 - \cos x}{\sin x}$

142. $\int \frac{dx}{1 - \cos x} = -\frac{1 + \cos x}{\sin x}$

143. $\int \frac{dx}{(1 + \cos x)^2} = \frac{(1 - \cos x)(2 + \cos x)}{(3 \sin x)(1 + \cos x)} = \frac{1}{2} \tan \frac{x}{2} + \frac{1}{6} \tan^3 \frac{x}{2}$

144. $\int \frac{dx}{(1 - \cos x)^2} = -\frac{(1 + \cos x)(2 - \cos x)}{2 \sin x(1 - \cos x)} = -\frac{1}{2} \cot \frac{x}{2} - \frac{1}{6} \cot^3 \frac{x}{2}$

145. $\int \sin mx \sin nx \, dx = \frac{\sin (m - n)x}{2(m - n)} - \frac{\sin (m + n)x}{2(m + n)}, \quad m^2 \neq n^2$

146. $\int \sin mx \cos nx \, dx = -\frac{\cos (m - n)x}{2(m - n)} - \frac{\cos (m + n)x}{2(m + n)}, \quad m^2 \neq n^2$

**318**

147. $\displaystyle\int \cos mx \cos nx \, dx = \frac{\sin (m-n)x}{2(m-n)} + \frac{\sin (m+n)x}{2(m+n)}, \quad m^2 \neq n^2$

148. $\displaystyle\int \sin^m x \cos^n x \, dx = \frac{\sin^{m+1} x \cos^{n-1} x}{m+n} + \frac{n-1}{m+n} \int \sin^m x \cos^{n-2} x \, dx,$
$$m \neq -n$$

149. $\displaystyle\int \sin^m x \cos^n x \, dx = - \frac{\sin^{m-1} x \cos^{n+1} x}{m+n} + \frac{m-1}{m+n} \int \sin^{m-2} x \cos^n x \, dx,$
$$m \neq -n$$

150. $\displaystyle\int \frac{\sin^m x}{\cos^n x} \, dx = - \frac{\sin^{m-1} x}{(m-n) \cos^{n-1} x} + \frac{m-1}{m-n} \int \frac{\sin^{m-2} x}{\cos^n x} \, dx, \quad m \neq n$

151. $\displaystyle\int \frac{\cos^n x}{\sin^m x} \, dx = \frac{\cos^{n-1} x}{(n-m) \sin^{m-1} x} + \frac{n-1}{n-m} \int \frac{\cos^{n-2} x}{\sin^m x} \, dx, \quad m \neq n$

152. $\displaystyle\int \frac{dx}{\sin^m x \cos^n x} = \frac{1}{(n-1) \sin^{m-1} x \cos^{n-1} x}$
$$+ \frac{m+n-2}{n-1} \int \frac{dx}{\sin^m x \cos^{n-2} x}, \quad n > 1$$

153. $\displaystyle\int \frac{dx}{\sin^m x \cos^n x} = \frac{-1}{(m-1) \sin^{m-1} x \cos^{n-1} x}$
$$+ \frac{m+n-2}{m-1} \int \frac{dx}{\sin^{m-2} x \cos^n x}, \quad m > 1$$

## Forms Involving $e^{ax}$ or $\ln x$

154. $\displaystyle\int xe^{ax} \, dx = e^{ax} \left( \frac{x}{a} - \frac{1}{a^2} \right)$

155. $\displaystyle\int x^2 e^{ax} \, dx = e^{ax} \left( \frac{x^2}{a} - \frac{2x}{a^2} + \frac{2}{a^3} \right)$

156. $\displaystyle\int x^3 e^{ax} \, dx = e^{ax} \left( \frac{x^3}{a} - \frac{3x^2}{a^2} + \frac{6x}{a^3} - \frac{6}{a^4} \right)$

157. $\displaystyle\int x^4 e^{ax} \, dx = e^{ax} \left( \frac{x^4}{a} - \frac{4x^3}{a^2} + \frac{12x^2}{a^3} - \frac{24x}{a^4} + \frac{24}{a^5} \right)$

158. $\displaystyle\int x^n e^{ax} \, dx$
$$= e^{ax} \left[ \frac{x^n}{a} - \frac{nx^{n-1}}{a^2} + \frac{n(n-1)x^{n-2}}{a^3} - \cdots + (-1)^{n-1} \frac{n!x}{a^n} + (-1)^n \frac{n!}{a^{n+1}} \right]$$

159. $\displaystyle\int \frac{e^{ax}}{x^n} \, dx = - \frac{e^{ax}}{(n-1)x^{n-1}} + \frac{a}{n-1} \int \frac{e^{ax} \, dx}{x^{n-1}}, \quad n > 1$

160. $\displaystyle\int \frac{dx}{a + be^{cx}} = \frac{x}{a} - \frac{1}{ac} \ln (a + be^{cx}), \quad ac \neq 0$

319

161. $\displaystyle\int \ln x \, dx = x \ln x - x$

162. $\displaystyle\int x \ln x \, dx = \frac{x^2}{2} \ln x - \frac{x^2}{4}$

163. $\displaystyle\int x^2 \ln x \, dx = \frac{x^3}{3} \ln x - \frac{x^3}{9}$

164. $\displaystyle\int x^3 \ln x \, dx = \frac{x^4}{4} \ln x - \frac{x^4}{16}$

165. $\displaystyle\int x^n \ln x \, dx = \frac{x^{n+1}}{n+1} \ln x - \frac{x^{n+1}}{(n+1)^2}, \quad n \neq -1$

166. $\displaystyle\int \frac{\ln x}{x^n} \, dx = -\frac{\ln x}{(n-1)x^{n-1}} - \frac{1}{(n-1)^2 x^{n-1}}, \quad n \neq 1$

167. $\displaystyle\int \frac{(\ln x)^2}{x^n} \, dx = -\frac{(\ln x)^2}{(n-1)x^{n-1}} - \frac{2\ln x}{(n-1)^2 x^{n-1}} - \frac{2}{(n-1)^3 x^{n-1}}, \quad n \neq 1$

## Products of $e^{ax}$ and Powers of $\sin bx$ or $\cos bx$

168. $\displaystyle\int e^{ax} \sin bx \, dx = \frac{e^{ax}(a \sin bx - b \cos bx)}{a^2 + b^2}$

169. $\displaystyle\int e^{ax} \cos bx \, dx = \frac{e^{ax}(a \cos bx + b \sin bx)}{a^2 + b^2}$

170. $\displaystyle\int e^{ax} \sin^2 x \, dx = \frac{e^{ax}}{4 + a^2}\left[ (\sin x)(a \sin x - 2 \cos x) + \frac{2}{a} \right]$

171. $\displaystyle\int e^{ax} \cos^2 x \, dx = \frac{e^{ax}}{4 + a^2}\left[ (\cos x)(a \cos x + 2 \sin x) + \frac{2}{a} \right]$

172. $\displaystyle\int e^{ax} \sin^n x \, dx = \frac{e^{ax}(\sin^{n-1} x)(a \sin x - n \cos x)}{a^2 + n^2}$
$$+ \frac{n(n-1)}{a^2 + n^2} \int e^{ax} \sin^{n-2} x \, dx$$

173. $\displaystyle\int e^{ax} \cos^n x \, dx = \frac{e^{ax}(\cos^{n-1} x)(a \cos x + n \sin x)}{a^2 + n^2}$
$$+ \frac{n(n-1)}{a^2 + n^2} \int e^{ax} \cos^{n-2} x \, dx$$

# ANSWERS TO EXERCISES

## Exercise 2, pages 6–7

11. 2

12. $-\frac{2}{3}$

13. $\frac{1}{2}(2 + \sqrt{2})$

14. ln cos 1

15. $\frac{12}{5}, -\frac{2}{5}$

16. $-1, e^{-2}$

17. $\sqrt{2}, \frac{1}{2}$

18. $\pm 2, (n + \frac{2}{3})\pi$

19. $-\frac{7}{9}, \frac{7}{9}, -\frac{4}{3}$

20. $\frac{1}{2}, 0, \frac{1}{2}$

## Exercise 3, page 11

1. $x(y')^2 - 2yy' = x$

2. $(3x + y^4)y' = y$

3. $y' = (x + y)^2$

4. $(x^2 + 1)y' = 1 + xy$

5. $(x^3 + y^2)y' = 3x^2y$

6. $y(xy + 1) - xy'$

7. $(x \cot y)y' + 1 = \ln (x \sin y)$

8. $y'' - y + x = 0$

9. $y'' - 3y' + 2y = e^x$

10. $y'' + 4y = 0$

11. $y'' - 2y' + 2y = 0$

12. $x^2y'' - 2xy' + (x^2 + 2)y = 0$

14. $xy' + y = 0$

15. $yy'' + (y')^2 + 1 = 0$

16. $x^2 - y^2 + 2xyy' = 0$

17. $(x + 1)y' = y$

18. $y = xy' + f(y')$

19. $xy' - y \pm 5\sqrt{1 + (y')^2} = 0$

20. $(y')^2 = 4(xy' - y)$

21. $yy'' + (y')^2 = 0$

22. $2y'' + (y')^3 = 0$

## Exercise 5, pages 21–22

1. $(x^2 + 1)y^2 = C$

2. $1 + y^2 = C(1 - x^2)$

3. $x + y = C(1 - xy)$

4. $xy = C$

5. $y = Ce^{x^2}$

6. $(x^2 - 1)(y^2 + 1) = C$

7. $y\sqrt{1 - x^2} + x\sqrt{1 - y^2} = C$

8. $(1 - y)(1 + x) = C$

9. $y + 1 = C \sin x$

10. $y + 3 = C \cos x$

11. $x^2 - y^2 = C$

12. $x = t + \frac{1}{2} \cos 2t + C$

13. $xy = C(1 - y)$

14. $\sec x + \tan y = C$

15. $\tan x - \sec y = C$

16. $xy = Ce^{y-x}$

17. $ye^{\sqrt{1+x^2}} = C$

18. $xy = Ce^{-\frac{1}{x}}$

19. $\tan^2 x - \cot^2 y = C$

20. $\text{Arc tan } x + \ln \sqrt{y^2 - 1} = C$

21. $y = 3x$

22. $x^2y = 4$

23. $\cos y = \sec x$

24. $\dfrac{1}{x} + \dfrac{1}{y} = \dfrac{4}{3}$

25. $(1 - x)e^y = 1$

26. $e^x(e^y - 1) = e - 1$

27. $\text{Arc tan } y = \frac{1}{5}x^5 - \frac{1}{4}x^4 - \frac{12}{5}$

28. $27y^6(x + 3)^4 = 256x^4(y^2 + 2)^3$

29. $\dfrac{1}{2} \text{Arc tan} \dfrac{y + 1}{2} - \dfrac{2}{\sqrt{3}} \text{Arc tan} \dfrac{2x + 1}{\sqrt{3}} = \dfrac{9 - 16\sqrt{3}}{72} \pi$

30. $(x - 4)(y + 2)^2 + 8(x + 2)(y - 1)^2 = 0$

## Exercise 6, pages 25–26

1. $x = Ce^{\frac{y}{x}}$

2. $\sqrt{x^2 + y^2} = Ce^{\text{Arc tan} \frac{x}{y}}$

3. $x = Ce^{2\sqrt{\frac{y}{x}}}$

4. $x^2 - xy - 2y^2 = C$

321

5. $\ln x = \text{Arc} \sin \frac{y}{x} + C$

6. $y - x = Ce^{\frac{x}{y-x}}$

7. $y + \sqrt{y^2 - x^2} = C$

8. $x = Ce^{\frac{y^2}{2x^2}}$

9. $y = Ce^{\frac{y}{x}}$

10. $\sqrt{xy} - x = C$

11. $x^2 + 2xy - y^2 = C$

12. $xy = Ce^{-\text{Arc} \tan \frac{y}{x}}$

13. $\tan \frac{y}{2x} = Cx$

14. $2 \text{ Arc} \tan e^{\frac{y}{x}} = \ln x + C$

15. $y^2 = x^2 + x$

16. $y^2(2x^2 + y^2) = 1$

17. $\ln x + e^{-\frac{y}{x}} = 1$

18. $x^2 + y^2 = e^{2 \text{ Arc} \tan \frac{y}{x}}$

19. $y = x \text{ Arc} \sin \frac{x}{12}$

20. $y^2(x - y) = 2x^2$

21. $x = \frac{1}{2}(y^{1-k} - y^{1+k})$

22. $y^3 = 3x^3(9 + \ln x)$

23. $\sinh \frac{y}{x} = 5.32x$

## Exercise 7, pages 28–29

1. $\ln [(x + y)^2 + (x - y + 2)^2] + 2 \text{ Arc} \tan \frac{x - y + 2}{x + y} = C$

2. $(x + 2y - 2)^2(x - y + 1) = C$

3. $\ln [(2x - y + 1)^2 + 2(x + y)^2] = \sqrt{2} \text{ Arc} \tan \frac{2x - y + 1}{\sqrt{2}(x + y)} + C$

4. $\ln [(x + y - 1)^2 + (x - y + 2)^2] + 2 \text{ Arc} \tan \frac{x + y - 1}{x - y + 2} = C$

5. $(x - y)^2 + 2y = C$

6. $\ln (x^2 + y^2 - 2x + 1) + 2 \text{ Arc} \tan \frac{x - y - 1}{x + y - 1} = C$

7. $x + 2y + \ln (x + y - 1) = C$

8. $x + y + \ln (x - y) = C$

9. $x + 3y = 3 \ln (x + 2y + 3) + C$

10. $(x - y - 3)^3 = C(3x + 3y + 1)$

11. $(x - y - 1)(x + y + 3)^2 + 9 = 0$

12. $5(3x + y + 2) = 9 \ln (10x - 5y + 16)$

13. $\ln [(2x + 3y + 2)^2 + 2(x - y)(2x + 3y + 2) + 2(x - y)^2]$
$$= 4 \text{ Arc} \tan \frac{3x + 2y + 2}{x - y} + \pi + \ln 8$$

14. $(x + y + 1)^3 = e^{2y-x}$

15. $x + y - 4 + 3 \ln \frac{2x + 3y - 7}{2} = 0$

16. $\ln \frac{21x^2 + 14y^2 + 30x + 4y + 11}{11}$
$$+ \frac{\sqrt{6}}{3}\left[ \text{Arc} \tan \frac{\sqrt{6}(x + 2y + 1)}{2(3x - y + 2)} - \text{Arc} \tan \frac{\sqrt{6}}{4} \right] = 0$$

17. $(2x + 2y + 1)(3x - 2y + 9)^4 + 1 = 0$

18. $x - 2y + 7 = -e^{\frac{x-y+6}{4}}$

19. $6x + 12y + 1 = 2 \ln (6x + 3y + 2)$

20. $\ln (4u^2 + 10uv - 4v^2) + \dfrac{3}{\sqrt{41}} \ln \dfrac{4u + (5 - \sqrt{41})v}{4u + (5 + \sqrt{41})v} = 0$, where $u = 2x + y$,

$v = 4x - 2y + 1$

## Exercise 8, page 34

1. $x^2 - 2y^2 + 2xy = C$
2. Not exact
3. $a_1 x^2 + 2b_1 xy + b_2 y^2 + 2c_1 x + 2c_2 y = C$
4. $4x^3 y + 5x^2 + 3y^2 = C$
5. $2x^3 y + x^2 y^2 + 2e^x - 2 \cos y = C$
6. Not exact
7. $y \sin x - 2x \sin y = C$
8. $x^2 y - x + 3y \ln y = Cy$
9. Not exact
10. $ye^x - x^2 = C$
11. $3y \cos x + x \cos y = C$
12. Not exact
13. $2x^2 + y^2 = Cxy$
14. $x^2 y + 2x + 4y \ln y = Cy$
15. $x^3 y^2 - y = Cx^2$
16. $y^2 \cot x - 3x^2 y + 2x = C$
17. $x^4 - y^3 = Cx^2 y^2$
18. $3x \cos y + y^3 = C$

19. $y^4 - 8 \cos xy = C$
20. $x \sin \dfrac{x}{y} + \sin x = C$

21. $e^{xy} + x^2 y = C$
22. $y^{16} x^{18} = C(3x^2 + 4y^2)^5$
23. $(2x^2 + y^2)^3 y^2 = Cx^4$
24. $x \ln (x^2 + y^2) = C$

## Exercise 9, pages 38–39

1. $y = 1 + \ln x + Cx$
2. $3x^2 y^2 + 2y^3 = C$
3. $\ln x^3 y = 2y + C$
4. $3x^2 + y = Cx^3 y$
5. $2x^3 y^3 - 3x^2 = C$
6. $x^3 y^3 - 3 \ln y = C$

7. $x^2 + y = Cxy$
8. $xy \ln \dfrac{x}{y} - 1 = Cxy$

9. $y = x \sin (y + C)$
10. $x^2 + y \ln y = Cy$
11. $1 - 2x^2 y = Cx^2 y^2$
12. $e^x + x^2 y = Cy$
13. $y = x \tan (C - y)$
14. $xy^2(1 + xy) = C$
15. $x^2 e^x + y^2 = Cx^2$
16. $x^4 y^6 + 2x^3 y^4 = C$
17. $x^3 + y = Cxy^2$
18. $x^5 y^4 (5x + 4y^2)^3 = C$

19. $xy = Ce^{\frac{y}{x}}$
20. $x^4 y^2 - 2x^2 y^2 + 1 = 0$
21. $x^2 y + y = 4x$
22. $x^2 y^2 + y = 7x$

23. $x^2 + y^2 = e^y$
24. $2 \text{ Arc } \sin \dfrac{y}{x} = 1 + \pi - x^2$

25. $4(3x + y^2)^2 = 25x^3 y$

## Exercise 10, pages 41–42

1. $4x^2 y = x^4 + C$
2. $ye^{-\frac{1}{2}x^2} = \sin x + C$
3. $ye^{x^2} = x^2 + C$
4. $ye^{-x} = x^3 + C$
5. $xe^y = y + C$
6. $2xye^y = e^{2y} + C$
7. $y^2(x - y) = C$
8. $y = x^4 + Cx^2$
9. $xe^{-y} = y + C$
10. $xy^2 = 1 + Ce^{-y}$

11. $20y + 5x + 4 = 20Cx^5$
12. $y = x^2(2 + Ce^{\frac{1}{x}})$
13. $y(x + 1)^2 = e^x + C$
14. $x - \tan y + 1 = Ce^{-\tan y}$
15. $7x = y^4 + Cy^{\frac{1}{2}}$
16. $r \cos^2 \theta = 2 \sin \theta + C$

323

17. $r(\sec\theta + \tan\theta) = \theta + \ln\dfrac{\cot\theta(\csc\theta - \cot\theta)}{\sec\theta + \tan\theta} + C$

18. $x + 2ye^{3y} = Cy^2e^{3y}$

19. $3xy^2 + 3x = y^3 + 1$

20. $y\sin x + \ln\cos x = 0$

21. $x(1 + y^2)^2 = 2y^2 + 4\ln y - 2$

22. $x^2y + 3x + 3 = 7e^{x-1}$

23. $y^2(x - y^2) = 1$

24. $r\csc^2\theta + \cot\theta = 3$

25. $3(x - 1)^2y + (x^3 - 6x^2 + 21x + 18)(x + 1)^2 = 24(x + 1)^2\ln(x + 1)$

## Exercise 11, pages 45–46

1. $y^3e^{-\frac{1}{2}x^2} = \sin x + C$

2. $y^4e^{2x^2} = 2e^{x^2} + C$

3. $e^x\sinh y = x + C$

4. $t^2 + 2e^{-t}\cos\theta = C$

5. $2x^2y^2 - x^4 = C$

6. $3\sqrt{y} = e^{x^2} + Ce^{\frac{1}{4}x^2}$

7. $1 + x^2t^4 = Cx^2t^2$

8. $x = y\ln Cx$

9. $2e^x\csc y + e^{2x} = C$

10. $y^2 + 1 = Ce^{x^2}$

11. $1 + xy\sin x = Cxy$

12. $r^2 = 1 + Ce^{-\theta^2}$

13. $7 + 3x^3y^{\frac{1}{3}} = Cx^{\frac{2}{3}}y^{\frac{1}{3}}$

14. $12(x + 1)^2y^3 = 3x^4 + 8x^3 + 6x^2 + C$

15. $\sin y = 1 + Ce^{-\sin x}$

16. $\tan y = 2x^2 + Cx$

17. $1 - y^2 - 2y^2\sin x = Cy^2e^{2\sin x}$

18. $y = 2e^t$

19. $x^2 + 1 = e^{x^2-2y}$

20. $10x = (9 + xy^4)\sqrt{y}$

21. $x(y^2 + 2) = 3xe^{\frac{1}{2}y^2} - 1$

22. $3\sqrt{y} + 1 - x^2 = 4\sqrt[4]{1 - x^2}$

## Miscellaneous Problems — Exercise 12, pages 46–48

1. $(1 - x)(1 + y) = C$

2. $xy'' = C(x + 2y)$

3. $\ln(x^2 + y^2) - \text{Arc tan}\,\dfrac{y}{x} = C$

4. $y\ln x = x + C$

5. $\ln(x - y - 1) = \dfrac{x - 2y + 1}{x - y - 1} + C$

6. $x^2y - x^2y^3 + \frac{1}{3}y^3 + \frac{1}{4}x^4 = C$

7. $4t^2e^x - t^4 = C$

8. $x^2(y + 3)^3 = Ce^y$

9. $2x + 2y + \ln(x - 3y - \frac{1}{2}) = C$

10. $y\cos x + 2x\cos y + \ln\cos x - \cos y = C$

11. $x^3 = 3y^3\ln Cy$

12. $(2 + x)(2y - 1) = Cy$

13. $3x + 4 = C\sin^3 y$

14. $\ln y = 2\cos x\ln(\sec x + \tan x) + C\cos x$

15. $x^2 + xy^3 = Cy^2$

16. $2xy^3 = y^4 + C$

17. $r = C\sin\theta$

18. $\ln(x^2 + 2xy + 2y^2) + \text{Arc tan}\,\dfrac{x + 2y}{x} = C$

19. $x^3 + y^3 - 3x\ln x = Cx$

20. $y + \sqrt{x^2 + y^2} = Cx^2$

21. $1 + re^{-2\theta} = Cre^\theta$

22. $\ln(\sec y + \tan y) = \frac{1}{4}\sin 2x + \frac{1}{2}x + C$

23. $\ln(x^2 + 3xy + 3y^2 - x - 3y + 1) = \dfrac{2\sqrt{3}}{3}\,\text{Arc tan}\,\dfrac{\sqrt{3}(1 - y)}{2x + 3y - 1} + C$

24. $x + ye^{\frac{x}{y}} = C$

25. $(y + 1) \sin x = x \cos x + C$

26. $6x - y^2 - 12 \ln x = C$

27. $x^2 + y^2 - 2x^2y + 2xe^y = C$

28. $y^3 + 3x^2 = Cx^{\frac{3}{2}}$

29. $y^2 + 1 = Cx^2y^2$

30. $x(x + \sqrt{x^2 + y^2}) = Cy$

31. $(1 - e^x)^3 \tan y = C$

32. $e^{-x} \tan y = x^2 + C$

33. $3x^2 \tan y + 9xy^2 + x^3 - y^3 = C$

34. $r \sec \theta + 2 \ln (\sec \theta + \tan \theta) = C$

35. $\sin \dfrac{x}{y} = \ln Cy$

36. $y(5x^2 - y)^4 = Cx^5$

37. $\ln (3x^2 + 6xy + 9y^2 + 4x + 12y + 4) + \sqrt{2} \text{ Arc tan } \dfrac{x + 3y + 2}{\sqrt{2}x} = C$

38. $3\sqrt{y} + x = Cx^2\sqrt{x}$

39. $2\sqrt{1 - y} - \sqrt{1 - x^2} = 1$

40. $x = e^{\frac{x}{y}-1}$

41. $x^2 + e^{y^2} = 1$

42. $2y \ln x + x \ln y = x^2y + \dfrac{x}{y^2} - 2$

43. $2x^4 + x^3y^2 = 3y^2$

44. $y^2(x + y) = 2x$

45. $x = e^{\frac{y}{x^4}}$

46. $x^3y^5(5 - 3x^2) = 2$

47. $r \sec \theta = \sqrt{2 - \sec^2 \theta}$

48. $2x = 2e^\theta + xe^{2\theta}$

49. $x^2 - y^2 = 2x$

50. $6x^2y^2 + y^4 = 1$

51. $4ye^{2x} = 3e^{4x} + 1$

52. $2 \ln (x^2 + 1) = \dfrac{1}{y} - 1$

53. $x - y + 2 = 2 \ln (x - 2y + 5)$

54. $4y^3(2x^2 - 3y) = 5x^2$

55. $x^2y + x + \ln (x - 1) = 10$

56. $\sqrt{2}y^3 = x\sqrt{x^2 + y^2}$

57. $y^2\sqrt{1 + x^2} + 1 = 2y^2$

## Exercise 13, pages 53–54

1. $xy = C$

2. $xy^2 = C$

3. $x + y \ln y = Cy$

4. $y + 2x \ln x = Cx$

5. $y^2 = 2x^2 + C$

6. $y = Ce^{\frac{x}{k}}$

7. $y^2 \pm y\sqrt{y^2 - x^2} = x^2 \ln \dfrac{C(y \pm \sqrt{y^2 - x^2})}{x^3}$

8. $y = 2e^{\frac{x}{y}}$

9. $y = C; \; x^2 + y^2 + Cy = 0$

10. $5 \ln y = - (x^2 - 10x + 16)$

11. $xy = 2$

12. $2x^2 + 2y^2 - 5y = 0$

13. $\sqrt{x^2 + y^2} = x + C$

14. $y = Ce^{\frac{x}{k}}$

15. $\dfrac{2y}{k} = Ce^{\frac{x}{k}} + \dfrac{1}{Ce^{\frac{x}{k}}}; \; y = \pm k$

16. $y^2 = Cx, \quad x^2 = Cy$

17. $y^3 = 3(19 - 10x); \; y^3 = 3(10x - 1)$

18. $xy \pm 16 = Cy$

19. $\ln (x^2 + y^2) + 2 \text{ Arc tan } \dfrac{y}{x} = C$

20. $y^2 = Cx$

21. $x + 2y = 0, \quad xy = -2$

22. $r = Ce^\theta$

23. $r = C \sin \theta$

24. $r = C\theta$

25. $r = k; \; r \cos (C + \theta) = k$

26. $r\theta = Cr - 2k$

# ANSWERS TO EXERCISES

## Exercise 14, pages 58–59

1. $x^2 - y^2 = C$
2. $y = Ce^{2x}$
3. $x^2 + 2y^2 = C$
4. $x^2 + y^2 = \ln Cx^{12}$
5. $xy^3 = C$
6. $y = Cx,\ x = 0$
7. $x^2 + y^2 + 25 = Cx$
8. $(x - 5)(x - C) + y^2 = 0$
9. $x(x^2 + 3y^2) = C$
10. $y^{b^2} = Cx^{a^2}$

13. $x^2 - 2xy - y^2 = C$
14. $2 \operatorname{Arc} \tan \dfrac{y}{x} + \ln (x^2 + y^2) = C$

15. $r = C \csc \theta$
16. $r = C(1 + \cos \theta)$
17. $\theta^2 + \ln^2 r = C$
18. $r^2 = C \sin 2\theta$
19. $(r^2 - 5) \sin \theta = Cr$
20. $r(1 + 2 \cos \theta) = C$
21. $r = C \cos \theta$
22. $r = C \cos^4 \tfrac{1}{2}\theta$
23. $r = Ce^{-\sin \theta}$

## Exercise 15, pages 63–65

1. 1599
2. 88%
3. 53.0
4. 85

5. $0.62x_0$; 8.5
6. 151,000
7. $\dfrac{10^7}{3^4}$
8. $p = p_0 e^{-kh}$

9. $2\tfrac{1}{4}$ cu. ft.
10. \$674.95
11. 6.9%
12. \$8535
13. 39.0°; 70 min.
14. 65 min.; 83.5°
15. 51,400
16. 28.3
17. 12.3
18. 39.2 min.
19. 299.9 lb.
20. 35.6 min.
21. 33 min.
22. 218

## Exercise 16, pages 69–71

1. $T = 40 - \tfrac{8}{5}x$; 2,070,000 calories
2. $T = 498 - 173 \ln r$; 70,300 calories
3. $T = \dfrac{2800}{r} - 250$
4. 110 sec.
5. 21.7 gal.
6. 12.1
7. 232
8. 201 sec.; 1.43 ft.
9. 2.6 units
10. 27.8 min.
11. 7.4 lb.
12. 164 min.
13. 5.7 lb.
14. 0.069; 92,600 ft.
15. 66.2

## Exercise 17, pages 78–79

9. $x \neq 0$
10. $x \neq 0$
11. $x \neq 2$
12. $x \neq 0,\ \pm \tfrac{1}{2}\sqrt{6}$
13. $x \neq -1$
14. $x \neq \tfrac{1}{2}\sqrt{2}$
15. $ce^x$
16. $c_1 e^{2x} + c_2 e^{-2x}$
17. $c_1 e^{-4x} + c_2 e^{-3x}$
18. $c_1 e^x + c_2 e^{2x}$
19. $c_1 e^x + c_2 e^{6x}$
20. $c_1 e^{\frac{1}{2}x} + c_2 e^{-2x}$
21. $e^x(c_1 e^{\sqrt{2}x} + c_2 e^{-\sqrt{2}x})$
22. $e^x(c_1 e^{\sqrt{3}x} + c_2 e^{-\sqrt{3}x})$
23. $e^{\frac{3}{2}x}(c_1 e^{\frac{1}{2}\sqrt{5}x} + c_2 e^{-\frac{1}{2}\sqrt{5}x})$
24. $e^{-\frac{1}{2}x}(c_1 e^{\frac{1}{2}\sqrt{3}x} + c_2 e^{-\frac{1}{2}\sqrt{3}x})$
25. $c_1 e^x + c_2 e^{-x} + c_3 e^{\frac{1}{2}x}$
26. $c_1 e^{2x} + c_2 e^{-2x} + c_3 e^{3x}$
27. $c_1 e^{2x} + c_2 e^{3x} + c_3 e^{-x}$
28. $c_1 e^{2x} + c_2 e^{-2x} + c_3 e^{\sqrt{2}x} + c_4 e^{-\sqrt{2}x}$
29. $c_1 e^x + c_2 e^{2x} + c_3 e^{-3x}$
30. $c_1 e^x + c_2 e^{2x} + c_3 e^{3x}$
31. $c_1 e^{3x} + c_2 e^{5x} + c_3 e^{-4x}$
32. $c_1 e^x + c_2 e^{3x} + c_3 e^{5x}$
33. $c_1 e^x + c_2 e^{-x} + c_3 e^{2x} + c_4 e^{-3x}$
34. $c_1 e^{2x} + c_2 e^{3x} + c_3 e^{-3x} + c_4 e^{-\frac{1}{2}x}$
35. $c_1 + c_2 e^{\frac{1}{2}x} + c_3 e^{-\frac{1}{2}x} + c_4 e^{\frac{1}{3}x}$
36. $c_1 + c_2 e^x + c_2 e^{3x}$

326

37. $c_1 e^{\frac{1}{2}x} + e^{-\frac{1}{2}x}(c_2 e^{\frac{1}{2}\sqrt{3}x} + c_3 e^{-\frac{1}{2}\sqrt{3}x})$      38. $c_1 e^{3x} + c_2 e^{4x} + c_3 e^{-2x}$

39. $c_1 e^x + c_2 e^{2x} + c_3 e^{-2x} + c_4 e^{-3x}$

40. $c_1 e^x + c_2 e^{-x} + c_3 e^{2x} + c_4 e^{-2x} + c_5 e^{3x}$

41. $c_1 e^{-3x} + c_2 e^{-2x} + c_3 e^{-x} + c_4 e^{2x} + c_5 e^{3x}$

42. $c_1 e^{-5x} + c_2 e^{-2x} + c_3 + c_4 e^x + c_5 e^{3x}$

43. $c_1 e^x + c_2 e^{-x} + c_4 e^{2ix} + c_5 e^{-2ix}$

44. $c_1 + c_2 e^{ix} + c_3 e^{-ix} + c_4 e^{\sqrt{2}ix} + c_5 e^{-\sqrt{2}ix}$

## Exercise 18, pages 82–83

1. $(c_1 + c_2 x)e^x$      2. $c_1 + c_2 x$

3. $c_1 e^{\frac{3}{2}x} + (c_2 + c_3 x)e^{-x}$      4. $(c_1 + c_2 x + c_3 x^2)e^x$

5. $c_1 + c_2 x + c_3 x^2 + c_4 x^3$      6. $c_1 e^x + (c_2 + c_3 x)e^{-x}$

7. $c_1 e^{-x} + (c_2 + c_3 x)e^{\frac{1}{2}x}$      8. $c_1 + c_2 x + (c_3 + c_4 x)e^{-\frac{1}{2}x} + c_5 e^x$

9. $c_1 e^{3x} + (c_2 + c_3 x)e^{2x}$      10. $c_1 e^x + (c_2 + c_3 x)e^{\frac{1}{2}x}$

11. $c_1 e^x + c_2 e^{-x} + c_3 \cos x + c_4 \sin x$

12. $c_1 e^{2x} + e^{-x}(c_2 \cos \sqrt{3}x + c_3 \sin \sqrt{3}x)$

13. $e^x(c_1 \cos \sqrt{2}x + c_2 \sin \sqrt{2}x)$

14. $c_1 e^{2x} + c_2 e^{-2x} + c_3 \cos \sqrt{5}x + c_4 \sin \sqrt{5}x$

15. $c_1 \cos \sqrt{2}x + c_2 \sin \sqrt{2}x + c_3 \cos \sqrt{3}x + c_4 \sin \sqrt{3}x$

16. $(c_1 + c_2 x)e^{2x} + c_3 \cos \sqrt{2}x + c_4 \sin \sqrt{2}x$

17. $c_1 e^x + c_2 e^{2x} + e^{-\frac{1}{2}x}(c_3 \cos \frac{1}{2}\sqrt{3}x + c_4 \sin \frac{1}{2}\sqrt{3}x)$

18. $c_1 e^{2x} + c_2 e^{-2x} + e^{-\frac{1}{2}x}(c_3 \cos \frac{1}{2}\sqrt{3}x + c_4 \sin \frac{1}{2}\sqrt{3}x)$

19. $c_1 e^{\frac{3}{2}x} + c_2 \cos \sqrt{5}x + c_3 \sin \sqrt{5}x$

20. $c_1 e^{\frac{5}{2}x} + e^{-\frac{1}{2}x}(c_2 \cos \frac{1}{2}\sqrt{31}x + c_3 \sin \frac{1}{2}\sqrt{31}x)$

21. $(c_1 + c_2 x)e^{2x} + e^{-\frac{1}{2}x}(c_3 \cos \frac{1}{2}\sqrt{15}x + c_4 \sin \frac{1}{2}\sqrt{15}x)$

22. $c_1 e^{-\frac{7}{2}x} + e^{\frac{1}{4}x}(c_3 \cos \frac{1}{4}\sqrt{15}x + c_3 \sin \frac{1}{4}\sqrt{15}x)$

23. $c_1 e^x + c_2 \cos 2x + c_3 \sin 2x + c_4 \cos \sqrt{2}x + c_5 \sin \sqrt{2}x$

24. $c_1 e^{kx} + c_2 e^{-kx} + (c_3 + c_4 x) \cos kx + (c_5 + c_6 x) \sin kx$

25. $c_1 e^x + (c_2 + c_3 x) \cos x + (c_4 + c_5 x) \sin x$

26. $c_1 e^{-x} + (c_2 + c_3 x) \cos 2x + (c_4 + c_5 x) \sin 2x$

## Exercise 19, pages 86–87

1. $c_1 e^{2x} + c_2 e^{-2x} - \frac{3}{5} \cos x$      2. $c_1 \cos x + c_2 \sin x - \frac{1}{3} \sin 2x$

3. $c_1 e^x + c_2 e^{-2x} + \frac{1}{3}xe^x$      4. $c_1 e^{-x} + c_2 e^{-2x} - xe^{-2x}$

5. $e^{-\frac{1}{2}x}(c_1 \cos \frac{1}{2}\sqrt{3}x + c \sin \frac{1}{2}\sqrt{3}x) - \cos x$

6. $e^{-\frac{1}{2}x}(c_1 \cos \frac{1}{2}\sqrt{3}x + c_2 \sin \frac{1}{2}\sqrt{3}x) + x^2 - 2x$

7. $c_1 e^{-x} + c_2 e^{-2x} + (\frac{1}{2}x^2 - x)e^{-x}$

8. $c_1 e^x + c_2 e^{-x} + c_3 \cos x + c_4 \sin x + \frac{1}{4}xe^x$

9. $c_1 e^{2x} + c_2 e^{-2x} + \frac{1}{4}x(e^{2x} - 1)$

10. $c_1 e^{3x} + c_2 e^{-3x} + \frac{1}{6}xe^{3x} - \frac{1}{18} \sin 3x$

11. $c_1 e^{3x} + c_2 e^{-2x} - \frac{1}{6}x^3 + \frac{1}{12}x^2 - \frac{7}{36}x + \frac{13}{216}$

12. $e^{\frac{3}{2}x}(c_1 \cos \frac{1}{2}\sqrt{3}x + c_2 \sin \frac{1}{2}\sqrt{3}x) + (x + 1)e^x$

13. $c_1 \cos 2x + c_2 \sin 2x + \frac{1}{3}x \sin x - \frac{2}{9} \cos x$

14. $c_1 + c_2 x + c_3 e^{4x} - \frac{1}{48}x^4 - \frac{1}{48}x^3 - \frac{65}{64}x^2$

15. $e^{-\frac{1}{2}x}(c_1 \cos \frac{1}{2}\sqrt{3}x + c_2 \sin \frac{1}{2}\sqrt{3}x) - \frac{1}{39}e^x(2 \sin 3x + 3 \cos 3x)$

16. $c_1 e^{3x} + c_2 \cos 2x + c_3 \sin 2x - \frac{1}{8}e^{2x} - \frac{1}{12}x - \frac{1}{36}$

17. $c_1 e^{4x} + c_2 \cos x + c_3 \sin x - \frac{1}{40}e^{4x}(\sin x + 2 \cos x)$

18. $(c_1 + c_2 x)e^{-2x} + \frac{1}{128}e^{2x}(8x^3 - 12x^2 + 9x - 3)$

19. $c_1 e^{2x} + c_2 \cos x + c_3 \sin x + (\frac{1}{10}x^2 - \frac{4}{25}x)e^{2x}$

20. $(c_1 x + c_2) \cos nx + (c_3 x + c_4) \sin nx + \dfrac{\sin kx}{(k^2 - n^2)^2}$

21. $(c_1 + c_2 x)e^{-nx} + \dfrac{5(n^2 - 36) \cos 6x + 60n \sin 6x}{(n^2 + 36)^2}$

22. $c_1 \cos 3x + c_2 \sin 3x + \frac{1}{5} \cos 2x + \frac{1}{16} \sin x - \frac{1}{32} \sin 5x$

23. $e^{-2x}(c_1 \cos x + c_2 \sin x) + \frac{2}{5}x - \frac{8}{25} - \frac{1}{5}e^{-4x} + \frac{1}{65}(\sin 2x - 8 \cos 2x)$

24. $c_1 + c_2 x + c_3 e^{-2x} + (\frac{1}{6}x^3 + \frac{5}{8}x^2 + x)e^{-2x} - \frac{1}{117}(2 \cos 3x + 3 \sin 3x)$

25. $c_1 \cos 2x + c_2 \sin 2x + 1 - x \sin 2x$

26. $e^x(c_1 \cos x + c_2 \sin x) + e^{-x}(c_3 \cos x + c_4 \sin x)$
$$+ \tfrac{1}{1105}e^{2x}(24 \cos 3x - 23 \sin 3x)$$

27. $\frac{10}{21}e^{6x} + \frac{4}{28}e^{-x} - \frac{1}{12}e^{3x}$  \qquad 28. $\frac{3}{2}[\cos 2x + (x - \frac{2}{3}\pi) \sin 2x + 1]$

29. $\frac{1}{36}[(6x + 5)e^{-x} - e^x]$

30. $\frac{1}{5}(17 \cos x + 11 \sin x + e^x \sin x - 2e^x \cos x)$

31. $6 - \frac{98}{17}e^{-\frac{1}{2}x} + e^{-x} - \frac{4}{17}(4 \sin 2x + \cos 2x)$

32. $2 \cos x + \sin x - \frac{3}{4}(x^2 \cos x - x \sin x)$

33. $-\frac{136}{35}e^{\frac{1}{2}x} - \frac{13}{315}e^{-3x} - \frac{1}{10}(\sin x + \cos x) + \frac{8}{9}(3x + 5)$

34. $\frac{1}{2}(16\sqrt{2} - 5)e^{\frac{1}{4}\sqrt{2}x} - \frac{1}{2}(16\sqrt{2} + 5)e^{-\frac{1}{4}\sqrt{2}x} + (x + 8)e^{-\frac{1}{2}x}$

## Exercise 20, pages 90–91

1. $c_1 \cos x + c_2 \sin x + x \sin x + \cos x \ln \cos x$

2. $(c_1 + c_2 x)e^{-2x} + \frac{1}{9}e^x$

3. $c_1 \cos x + c_2 \sin x + x^2 - 2$

4. $(c_1 + c_2 x)e^x + e^{2x}$

5. $c_1 \cos x + c_2 \sin x - \frac{1}{3} \sin 2x$

6. $c_1 \cos 2x + c_2 \sin 2x + \frac{1}{2}x(1 + \cos 2x)$

7. $c_1 e^x + c_2 e^{-x} - 3x + \frac{5}{2}xe^x$

8. $c_1 \cos 3x + c_2 \sin 3x + \frac{1}{10}e^x - \frac{1}{7} \sin 4x$

9. $c_1 + c_2 e^x + c_3 e^{-4x} - \frac{1}{100}(4 \sin 2x + 3 \cos 2x)$

10. $c_1 + c_2 e^x + c_3 e^{-5x} + \frac{1}{48}e^{3x}$

11. $c_1 \cos x + c_2 \sin x - \cos x \ln (\sec x + \tan x)$

12. $c_1 \cos ax + c_2 \sin ax + \dfrac{x \sin ax}{a} + \dfrac{\cos ax \ln \cos ax}{a^2}$

13. $c_1 + (c_2 + c_3 x)e^x + \frac{1}{2}e^{2x}$

14. $c_1 + c_2 x + (c_3 + c_4 x)e^x + \frac{1}{12}x^4 + \frac{2}{3}x^3 + 3x^2$

15. $c_1 + c_2 e^{-x} + c_3 e^{4x} - \frac{1}{12}e^{2x} + \frac{1}{34}(3 \sin x + 5 \cos x)$

16. $(c_1 + c_2 x)e^x - e^x \ln (1 - x)$

17. $c_1 e^x + c_2 e^{2x} - e^{2x} \sin e^{-x}$

18. $c_1 \cos 2x + c_2 \sin 2x - 2 \sin x - \cos 2x \ln (\sec x + \tan x)$

19. $c_1 e^{\sqrt{2}x} + c_2 e^{-\sqrt{2}x} + \frac{1}{41}e^{-x}(4 \cos 2x - 5 \sin 2x)$

20. $c_1 \cos 3x + c_2 \sin 3x + \frac{4}{3} \sin 2x + \frac{1}{3} \cos 3x \ln (\sec x + \tan x)$
$$+ \tfrac{1}{3} \sin 3x \ln (\csc x - \cot x)$$

21. $c_1 \cos 3x + c_2 \sin 3x + \frac{2}{3} \sin 2x + \frac{1}{6} \cos 3x \ln (\sec x + \tan x)$
$$+ \tfrac{1}{6} \sin 3x \ln (\csc x - \cot x)$$

22. $c_1 \cos \dfrac{x}{3} + c_2 \sin \dfrac{x}{3} + \sin \dfrac{x}{3} \ln \left(\sec \dfrac{x}{3} + \tan \dfrac{x}{3}\right) - 2$

23. $c_1 + c_2 \cos x + c_3 \sin x - \ln \cos x - \sin x \ln (\sec x + \tan x)$

24. $(c_1 + c_2 x)e^{\frac{1}{2}x} + \frac{1}{16}x^2 e^{\frac{1}{2}x}(2 \ln x - 3)$

## Exercise 21, pages 95-96

1. $30 \sin 5x - 20 \cos 5x$
2. $27e^{4x}$
3. $e^{3x} \sec x (2 \sec^2 x - 1)$
4. $2575 \sin 5x$
5. $2x(1 - ax)e^{-ax}$
6. $2(13x-12) \sin 3x - 18(x+1) \cos 3x$
7. $x^5 + 15x^4 + 60x^3 + 60x^2 + x + 3$
8. $- (k^2 + a^2) \cos kx$
9. $\frac{1}{4}x^4 + C$
10. $\frac{1}{10}x^6 + c_1 x + c_2$
11. $\frac{7}{24}x^4 + c_1 x^2 + c_2 x + c_3$
12. $\frac{1}{56}x^8 + c_1 x + c_2$
13. $\frac{e^{2x}}{2a + b} + Ce^{-\frac{bx}{a}}$
14. $e^{3x} + (c_1 x + c_2)e^{ax}$
15. $\frac{1}{17}(4 \sin 2x - \cos 2x) + Ce^{\frac{1}{2}x}$
16. $-\frac{5}{b^3} + (c_1 x^2 + c_2 x + c_3)e^{bx}$
17. $e^{-3x}(\sin x - \cos x)$
18. $e^{2x}(26 \sin x + 44 \cos x)$
19. $15x^2(x - 2)^2 e^{-x}$
20. $32e^{3x} \sec^2 4x \tan 4x$
21. $e^{5x} \sec x(2 \tan^2 x + 11 \tan x + 31)$
22. $e^{5x}\left(10 \ln 2x + \frac{5}{x} - \frac{1}{x^2}\right)$
23. $e^x \sin x$
24. $- e^{-x} \sin x$
25. $2e^{-2x} \sec^2 x \tan x$
26. $\frac{2e^{2x}}{x^3}$
27. $16e^{3x} \sin 2x$
28. $xe^x(1 - x^2)^{-\frac{3}{2}}$
29. $656e^{5x}$
30. $0$
31. $0$
32. $- 90e^{-4x}$
33. $239e^{12x}$
34. $\frac{37}{6}e^{16x}$
35. $(a + b)^2 e^{(a+b)x}$
36. $\frac{2ab}{c} e^{(a+b-c)x}$

## Exercise 22, page 99

1. $(c_1 + c_2 x)e^{3x} + \frac{1}{2}x^2 e^{3x}$
2. $(c_1 + c_2 x)e^{-2x} + \frac{1}{2}x^2 e^{-2x}$
3. $(c_1 + c_2 x + c_3 x^2)e^x + \frac{1}{6}x^3 e^x$
4. $(c_1 + c_2 x + c_3 x^2)e^{2x} - e^x$
5. $c_1 e^{2x} + c_2 e^{3x} + \frac{1}{6}x^2 + \frac{5}{18}x + \frac{19}{108}$
6. $c_1 e^{-2x} + c_2 e^{-3x} + \frac{1}{20}xe^{-2x} - \frac{9}{400}e^{2x}$
7. $(c_1 + c_2 x + c_3 x^2)e^{-2x} + \frac{1}{8}x - \frac{3}{16}$
8. $c_1 e^{-x} + c_2 e^{-2x} + \frac{1}{10}(\sin x - 3 \cos x)$
9. $c_1 e^x + c_2 e^{-x} - \frac{1}{2} \cos x$
10. $(c_1 + c_2 x)e^x + c_3 e^{-x} + \frac{1}{24}x^2 e^x(x^2 - 2x + 3)$
11. $(c_1 + c_2 x)e^{-2x} + c_3 e^{3x} - \frac{1}{150}x^2 e^{-2x}(5x + 3)$
12. $c_1 + c_2 x + c_3 x^2 + c_4 e^{-x} + \frac{1}{40}(2 \cos 2x - \sin 2x)$
13. $(c_1 + c_2 x)e^{-x} + xe^{-x} (\ln x - 1)$
14. $(c_1 + c_2 x)e^x + \frac{1}{2}x^2 e^x \ln x - \frac{3}{4}x^2 e^x$
15. $(c_1 + c_2 x)e^{-x} + (c_3 + c_4 x + c_5 x^2)e^x - x - 1$
16. $c_1 e^{2x} + c_2 e^{-2x} - \frac{1}{8}xe^{-2x} + \frac{1}{40}(2 \sin 2x + \cos 2x)$
17. $(c_1 + c_2 x)e^{-x} - \frac{1}{2}(x \cos x - \sin x - \cos x)$
18. $(c_1 + c_2 x)e^x - \frac{1}{2}(x \sin x + \sin x + \cos x)$
19. $c_1 e^{a_1 x} + c_2 e^{a_2 x} + c_3 e^{a_3 x} + e^{a_3 x}\int e^{(a_2-a_3)x}\int e^{(a_1-a_2)x}\int e^{-a_1 x}Q(x)\, dx\, dx\, dx$
20. $c_1 e^{a_1 x} + c_2 e^{a_2 x} + \cdots + c_n e^{a_n x} + e^{a_n x}\int e^{(a_{n-1}-a_n)x}\int \cdots e^{(a_1-a_2)x}\int e^{-a_1 x}Q(x)\, (dx)^n$

## Exercise 23, page 106

1. $\frac{2}{5}e^x$
2. $\frac{3}{19}e^{-4x}$
3. $\frac{1}{18}(e^x + 9e^{-x})$
4. $- \frac{1}{3}xe^{-2x}$
5. $\sin x$
6. $\frac{1}{50}(e^{3x} - 25e^{-3x})$
7. $- \frac{1}{12}(\sin 2x + \cos 2x)$
8. $\frac{1}{10}e^x(\sin x - \cos x)$

329

9. $\frac{1}{3}xe^x$

10. $\frac{1}{34}x(4\cos x - \sin x - 2e^{4x})$

11. $\frac{1}{20}x(8e^x - 3\sin 2x)$

12. $\frac{1}{30}e^{3x}(\sin 2x - 2\cos 2x + 3)$

13. $\dfrac{(n^4 - k^2)\sin kx - 2n^2k\cos kx}{(n^4 + k^2)^2}$

14. $\frac{1}{20}(e^x + 5e^{-x})$

15. $\frac{1}{4}e^{-x}(1 - 2x)$

16. $\frac{1}{25}(5x - 2)e^x$

17. $\frac{1}{27}(9x^2 + 12x + 2)e^{-x}$

18. $\frac{1}{4}(13 + 2x - 2x^2)$

19. $-x^2$

20. $\frac{1}{64}e^{-x}(8x^2 + 20x + 23)$

21. $\frac{1}{12}(x^4 + 8x^3 + 36x^2)$

22. $-\frac{1}{12}e^x(2x^3 - 9x^2 + 21x) - \frac{1}{10}e^x(\cos x + 3\sin x)$

23. $\frac{1}{16}e^{2x}(7 - 2x)$

24. $\frac{1}{162}\cos 3x + \frac{1}{32}e^x(2x - 5)$

25. $-\frac{1}{3}(x^3 + 6x)e^{2x}$

26. $\frac{1}{6}x^3 - \frac{1}{2}x + \sin x$

27. $\frac{1}{20}(3\sin 2x + \cos 2x)$

28. $\dfrac{x}{10}(2\sin x - \cos x)$

29. $\dfrac{x^2}{16}(\sin x + \cos x)$

30. $\frac{1}{4}x^4 - 2x^3 + 12x^2 - 54x - \frac{1}{68}(4\cos 2x + \sin 2x)$

31. $-\frac{1}{10}xe^{-2x}(2\sin x + \cos x)$

32. $\frac{1}{104}e^{-2x}(5\cos 2x + \sin 2x)$

33. $(8 - x^2)\cos x - 2x\sin x$

34. $\frac{1}{24}[(15x - 2x^3)\sin x - 9x^2\cos x]$

## Exercise 24, page 109

1. $\frac{1}{9}(3x\sin x - 2\cos x)$

2. $\frac{1}{12}(2x^3\sin x + 3x^2\cos x - 3x\sin x)$

3. $\frac{1}{8}(-x^3\cos x + 3x^2\sin x + 3x\cos x)$

4. $\frac{1}{15}(3e^x - 5\cos x)$

5. $\frac{1}{360}(x^6 - 6x^5 + 30x^4)$

6. $\frac{1}{27}(9x^2 - 42x + 86)e^x$

7. $\frac{1}{8}(x^4 + 4x^3 + 6x^2)e^{-x}$

8. $-\frac{1}{2}x\sin x$

9. $\frac{1}{2}x\cos x - \sin x$

10. $-\frac{1}{32}[(2x + 2)\cos 2x + (2x - 3)\sin 2x]$

11. $\frac{1}{250}[(25x^2 + 60x - 133)\cos x + (75x^2 - 170x + 81)\sin x]$

12. $\frac{1}{250}[(25x^2 - 20x - 67)\sin x + (50x^2 + 110x + 56)\cos x]$

13. $-\frac{1}{25}(5x\sin 2x + 4\cos 2x)$

14. $-\frac{1}{64}[(8x^3 - 24x^2 - 6x + 15)\sin 2x + (8x^3 + 12x^2 - 30x)\cos 2x]$

15. $-\frac{1}{2}xe^x(\sin x + \cos x) + \frac{1}{2}e^x(2\sin x - \cos x)$

16. $\frac{1}{17}xe^{2x}(4\sin x - \cos x) + \frac{1}{289}e^{2x}(2\sin x + 76\cos x)$

17. $-\frac{1}{2}e^{-x}(x^2\sin x + 2x\cos x - \sin x)$

## Exercise 25, page 112

1. $c_1 x^{\frac{1}{2}(5+\sqrt{21})} + c_2 x^{\frac{1}{2}(5-\sqrt{21})}$

2. $c_1\cos(4\ln x) + c_2\sin(4\ln x)$

3. $(c_1 + c_2\ln x)x^{\frac{5}{2}}$

4. $x^{-2}[c_1\cos(\sqrt{6}\ln x) + c_2\sin(\sqrt{6}\ln x)]$

5. $c_1 x^{\frac{9}{2}} + c_2 x^{-2} - \frac{1}{18}\ln x + \frac{5}{324}$

6. $c_1 x^2 + c_2 x^{\frac{1}{2}} + \frac{3}{2}\ln x + \frac{15}{4}$

7. $(c_1 + c_2\ln x)x^2 + x^3$

8. $\dfrac{c_1 + c_2\ln x}{x} + 1 - \frac{1}{4}x$

9. $(c_1 + c_2\ln x)x + \dfrac{c_3}{x} + \dfrac{\ln x}{4x}$

10. $c_1 x + c_2 x^2 - 4x\ln x + \frac{1}{10}[\sin(\ln x) + 3\cos(\ln x)]$

11. $x[c_1\cos(\ln x) + c_2\sin(\ln x)] + \frac{1}{2}x^2(\ln x - 1)$

12. $x^{-\frac{3}{2}}[c_1\cos(\frac{1}{2}\sqrt{3}\ln x) + c_2\sin(\frac{1}{2}\sqrt{3}\ln x)] + \frac{1}{7}x\ln x - \frac{5}{49}x + \frac{1}{3}(1 - \ln x)$

13. $c_1 x + c_2 x^{\frac{1}{2}} + c_3 x^{-\frac{1}{2}} + \frac{1}{3}x\ln x + \ln x + 1$

14. $c_1 x + c_2 x^{\frac{1}{3}(+\sqrt{31})} + c_3 x^{\frac{1}{3}(1-\sqrt{31})} - \dfrac{2}{9x^2}$

15. $c_1x^2 + \dfrac{1}{x}\left[c_2 + c_3\cos(\sqrt{2}\ln x) + c_4\sin(\sqrt{2}\ln x)\right]$

$\qquad\qquad\qquad\qquad -\frac{1}{20}[\cos(\ln x) + 2\sin(\ln x)]$

16. $c_1x^4 + c_2x^{\frac{1}{2}(1+\sqrt{5})} + c_3x^{\frac{1}{2}(1-\sqrt{5})} + \frac{1}{85}[9\sin(\ln x) - 2\cos(\ln x)]$

## Exercise 26, page 115

1. $x = c_1e^t + \frac{1}{2}(\sin t - \cos t),\quad y = c_2e^{-t} + 4t - 4$
2. $x = c_1e^{-5t} + \frac{3}{5}t^2 - \frac{6}{25}t + \frac{6}{125},\quad y = c_2e^{-t} + \frac{1}{4}e^{3t}$
3. $x = 3c_1e^{-2t} + \frac{3}{2}t - \frac{3}{4}$
   $y = -2c_1e^{-2t} + c_2e^{\frac{1}{2}t} + \frac{1}{17}(\cos 2t + 4\sin 2t) - \frac{3}{2}$
4. $x = c_1 + c_2e^{5t} - \frac{2}{13}(8\cos t + \sin t)$
   $y = c_1 - 4c_2e^{5t} + \frac{2}{13}(4\sin t - 7\cos t)$
5. $x = c_1e^{-2t} + 3c_2e^{\frac{1}{6}t} + \frac{4}{15}e^t + t + \frac{11}{2}$
   $y = -c_1e^{-2t} + 10c_2e^{\frac{1}{6}t} + \frac{1}{3}e^t + 3t - \frac{37}{2}$
6. $x = 5c_1e^{\frac{2}{5}t} + \frac{5}{2},\quad y = -2c_1e^{\frac{2}{5}t} - t - 1$
7. $x = -3(c_1e^t + c_2e^{-t}) - 2(c_3e^{\sqrt{2}t} + c_4e^{-\sqrt{2}t}) - \frac{5}{6}\sin t - \cos t$
   $y = c_1e^t + c_2e^{-t} + c_3e^{\sqrt{2}t} + c_4e^{-\sqrt{2}t} + \frac{1}{6}\sin t$
8. $x = c_1e^t + c_2\sin t + c_3\cos t - \frac{1}{15}(3\cos 2t + 4\sin 2t)$
   $y = c_1e^t + (c_2 - c_3)\sin t + (c_2 + c_3)\cos t - \frac{1}{15}(2\cos 2t + \sin 2t)$
9. $x = c_1 + c_2e^{-\frac{1}{3}t} - \frac{1}{74}(6\sin 2t + \cos 2t) + \frac{1}{3}t^3 - 3t^2 + 18t$
   $y = c_3 + c_4t + 2c_2e^{-\frac{1}{3}t} - \frac{1}{37}(6\sin 2t + \cos 2t) - \frac{1}{12}t^4 + \frac{2}{3}t^3 - 6t^2$
10. $x = c_1 + c_2t + 5c_3\cos\sqrt{3}t + 5c_4\sin\sqrt{3}t - \frac{5}{3}t^3$
    $y = -c_1 + (\frac{2}{3} - c_2)t - 2c_3\cos\sqrt{3}t - 2c_4\sin\sqrt{3}t + \frac{5}{3}t^3$
11. $x = c_1e^{\sqrt{3}t} + c_2e^{-\sqrt{3}t} + c_3\cos\sqrt{3}t + c_4\sin\sqrt{3}t + \frac{23}{7}e^{2t} - \frac{1}{3}$
    $y = c_1e^{\sqrt{3}t} + c_2e^{-\sqrt{3}t} - 5(c_3\cos\sqrt{3}t + c_4\sin\sqrt{3}t) + \frac{25}{7}e^{2t} - \frac{1}{3}$
12. $x = 25c_1e^{3t},\quad y = 50c_1te^{3t} + 5c_2e^{3t}$
    $z = 30c_1te^{3t} + 3(c_2 - 2c_1)e^{3t} + c_3e^{-2t}$

## Exercise 27, pages 125–126

1. $x = \frac{1}{4}\cos 8\sqrt{2}t$ 
$\qquad\qquad\qquad$ 2. $-\dfrac{\pi\sqrt{15}}{3}$ ft./sec.; $-\dfrac{4}{9}\pi^2$ ft./sec.$^2$

4. $-98.4$ ft./sec.; $-288$ ft. $\qquad$ 6. $203$ ft.; $64$ ft.

7. $161.7$ ft. from base; $64\ 3°$ with horizontal.

8. $28.64$ in./sec. $\qquad\qquad\qquad$ 9. $42.5$ min.

10. $x = 0.54$ ft.; $v = -2.24$ ft./sec.; $t = 0.30$ sec.; $v = 3.74$ ft./sec.

11. $\dfrac{d^2x}{dt^2} + 0.077\dfrac{dx}{dt} + 6.318x = 0$ $\qquad$ 12. $0.17$ sec.

13. $x = \frac{1}{4}\cos 8t - \frac{6}{5}\sin 8t + \frac{16}{5}\sin 3t$; $0.06$ sec.

## Exercise 28, pages 129–130

1. $i = 3e^{-600t}\sin 200t$ $\qquad\qquad$ 2. $i = \frac{1}{6}e^{-\frac{1000}{3}t}$

3. $i = 4.3\cos 120\pi t + 7.5\sin 120\pi t - e^{-600t}(4.3\cos 200t + 27.1\sin 200t)$

4. $i = 0.018e^{-1710t} - 0.041e^{-293t} + 0.049\sin 120\pi t + 0.023\cos 120\pi t$

5. $i = 0.5(1 - e^{-1200t})$

6. $v = 100$ cycles per second

7. $L_2 \dfrac{di_2}{dt} + R(i_1 + i_2) = E, \qquad L_2 \dfrac{d^2 i_2}{dt^2} - R \dfrac{di_1}{dt} - \dfrac{1}{C_1} i_1 = 0$

8. $L_2 \dfrac{di_2}{dt} + R(i_1 + i_2) = E, \qquad L_1 \dfrac{di_1}{dt} - L_2 \dfrac{di_2}{dt} + R_1 i_1 = 0$

9. $R \left( \dfrac{di_1}{dt} + \dfrac{di_2}{dt} \right) + \dfrac{1}{C_2} i_2 = 0, \qquad L_1 \dfrac{d^2 i_1}{dt^2} + R_1 \dfrac{di_1}{dt} - \dfrac{1}{C_2} i_2 = 0$

### Exercise 29, page 135

1. $\phi_4(x) = 1 - x + x^2 - \frac{1}{3}x^3 + \frac{1}{24}x^4$
   $\phi_5(x) = 1 - x + x^2 - \frac{1}{3}x^3 + \frac{1}{12}x^4 - \frac{1}{120}x^5$
   $y(x) = -1 + x + 2e^{-x}$
   $\phi_4(0.5) = 0.7109, \quad \phi_5(0.5) = 0.7133, \quad y(0.5) = 0.7130$

2. $\phi_4(x) = 1 + x + x^2 + \frac{1}{3}x^3 + \frac{1}{24}x^4$
   $\phi_5(x) = 1 + x + x^2 + \frac{1}{3}x^3 + \frac{1}{12}x^4 + \frac{1}{120}x^5$
   $y(x) = -1 - x + 2e^x$
   $\phi_4(0.5) = 1.7943, \quad \phi_5(0.5) = 1.7971, \quad y(0.5) = 1.7974$

3. $\phi_4(x) = \frac{43}{60} + \frac{17}{12}x - \frac{1}{6}x^2 + \frac{5}{6}x^3 + \frac{1}{12}x^4 + \frac{1}{60}x^5$
   $\phi_5(x) = \frac{349}{360} + \frac{43}{60}x + \frac{17}{24}x^2 + \frac{5}{18}x^3 + \frac{5}{24}x^4 + \frac{1}{60}x^5 + \frac{1}{360}x^6$
   $y(x) = 8e^{x-1} - x^2 - 2x - 2$
   $\phi_4(2) = 11.517, \quad \phi_5(2) = 11.703, \quad y(2) = 11.746$

4. $\phi_4(x) = \frac{23}{20} - \frac{53}{12}x + \frac{11}{6}x^2 - \frac{1}{12}x^4 + \frac{1}{60}x^5$
   $\phi_5(x) = \frac{847}{180} - \frac{23}{20}x + \frac{53}{24}x^2 - \frac{5}{18}x^3 + \frac{1}{60}x^5 - \frac{1}{360}x^6$
   $y(x) = 2 - 2x + x^2 + e^{1-x}$
   $\phi_4(0.5) = 2.8953, \quad \phi_5(0.5) = 2.8984, \quad y(0.5) = 2.8987$

5. $\phi_4(x) = \frac{2}{3} + e^x + \frac{1}{3}e^{3x}$
   $\phi_5(x) = \frac{3}{4} + \frac{2}{3}e^x + \frac{1}{2}e^{2x} + \frac{1}{12}e^{4x}$
   $y(x) = 2e^{e^x - 1}$
   $\phi_4(1.5) = 35.15, \quad \phi_5(1.5) = 47.40, \quad y(1.5) = 65.03$

6. $\phi_4(x) = 0.5 + 1.5x + 0.75x^2 + \frac{1}{3}(0.25)x^3 - \sin x$
   $\phi_5(x) = 0.5 + 0.5x + 0.75x^2 + 0.25x^3 + \frac{1}{3}(0.0625)x^4$
   $y(x) = e^x - \frac{1}{2}(\sin x + \cos x)$
   $\phi_4(0.4) = 0.8359, \quad \phi_5(0.4) = 0.8365, \quad y(0.4) = 0.8366$

7. $\phi_4(x) = 0.45 - 0.45x + 0.35x^2 - \frac{1}{3}(0.35)x^3 + \frac{3}{8}\sin 2x + \frac{1}{4}\cos 2x$
   $\phi_5(x) = 0.5125 - 0.45x + 0.225x^2 - \frac{1}{3}(0.35)x^3 + \frac{1}{12}(0.35)x^4 + \frac{3}{8}\sin 2x$
   $\qquad\qquad + \frac{3}{16}\cos 2x$

   $y(x) = \frac{1}{5}(2\sin 2x + \cos 2x) + \frac{1}{2}e^{-x}$
   $\phi_4(0.3) = 0.7614, \quad \phi_5(0.3) = 0.7613, \quad y(0.3) = 0.7613$

8. $\phi_3(x) = 1 + 2x + 2x^2 + \frac{4}{3}x^3$
   $\phi_4(x) = 1 + 2x + 2x^2 + \frac{8}{3}x^3 + \frac{8}{3}x^4 + \frac{28}{15}x^5 + \frac{8}{9}x^6 + \frac{16}{63}x^7$

   $y(x) = \tan \left( x + \dfrac{\pi}{4} \right)$

   $\phi_3(0.3) = 1.8160, \quad \phi_4(0.3) = 1.8788, \quad y(0.3) = 1.896$

9. $\phi_2(x) = 0.4 + 0.16x + \frac{1}{2}x^2$
   $\phi_3(x) = 0.4 + 0.16x + 0.564x^2 + \frac{1}{3}(0.4256)x^3 + 0.04x^4 + 0.05x^5$
   $\phi_2(0.2) = 0.4520, \quad \phi_3(0.2) = 0.4558$

10. $\phi_2(x) = 1 + \frac{1}{2}x^2 + \sin x$
    $\phi_3(x) = 1 + \frac{1}{2}x^2 + x \cos x + \frac{1}{2}x^2 \sin x + \frac{1}{2}\sin^2 x$
    $\phi_2(0.6) = 1.7446, \quad \phi_3(0.6) = 1.9362$

ANSWERS TO EXERCISES

## Exercise 30, page 140

1. 1.656  2. 1.429  3. 0.6666  4. 0.5101  5. 2.990
6. 0.8012  7. 0.7798  8. − 0.2090  9. 1.774  10. 1.201

## Exercise 31, page 144

1. 2.896, 2.785, 2.665, 2.534, 2.389
2. 0.9052, 0.8213, 0.7492, 0.6897, 0.6435
3. 0.5578, 0.6323, 0.7256, 0.8402, 0.9793
4. 0.2826, 0.3666, 0.4519, 0.5384, 0.6260
5. − 0.3357, − 0.1446, 0.0770, 0.3328, 0.6254
6. 1.005, 1.020, 1.045, 1.081, 1.127
7. 0.6640, 0.7436, 0.8396, 0.9525, 1.0825
8. 2.076, 2.165, 2.267, 2.381, 2.508
9. $y = 0.9050, 0.8199, 0.7444$; $y' = − 0.9003, − 0.8023, − 0.7074$
10. $y = − 1.710, − 1.440, − 1.190$; $y' = 2.800, 2.602, 2.408$
11. $y = 0.7955, 0.8199, 0.7444$; $y' = − 2.088, − 2.142, − 2.177$
12. $y = 2.186, 2.349, 2.494$; $y' = 1.731, 1.527, 1.368$

## Exercise 32, page 147

1. 2.389  2. − 0.5696  3. 0.9793
4. 0.6260  5. 0.6257  6. 1.128
7. 1.0825  8. 2.507  9. 0.669, − 0.616
10. − 0.821, 2.843  11. 0.146, − 2.192  12. 2.624, 1.240

## Exercise 34, page 153

1. 0.110, 1.090; 0.237, 1.161; 0.381, 1.215
2. 0.498, 1.076; 0.795, 1.143; 1.090, 1.207
3. 1.000, − 0.111; 0.997, − 0.246; 0.990, − 0.410
4. 1.145, 1.216; 1.309, 1.466; 1.494, 1.755
5. 0.092, − 0.500; 0.194, − 0.499; 0.307, − 0.499
6. 0.540, 1.254  7. 1.388, 1.271  8. 0.977, − 0.610
9. 1.704, 2.089  10. 0.432, − 0.500

## Exercise 35, pages 157–159

1. $y = − \cos \theta + c_1\theta + c_2$
2. $\ln (ky + \sqrt{k^2y^2 + c_1}) = kx + c_2$
3. $kx = c_1 \sin (kt + c_2)$
4. $\pm \sqrt{4 + c_1y^2} = c_1x + c_2$
5. $\sqrt{c_1x} \sqrt{c_1x − 2k^2} + 2k^2 \ln (\sqrt{c_1x} + \sqrt{c_1x − 2k^2}) = c_1^{\frac{3}{2}}t + c_2$
6. $y = x \ln x + \frac{1}{6}x^3 + c_1x + c_2$
7. $y + c_1 \ln (1 − x) = c_2$
8. $y + x + c_2 = c_1 \text{ Arc tan } x$
9. $c_1e^x = \sin (y + c_2)$
10. $2y = − x^2 \ln x + c_1x^2 + c_2$
11. $x = \frac{1}{3}t^3 − 2t + c_1 \int e^{-\frac{1}{2}t^2} dt + c_2$
12. $2y = − \ln x + c_1x^2 + c_2$
13. $y = \ln \sec (x + c_1) + c_2$
14. $2y = x^2 + c_1(x\sqrt{1 − x^2} + \text{Arc sin } x) + c_2$
15. $y = \cosh (x + c_1) + c_2$
16. $y = c_2 − \ln (c_1 − e^x)$
17. $y = 2c_1 \tan (c_1x + c^2)$
18. $y + c_1x + c_2 = (1 + c_1^2) \ln (x + c_1)$
19. $y = \dfrac{c_1(e^{c_1x} − c_2)}{e^{c_1x} + c_2}$
20. $y = k$, $2y = \ln (2x − c_1) + c_2$

333

**21.** $y^2 + c_1^2 = (x + c_2)^2$

**22.** $c_1 y = \sinh (c_1 x + c_2)$

**23.** $y = c_1 \sinh (x + c_2)$

**24.** $y^2 + c_1 = c_2 e^x$

**25.** $4y = (c_1 x + c_2)^2$

**26.** $2y = c_2 + \ln (c_1 e^{2x} + e^{-2x})$

**27.** $y + c_2 = \ln (\sqrt{c_1 + e^{-2x}} + e^{-x})$

**28.** $y + 1 = (c_1 x + c_2)^{-\frac{1}{2}}$

**29.** $\sqrt{2} \sin \theta = e^t$

**30.** $e^{\frac{1}{2}y} = \dfrac{2}{2 - x}$

**31.** $xy + \sqrt{2}(1 + y) = 0$

**32.** $y = 1 + \sec x + \tan x$

**33.** $y(4 - e^{\frac{3}{2}x}) = 6$

**34.** $x + y - 1 = 2 \ln (x + 1)$

**35.** $\dfrac{\sqrt{y + 1} - 1}{\sqrt{y + 1} + 1} = \dfrac{\sqrt{2} - 1}{\sqrt{2} + 1} e^{\sqrt{2}x}$

**36.** $4x + 3\sqrt{2} = \sqrt{(6 - y)(4y - 6)} + 9 \operatorname{Arc} \tan \dfrac{\sqrt{4y - 6}}{2\sqrt{6 - y}} - 9 \operatorname{Arc} \tan \dfrac{\sqrt{2}}{2}$

**37.** $y = \tan \dfrac{x}{2}$

**38.** $y = - \operatorname{sech}^2 \dfrac{x}{2}$

**39.** $kx + \sqrt{v_0^2 + k^2 x^2} = v_0 e^t$

**40.** $y = \dfrac{1}{2} \sec \left(x + \dfrac{\pi}{3}\right)$

**41.** $y = (e - 1)[\ln (e^{-x} - 1) - \ln (e^{-1} - 1)]$

**42.** $(x + c_1)^2 + (y + c_2)^2 = \dfrac{1}{k^2}$

**43.** $3y = 2 + \cosh 3x; \quad 10.02$

**44.** $v = v_0 \sqrt{1 - e^{\dfrac{-2gy}{v_0^2}}}; \quad y = \dfrac{v_0^2}{g} \ln \cosh \dfrac{gt}{v_0}$

**45.** (a) $v = \dfrac{8t}{3\sqrt{8t^2 + 81}}$
(b) $v = \dfrac{2\sqrt{2}\sqrt{s^2 + 6s}}{3(s + 3)}$

(c) $s = - 3 + \frac{1}{3}\sqrt{8t^2 + 81}$

**46.** $v = \pm \sqrt{v_0^2 - 2gR \left(1 + \dfrac{R}{y}\right)}; \quad \pm \sqrt{v_0^2 - gR}; \quad - \sqrt{v_0^2 - 2gR}$

**47.** 116 hr.

## Exercise 36, pages 166–167

**2.** $y = 14 \cosh \dfrac{x}{14}$

**3.** 6.50

**4.** 0.480

**5.** 76.2 ft.

**7.** 14.3 pounds, 11.8 pounds

**8.** 258 ft.

## Exercise 37, pages 171–172

**1.** $y = Cx^2, \quad x^2 y = C'$

**2.** $y = \ln \dfrac{C}{x}, \quad y^2 + 2x = C'$

**3.** $y^2 + x = C, \quad xy + 1 = C'x$

**4.** $y \pm \sqrt{x^2 + y^2} = C$

**5.** $2x + C = \pm (y\sqrt{1 - y^2} + \operatorname{Arc} \sin y)$

**6.** $y = Ce^{-x}, \quad x = C'e^{\frac{1}{2}y^2}$

**7.** $x^2 - y^2 = C, \quad 2x^2 + y^2 = C'$

**8.** $\sqrt{x^2 - y^2} = C \pm \sqrt{2}x$

**9.** $y = C, \quad y = C'e^{x^2}, \quad x + y - 1 = C''e^{-x}$

**10.** $y = Ce^{-x}, \quad x^2 + y^2 + 1 = C'e^{x^2}$

**11.** $p^2 x = Ce^{\frac{1}{p}}$, D.E.

**12.** $\dfrac{p - 1}{p} = Ce^{\frac{1}{3}x}$, D.E.

**13.** $\dfrac{p}{p^2 + 1} + \operatorname{Arc} \tan p = C - \dfrac{x}{2}$, D.E. $\quad y = 2$ (s.s.)

**14.** $y^2 = 2Cx - C^2. \quad y = \pm x$ (s.s.)

**15.** $y = \cos (x + C). \quad y = \pm 1$ (s.s.)

**16.** $C^2 x^2 - 2Cy = 1$

**17.** $x^2 = Cy - C^2. \quad y = \pm 2x$ (s.s.)

18. $y = Cx^2 - 2C^2$.   $8y = x^4$ (s.s.)

19. $Cx^8 = \dfrac{(p^2 - 1)^8}{p^6(p^2 - 4)^5}$, D.E.

20. $(8x + 1)^3(p^3 - 8)^2 = Cp^6$, D.E.

21. $\dfrac{3p + 2}{p^3} = C - 3x$, D.E.

22. $Cx = pe^p$, D.E.   $y = x$ (s.s.)

23. $3Cy = 1 + C^2x^3$.   $9y^2 = 4x^3$ (s.s.)

24. $x^3p^2(p - 3)^4 = C$, D.E.

### Exercise 38, page 173

1. $6y = 4p^3 + 3p^2 + C$, D.E.
2. $2y = 2p^3 + 3p^2 + 6p + 6 \ln (p - 1) + C$, D.E.
3. $C^2x^2 = 4(1 + Cy)$.   $x^2 + y^2 = 0$ (s.s.)
4. $C^2x^2 = 4Cy - 16$.   $y = \pm 2x$ (s.s.)
5. $2p(p - 1)^2y = 3p - 2 + Cp^3$, D.E.
6. $y^2 - 2Cx + C^2 = 0$.   $y = \pm x$ (s.s.)
7. $C^2x^2 = 4(Cy - 2)$.   $y = \pm \sqrt{2x}$ (s.s.)
8. $(y + p)\sqrt{p^2 - 1} + \ln (p + \sqrt{p^2 - 1}) = C$, D.E.
9. $Cx = (y - C)^2$.   $x + 4y = 0$ (s.s.)
10. $py = C(p + 1)e^{\frac{1}{p}}$, D.E.
11. $p^2y + 3 = Cp$, D.E.
12. $4y = C(C + x)^2$.   $x^3 + 27y = 0$ (s.s.)
13. $5p^3y = 4 + Cp^{\frac{5}{2}}$, D.E.
14. $3py + 4p^0 = C$, D.E.
15. $4y = 3p^{-2} + Cp^2$, D.E.
16. $y = \dfrac{1}{2} + \ln p + \dfrac{C}{p^2}$, D.E.

### Exercise 39, pages 178–179

1. $x^2 + y^2 = p^2$
2. $y^2 = a^2$
3. $2xy = k$
4. $y^2 = 4ax$
5. $4y = x^2 - 2x$
6. $y^2 = \frac{4}{27}x^3$
7. $y^2 = 4x^2$
8. $y = 0$
9. $y = \pm x$

21. $xy = \pm \dfrac{A}{2\pi}$

22. $(x^2 + y^2)^2 = 16xy$

23. $y = Cx + C^2$;   $x^2 + 4y = 0$

24. $y = Cx + \dfrac{1}{C}$;   $y^2 = 4x$

25. $y = Cx - \sqrt{C}$;   $4xy + 1 = 0$

26. $y = Cx + \ln C$;   $y + 1 + \ln (- x) = 0$

27. $y = Cx + \dfrac{3}{C^2}$;   $y = 9\left(\dfrac{x}{6}\right)^{\frac{2}{3}}$

28. $y = Cx - C^{\frac{2}{3}}$;   $27x^2y + 4 = 0$

29. $y = Cx + e^{-C}$;   $y = x(1 - \ln x)$
30. $(y - Cx)^2 = C^2 + 1$;   $x^2 + y^2 = 1$
31. $C^2x - Cy - 2 = 0$;   $y^2 + 8x = 0$
32. $y^2 - 2Cxy + C^2(x^2 - 1) = 0$;   $x = \pm 1$

### Exercise 40, page 186

1. $x - \frac{1}{4}x^2$
2. $2 + x^2 - \frac{1}{3}x^3 + \frac{1}{4}x^4 - \frac{1}{15}x^5$
3. $(x - 1) + (x - 1)^2 - \frac{1}{2}(x - 1)^4 - \frac{1}{5}(x - 1)^5$
4. $3 + 6(x - 1) + 3(x - 1)^2$

5. $1 + \frac{1}{2}(x-1)^2 + \frac{1}{12}(x-1)^4 - \frac{7}{120}(x-1)^5$

6. $-1 + 2(x-1) - 2(x-1)^2 + \frac{8}{3}(x-1)^3 - \frac{10}{3}(x-1)^4 + \frac{64}{15}(x-1)^5$

7. $4(x-2) + 2(x-2)^2 + \frac{17}{3}(x-2)^3 + 4(x-2)^4 + \frac{148}{15}(x-2)^5 + \frac{82}{9}(x-2)^6$

8. $1 + x + \frac{1}{4}x^2 + \frac{1}{8}x^3 - \frac{1}{64}x^4$

9. $\frac{\pi}{2} + \left(x - \frac{\pi}{2}\right) - \frac{1}{2}\left(x - \frac{\pi}{2}\right)^2 - \frac{1}{6}\left(x - \frac{\pi}{2}\right)^3 + \frac{1}{6}\left(x - \frac{\pi}{2}\right)^4 + \frac{1}{60}\left(x - \frac{\pi}{2}\right)^5$

10. $1 + 2x + \frac{1}{2}x^2 + \frac{1}{2}x^3 + \frac{1}{24}x^4 + \frac{1}{60}x^5 + \frac{1}{720}x^6 + \frac{1}{1680}x^7$

11. $2 + 2x + \frac{5}{2}x^2 + x^3 + \frac{7}{12}x^4 + \frac{1}{6}x^5 + \frac{1}{180}x^6 + \frac{1}{70}x^7$

12. $x - \frac{1}{3}x^3 + \frac{2}{15}x^5 - \frac{17}{315}x^7$

13. $\frac{\pi}{4} + \frac{\sqrt{2}}{4}x^2 + \frac{1}{48}x^4 - \frac{\sqrt{2}}{1440}x^6$

14. $1 + x + \frac{1}{4}x^2 + \frac{1}{12}x^3 - \frac{1}{96}x^4 - \frac{1}{1440}x^6 + \frac{1}{2880}x^7$

15. $1 + \left(x - \frac{\pi}{2}\right) + \frac{1}{2}\left(x - \frac{\pi}{2}\right)^2 - \frac{1}{24}\left(1 + \frac{\pi}{2}\right)^2\left(x - \frac{\pi}{2}\right)^4$
$$- \frac{1}{40}\left(1 + \frac{\pi}{2}\right)\left(2 + \frac{\pi}{2}\right)\left(x - \frac{\pi}{2}\right)^5$$

16. $1 + \left(x - \frac{\pi}{2}\right) - \frac{1}{6}\left(1 + \frac{\pi}{2}\right)\left(x - \frac{\pi}{2}\right)^3 - \frac{1}{12}\left(x - \frac{\pi}{2}\right)^4$
$$+ \frac{1}{120}\left(1 + \frac{\pi}{2}\right)\left(1 + \frac{3\pi}{2} + \frac{\pi^2}{4}\right)\left(x - \frac{\pi}{2}\right)^5$$

## Exercise 41, pages 195–196

1. $y_1 = 1 - \dfrac{x^2}{2 \cdot 7} + \dfrac{x^4}{2 \cdot 4 \cdot 7 \cdot 11} - \cdots$
$$+ (-1)^m \frac{x^{2m}}{[2 \cdot 4 \cdots 2m][7 \cdot 11 \cdots (4m+3)]} + \cdots$$

$y_2 = x^{-\frac{3}{2}}\left[1 - \dfrac{x^2}{1 \cdot 2} + \dfrac{x^4}{1 \cdot 5 \cdot 2 \cdot 4} - \cdots \right.$
$$\left. + (-1)^m \frac{x^{2m}}{[1 \cdot 5 \cdots (4m-3)][2 \cdot 4 \cdots 2m]} + \cdots \right]$$

2. $y_1 = 1 + x - x^2 + \frac{11}{12}x^3 - \frac{319}{336}x^4 + \cdots$
$y_2 = x^{\frac{5}{3}}[1 - \frac{7}{8}x + \frac{7}{8}x^2 - \frac{23}{24}x^3 + \frac{1817}{1632}x^4 - \cdots]$

3. $y_1 = x^{-1}(x+2)$
$$y_2 = x^{\frac{1}{4}}\left[1 + \frac{3x}{9 \cdot 4^2} - \frac{3 \cdot 5x^2}{9 \cdot 13 \cdot 4^4 \cdot 2!} + \frac{3 \cdot 5^2 \cdot 9x^3}{9 \cdot 13 \cdot 17 \cdot 4^6 \cdot 3!} - \cdots \right]$$

4. $y_1 = x\left[1 + \frac{x}{5} + \frac{x^2}{5 \cdot 7} + \cdots + \frac{x^m}{5 \cdot 7 \cdots (2m+3)} + \cdots \right]$
$y_2 = x^{-\frac{1}{2}}\left[1 + \frac{x}{2} + \frac{x^2}{2 \cdot 4} + \cdots + \frac{x^m}{2^m \cdot m!} + \cdots \right]$

5. $y_1 = x^{-1}\left[1 - \frac{2x}{2!} + \frac{(2x)^2}{4!} - \cdots + (-1)^m\frac{(2x)^m}{(2m)!} + \cdots \right]$
$y_2 = x^{-\frac{1}{2}}\left[1 - \frac{2x}{3!} + \frac{(2x)^2}{5!} - \cdots + (-1)^m\frac{(2x)^m}{(2m+1)!} + \cdots \right]$

6. $y_1 = x^{\frac{1}{3}}\left[1 - \frac{x}{2} + \frac{x^2}{2! 2 \cdot 5} - \cdots + (-1)^m\frac{x^m}{m! 2 \cdot 5 \cdots (3m-1)} + \cdots \right]$
$y_2 = x^{\frac{2}{3}}\left[1 - \frac{x}{4} + \frac{x^2}{2! 4 \cdot 7} - \cdots + (-1)^m\frac{x^m}{m! 4 \cdot 7 \cdots (3m+1)} + \cdots \right]$

7. $y_1 = x\left[1 + \dfrac{x}{3} - \dfrac{x^2}{2! \, 3 \cdot 5} + \dfrac{5x^3}{3! 3 \cdot 5 \cdot 7} - \cdots\right]$

$y_2 = x^{\frac{1}{2}}\left[1 + \dfrac{5x}{4} + \dfrac{5x^2}{4^2 2! 3} - \dfrac{55x^3}{4^3 3! 3 \cdot 5} + \cdots\right]$

8. $y_1 = x^2\left[1 + \dfrac{3x}{5} + \dfrac{(3x)^2}{5 \cdot 7} + \cdots + \dfrac{(3x)^m}{5 \cdot 7 \cdots (2m+3)} + \cdots\right]$

$y_2 = x^{\frac{1}{2}}\left[1 + \dfrac{3x}{2} + \dfrac{1}{2!}\left(\dfrac{3x}{2}\right)^2 + \cdots + \dfrac{1}{m!}\left(\dfrac{3x}{2}\right)^m + \cdots\right]$

9. $y_1 = x^{-1}[1 + x - \frac{1}{2}x^2 - \frac{1}{6}x^3 + \cdots]$

$y_2 = x^{\frac{1}{3}}\left[1 + \dfrac{x}{2!} - \dfrac{61}{630}x^2 - \dfrac{607}{73710}x^3 - \cdots\right]$

10. $y_1 = x^{\frac{1}{2}}\left[1 - \dfrac{x^2}{16} + \dfrac{5x^4}{2^6 \cdot 4!} + \cdots + (-1)^m \dfrac{1 \cdot 5 \cdots (4m-3)x^{2m}}{2^{3m}(2m)!} + \cdots\right]$

$y_2 = x^{\frac{3}{2}}\left[1 - \dfrac{x^2}{16} + \dfrac{7x^4}{2^6 \cdot 5!} + \cdots + (-1)^m \dfrac{3 \cdot 7 \cdots (4m-1)x^{2m}}{2^{3m}(2m+1)!} + \cdots\right]$

11. $y_1 = 1 - \dfrac{1}{2 \cdot 7}t^{-2} + \dfrac{1}{2 \cdot 4 \cdot 7 \cdot 11}t^{-4} - \dfrac{1}{2 \cdot 4 \cdot 6 \cdot 7 \cdot 11 \cdot 15}t^{-6} + \cdots$

$y_2 = t^{\frac{3}{2}}\left[1 - \dfrac{1}{2}t^{-2} + \dfrac{1}{2 \cdot 4 \cdot 1 \cdot 5}t^{-4} - \dfrac{1}{2 \cdot 4 \cdot 6 \cdot 1 \cdot 5 \cdot 9}t^{-6} + \cdots\right]$

12. $y_1 = t\left[1 - \dfrac{1}{2!}\dfrac{2}{t} + \dfrac{1}{4!}\left(\dfrac{2}{t}\right)^2 - \cdots + (-1)^m \dfrac{1}{(2m)!}\left(\dfrac{2}{t}\right)^m + \cdots\right]$

$y_2 = t^{\frac{1}{2}}\left[1 - \dfrac{1}{3!}\dfrac{2}{t} + \dfrac{1}{5!}\left(\dfrac{2}{t}\right)^2 - \cdots + (-1)^m \dfrac{1}{(2m+1)!}\left(\dfrac{2}{t}\right)^m + \cdots\right]$

13. $y_1 = t^{-\frac{1}{3}}\left[1 - \dfrac{1}{1 \cdot 2}t^{-1} + \dfrac{1}{2! 2 \cdot 5}t^{-2} - \cdots\right.$
$\left. + (-1)^m \dfrac{1}{m! 2 \cdot 5 \cdots (3m-1)}t^{-m} + \cdots\right]$

$y_2 = t^{-\frac{2}{3}}\left[1 - \dfrac{1}{1 \cdot 4}t^{-1} + \dfrac{1}{2! 4 \cdot 7}t^{-2} - \cdots\right.$
$\left. + (-1)^m \dfrac{1}{m! 4 \cdot 7 \cdots (3m+1)}t^{-m} + \cdots\right]$

14. $y_1 = t^{-2}\left[1 + \dfrac{1}{3}\left(\dfrac{3}{t}\right) + \dfrac{1}{5 \cdot 7}\left(\dfrac{3}{t}\right)^2 + \cdots + \dfrac{1}{5 \cdot 7 \cdots (2m+3)}\left(\dfrac{3}{t}\right)^m + \cdots\right]$

$y_2 = t^{-\frac{1}{2}}\left[1 + \dfrac{3}{2t} + \dfrac{1}{2!}\left(\dfrac{3}{2t}\right)^2 + \cdots + \dfrac{1}{m!}\left(\dfrac{3}{2t}\right)^m + \cdots\right]$

15. $y_1 = x^2\left[1 + \dfrac{2(3x)}{5} + \dfrac{3(3x)^2}{5 \cdot 7} + \cdots + \dfrac{(m+1)(3x)^m}{5 \cdot 7 \cdots (2m+3)} + \cdots\right]$

$y_2 = x^{\frac{1}{2}}\left[1 - \dfrac{3x}{2} - \dfrac{3(3x)^2}{2^2 2!} - \cdots - \dfrac{(2m-1)(3x)^m}{2^m m!} - \cdots\right]$

16. $y_1 = x^{\frac{1}{3}}\left[1 + \dfrac{2x}{3 \cdot 5} + \dfrac{2 \cdot 11 x^2}{3^2 2! 5 \cdot 8} + \cdots + \dfrac{2 \cdot 11 \cdots (9m-7)x^m}{3^m m! 5 \cdot 8 \cdots (3m+2)} + \cdots\right]$

$y_2 = x^{-\frac{1}{3}}\left[1 - \dfrac{4x}{3} - \dfrac{4 \cdot 5 x^2}{3^2 2! 1 \cdot 4} - \cdots - \dfrac{4 \cdot 5 \cdots (9m-13)x^m}{3^m m! 1 \cdot 4 \cdots (3m-2)} - \cdots\right]$

17. $y_1 = x[1 - \frac{6}{11}x + \frac{4}{55}x^2 + \frac{8}{1045}x^3 + \cdots]$

$y_2 = x^{-\frac{3}{4}}[1 - \frac{13}{4}x + \frac{117}{32}x^2 - \frac{195}{128}x^3 + \cdots]$

18. $y_1 = x^{-2}(1 - 12x + 72x^2)$

$y_2 = x^{\frac{1}{2}}\left[1 - \dfrac{3x}{14} - \dfrac{3x^2}{56} - \cdots - \dfrac{3^n[1 \cdot 3 \cdots (2m-3)]^2(2m-1)x^m}{2^m m! 7 \cdot 9 \cdots (2m+5)} + \cdots\right]$

# ANSWERS TO EXERCISES

19. $y_1 = x^2\left[1 - \frac{8x}{11} + \frac{32x^2}{55} - \cdots + (-1)^m \frac{4^m(m+1)!x^m}{11\cdot15\cdots(4m+7)} + \cdots\right]$

$\phantom{19.\ }y_2 = x^{\frac{1}{4}}\left[1 - \frac{x}{4} + \frac{1\cdot5x^2}{4^2\cdot2!} - \cdots + (-1)^m \frac{1\cdot5\cdots(4m-3)x^m}{4^m m!} + \cdots\right]$

20. $y_1 = x\left[1 - \frac{x}{7} + \frac{2!x^2}{7\cdot11} - \cdots + (-1)^m \frac{m!x^m}{7\cdot11\cdots(4m+3)} + \cdots\right]$

$\phantom{20.\ }y_2 = x^{\frac{1}{4}}\left[1 - \frac{x}{16} + \frac{5x^2}{16^2 2!} - \cdots + (-1)^m \frac{5\cdot9\cdots(4m-3)x^m}{16^m m!} + \cdots\right]$

21. $y_1 = x^{\frac{1}{2}}\left[1 - \frac{x}{8\cdot7} - \frac{1^2\cdot3x^2}{8^2 2!7\cdot11} - \cdots - \frac{[1\cdot3\cdots(2m-3)]^2(2m-1)x^m}{8^m m!7\cdot11\cdots(4m+3)} - \cdots\right]$

$\phantom{21.\ }y_2 = x^{-\frac{1}{4}}\left[1 + \frac{5x}{32} - \frac{5\cdot3x^2}{32^2 2!1\cdot5} - \cdots - \frac{5[3\cdot7\cdots(4m-9)]^2(4m-5)x^m}{32^m m!1\cdot5\cdots(4m-3)} - \cdots\right]$

22. $y_1 = x[1 + \frac{1}{5}x - \frac{2}{35}x^2 - \frac{16}{945}x^3 + \cdots]$

$\phantom{22.\ }y_2 = x^{-\frac{1}{2}}[1 - x - \frac{1}{4}x^2 + \frac{1}{36}x^3 + \cdots]$

23. $y_1 = x\left[1 - \frac{x^2}{2\cdot1\cdot5} + \frac{x^4}{2^2 2!5\cdot9} - \cdots + (-1)^m \frac{x^{2m}}{2^m m!5\cdot9\cdots(4m+1)} + \cdots\right]$

$\phantom{23.\ }y_2 = x^{\frac{1}{2}}\left[1 - \frac{x^2}{2\cdot1\cdot3} + \frac{x^4}{2^2 2!3\cdot7} - \cdots + (-1)^m \frac{x^{2m}}{2^m m!3\cdot7\cdots(4m-1)} + \cdots\right]$

24. $y_1 = x\left[1 - \frac{x^2}{2\cdot1\cdot11} + \frac{x^4}{2^2 2!11\cdot17} - \cdots\right.$

$\phantom{24.\ }\left. + (-1)^m \frac{x^{2m}}{2^m m!11\cdot17\cdots(6m+5)} + \cdots\right]$

$\phantom{24.\ }y_2 = x^{-\frac{2}{3}}\left[1 - \frac{x^2}{2\cdot1} + \frac{x^4}{2^2 2!1\cdot7} - \cdots + (-1)^m \frac{x^{2m}}{2^m m!1\cdot7\cdots(6m-5)} + \cdots\right]$

25. $y_1 = x^{-1}[1 - x - \frac{3}{4}x^2 - \frac{1}{20}x^3 - \cdots]$

$\phantom{25.\ }y_2 = x^{\frac{1}{3}}[1 + \frac{1}{4}x + \frac{23}{1260}x^2 - \frac{179}{16380}x^3 - \cdots]$

26. $y_1 = 1 + x - \frac{1}{2}x^2 + \frac{1}{18}x^3 + \cdots$

$\phantom{26.\ }y_2 = x^{\frac{3}{2}}[1 - \frac{1}{5}x + \frac{1}{70}x^2 + \frac{52}{945}x^3 - \cdots]$

## Exercise 42, page 206

1. $y_1 = 1 - 2x + \frac{(2x)^2}{(2!)^2} - \cdots + \frac{(-1)^m(2x)^m}{(m!)^2} + \cdots$

$\phantom{1.\ }y_2 = y_1 \ln x + 4x - 3x^2 + \frac{22}{27}x^3 - \cdots$

2. $y_1 = 1 - \frac{2}{2^2}x^2 + \frac{2^2 x^4}{2^4(2!)^2} - \cdots + \frac{(-1)^{m+1}x^{2m}}{2^{2m}(m!)^2} + \cdots$

$\phantom{2.\ }y_2 = y_1 \ln x + \frac{1}{2}x^2 - \frac{3}{32}x^4 + \frac{11}{1728}x^6 - \cdots$

3. $y_1 = x^2\left[1 - 4x + (4x)^2 - \cdots + \frac{(-1)^m(4x)^m}{(m!)^2} + \cdots\right]$

$\phantom{3.\ }y_2 = y_1 \ln x + x^2(8x - 12x^2 + \frac{176}{27}x^3 - \cdots)$

4. $y_1 = x\left[1 + x + \frac{x^2}{2!} + \cdots + \frac{x^m}{m!} + \cdots\right] = xe^x$

$\phantom{4.\ }y_2 = xe^x \ln x - x[x + \frac{3}{4}x^2 + \frac{11}{36}x^3 + \cdots]$

5. $y_1 = x^2\left[1 + 4x + 6x^2 + \cdots + \frac{2^m(m+1)x^m}{m!} + \cdots\right]$

$\phantom{5.\ }y_2 = y_1 \ln x - x^2[6x + 13x^2 + \frac{124}{9}x^3 + \cdots]$

6. $y_1 = x^3\left[1 + \frac{3}{2}x^2 + \frac{15}{8}x^4 + \cdots + \frac{3\cdot5\cdots(2m+1)x^{2m}}{2^m m!} + \cdots\right]$

$\phantom{6.\ }y_2 = y_1 \ln x - x^5[\frac{1}{4} + \frac{13}{32}x^2 + \frac{101}{192}x^4 + \cdots]$

**7.** $y_1 = x$

$$y_2 = x \ln x - x^3\left[\frac{1}{2^2} - \frac{x^2}{2 \cdot 4^2} + \frac{x^4}{2 \cdot 4 \cdot 6^2} - \cdots\right]$$

**8.** $y_1 = 1 - x + \frac{1}{3}x^3 - \frac{5}{24}x^4 + \cdots$

$y_2 = x^2 e^{-x}$

**9.** $y_1 = x^{-1}[1 + \frac{1}{2}x + \frac{1}{2}x^2 - \frac{1}{8}x^4 - \cdots]$

$y_2 = x^2[1 + \frac{1}{2}x + \frac{1}{20}x^2 - \frac{17}{60}x^3 - \cdots]$

**10.** $y_1 = x^{-1}[1 - x - \frac{3}{2}x^2 - \frac{3}{8}x^4 + \cdots]$

$y_2 = x^2[1 - x + \frac{9}{10}x^2 - \frac{17}{30}x^3 + \cdots]$

**11.** $y_1 = x^3[1 + \frac{3}{7}x + \frac{3}{14}x^2 + \frac{5}{42}x^3 + \cdots]$

$$y_2 = \frac{(1 - x)^3}{x^3}$$

**12.** $y_1 = 3 + 2x + x^2$

$y_2 = x^4[1 + 2x + 3x^2 + \cdots + (m + 1)x^m + \cdots]$

**13.** $y_1 = x^6\left[5 \cdot 6 - 6 \cdot 7x + \frac{7 \cdot 8}{2!}x^2 - \cdots + (-1)^m \frac{(m + 5)(m + 6)x^m}{m!} + \cdots\right]$

$y_2 = x^2[1 + x + x^2 + \frac{5}{3}x^3 - \cdots] - \frac{1}{12}y_1 \ln x$

**14.** $y_1 = x^4\left[1 - 4x + \frac{3 \cdot 4 \cdot 5}{3!}x^2 - \cdots + (-1)^m \frac{(m + 1)(m + 2)(m + 3)x^m}{3!} + \cdots\right]$

$y_2 = x[1 + \frac{1}{2}x + x^2 - 10x^3 - \cdots] - 3y_1 \ln x$

**15.** $y_1 = x\left[3 + \frac{1}{2^2}x^2 + \frac{3}{2^7}x^4 + \frac{1}{2^9}x^6 + \cdots\right]$

$$y_2 = x^{-3}\left[1 + \frac{3}{4}x^2 + \frac{19}{2^6}x^4 + \frac{5}{2^8}x^6 + \cdots\right] - \frac{1}{16}y_1 \ln x$$

## Exercise 43, page 209

**1.** $3! x^2\left[\dfrac{1}{2!\,4!} + \dfrac{x}{3!\,5!} + \dfrac{x^2}{4!\,6!} + \cdots + \dfrac{x^m}{(m + 2)!(m + 4)!} + \cdots\right]$

**2.** $x^3\left[\dfrac{1}{3^2} + \dfrac{2x^2}{(3 \cdot 5)^2} + \dfrac{2^2 x^4}{(3 \cdot 5 \cdot 7)^2} + \cdots + \dfrac{2^m x^{2m}}{[3 \cdot 5 \cdots (2m + 3)]^2} + \cdots\right]$

**3.** $3! x^4\left[\dfrac{1}{3 \cdot 4!} + \dfrac{x}{4 \cdot 5!} + \dfrac{x^2}{5 \cdot 6!} + \cdots + \dfrac{x^m}{(m + 3)(m + 4)!} + \cdots\right]$

**4.** $-\frac{1}{6}x^3[1 + x + \frac{4}{5}x^2 + \frac{2}{3}x^3 + \cdots] + x^4[\frac{1}{12} + \frac{1}{10}x + \frac{1}{10}x^2 + \frac{11}{105}x^3 + \cdots]$

**5.** $x\left[\dfrac{1}{13} - \dfrac{x}{13 \cdot 16} + \dfrac{x^2}{13 \cdot 16 \cdot 21} - \cdots + (-1)^m \dfrac{x^m}{13 \cdot 16 \cdots [12 + (m + 1)^2]} + \cdots\right]$

$\qquad + x^2\left[\dfrac{1}{16} - \dfrac{x}{16 \cdot 21} + \dfrac{x^2}{16 \cdot 21 \cdot 28} - \cdots\right.$

$\qquad\qquad \left. + (-1)^m \dfrac{x^m}{16 \cdot 21 \cdots [12 + (m + 2)^2]} + \cdots\right]$

**6.** $\frac{1}{4}x[1 - \frac{1}{16}x^2 + \frac{3}{200}x^3 + \frac{1}{4800}x^4 + \cdots] - \frac{1}{9}x^2[2 - \frac{1}{4}x - \frac{1}{10}x^2 + \frac{13}{240}x^3 - \cdots]$

**7.** $\frac{1}{4}x[1 + \frac{1}{15}x - \frac{1}{120}x^2 - \frac{7}{6600}x^3 + \cdots]$

$\qquad - \frac{1}{32}x^3[1 + \frac{3}{55}x - \frac{7}{330}x^2 - \frac{71}{39270}x^3 + \cdots]$

**8.** $2x^2\left[\dfrac{3^2 \cdot 2!}{6!} - \dfrac{3^3 \cdot 3!(3x)}{9!} + \dfrac{3^4 \cdot 4!(3x)^2}{12!} - \cdots + \dfrac{3^{m+2}(m + 2)!(-3x)^m}{[3(m + 2)]!} + \cdots\right]$

$\qquad + 2240 x^4\left[\dfrac{3^4 \cdot 4!}{12!} - \dfrac{3^5 \cdot 5!(3x)}{15!} + \dfrac{3^6 \cdot 6!(3x)^2}{18!} - \cdots\right.$

$\qquad\qquad \left. + \dfrac{3^{m+4}(m + 4)!(-3x)^m}{[3(m + 4)]!} + \cdots\right]$

**9.** $-1 + \frac{1}{11}x$

**10.** $-1 + A_1\left[x + \frac{x^2}{5} + \frac{x^3}{5 \cdot 7} + \cdots + \frac{x^m}{5 \cdot 7 \cdots (2m+1)} + \cdots\right]$

$$+ \frac{x^3}{14}\left[1 + \frac{x}{9} + \frac{x^2}{9 \cdot 11} + \cdots + \frac{x^m}{9 \cdot 11 \cdots (2m+7)} + \cdots\right]$$

**11.** $3x^2 - 24x^4\left[\frac{1}{4!} + \frac{3!\,x^2}{6!} + \frac{5!\,x^4}{8!} + \cdots + \frac{(2m+1)!\,x^{2m}}{(2m+4)!} + \cdots\right]$

$$+ 24x^6\left[\frac{3!}{6!} + \frac{5!\,x^2}{8!} + \frac{7!\,x^4}{10!} + \cdots + \frac{(2m+3)!\,x^{2m}}{(2m+6)!} + \cdots\right]$$

**12.** $4x^3\left[\frac{1}{3!} - \frac{x}{2 \cdot 4!} + \frac{2!\,x^2}{2^2 \cdot 5!} - \cdots + (-1)^m \frac{m!\,x^m}{2^m(m+3)!} + \cdots\right]$

$$+ 6x^4\left[\frac{1}{4!} - \frac{x}{5!} + \frac{3!\,x^2}{2^2 \cdot 6!} - \cdots + (-1)^m \frac{(m+1)!\,x^m}{2^m(m+4)!} + \cdots\right]$$

$$+ 2x^5\left[\frac{2!}{5!} - \frac{3!\,x}{2 \cdot 6!} + \frac{4!\,x^2}{2^2 \cdot 7!} - \cdots + (-1)^m \frac{(m+2)!\,x^m}{2^m(m+5)!} + \cdots\right]$$

**13.** $x\left[\frac{1}{3!} - \frac{2^2 x}{3 \cdot 5!} + \frac{2^3 x^2}{4 \cdot 7!} - \cdots + (-1)^m \frac{2^{m+1} x^m}{(m+2)(2m+3)!} + \cdots\right]$

$$+ 3 \cdot 2^4 x^2\left[\frac{1}{6!} - \frac{2x}{8!} + \frac{(2x)^2}{10!} - \cdots + (-1)^m \frac{(2x)^m}{(2m+6)!} + \cdots\right]$$

$$+ 2 \cdot 6!\,x^3\left[\frac{1}{8!} - \frac{2x}{10!} + \frac{(2x)^2}{12!} - \cdots + (-1)^m \frac{(2x)^m}{(2m+8)!} + \cdots\right]$$

**14.** $x^2\left[\frac{2}{3!} - \frac{2^2 x}{5!} + \frac{2^3 \cdot 5x^2}{7!} - \cdots + (-1)^m \frac{2^{m+1} 5 \cdot 11 \cdots (m^2+m-1)x^m}{(2m+3)!} + \cdots\right]$

$$+ 3x^3\left[\frac{2^2}{5!} - \frac{2^3 x}{7!} + \frac{2^4 \cdot 11 x^2}{9!} - \cdots\right.$$

$$\left. + (-1)^m \frac{2^{m+2} \cdot 11 \cdot 19 \cdots (m^2+3m+1)x^m}{(2m+5)!} + \cdots\right]$$

$$+ 3x^4\left[\frac{2^4 \cdot 5}{7!} - \frac{2^5 \cdot 5 \cdot 11 x}{9!} + \frac{2^6 \cdot 5 \cdot 11 \cdot 19 x^2}{11!} - \cdots\right.$$

$$\left. + (-1)^m \frac{2^{m+4} 5 \cdot 11 \cdots (m^2+5m+5)x^m}{(2m+7)!} + \cdots\right]$$

### Exercise 44, pages 213–214

**1.** $\frac{1}{8}x(63x^4 - 70x^2 + 15)$; $\frac{1}{16}(231x^6 - 315x^4 + 105x^2 - 5)$;
$\frac{1}{16}x(429x^6 - 693x^4 + 315x^2 - 35)$

**11.** $0.9776$; $0.9604$; $-0.0995$  **12.** $0.0995$; $0.1483$; $0.4925$; $0.4703$

### Exercise 45, page 221

**1.** $z = x^2 + y^2 + a$  **2.** $z = \frac{\ln k}{xy} + a$  **3.** $z = \frac{1}{y}\sin xy + a$

**4.** $yx^2(1 + z) = a$  **5.** Not integrable  **6.** $x^2 z(1 + y^2)^2 = a$

**7.** $x^2 \sin y + e^z = a$  **8.** Not integrable  **9.** $\frac{xe^{2y}}{1 + z^2} = a$

**10.** Not integrable  **11.** $\frac{z \tan y}{1 + x^2} = a$  **12.** $ye^{\frac{z}{y}} + \ln \cos x = a$

**13.** Arc $\tan \frac{z}{x} = z - y^2 + a$  **14.** $ye^{x^2-z} = e^z + a$

### Exercise 46, page 223

1. $u = z \cos xy + a$
2. $u = axy \sin z$
3. $u = axze^y$
4. $u = aze^x \sin y$
5. $u = ax^2y^3z$
6. $u = ax^2z(\csc 2y - \cot 2y)$
7. $u = e^{xy} + \ln axyz$
8. $u = e^{yz^2} + \text{Arc} \tan xy + a$
9. $u^2 = \sin xy + \cos xz + a$
10. $u^3 = \sin xyz + a$

### Exercise 47, page 226

1. $x^2y + y^2z = C$
2. $x(y^2 + 1) - y \tan z = C$
3. Not exact
4. $x + \ln xz - \dfrac{y}{z} = C$
5. Not exact
6. $y \text{ Arc} \tan x + z(y - x^2 - 1) = C$
7. Not exact
8. $(x + y)e^z = C$
9. $\sin xy - x \sin y + z^2 = C$
10. $ye^{2x} - 3xe^y + e^z = C$
11. Not exact
12. $xyz + \ln xyz = C$
13. Not exact
14. $(x^2 + y^2)e^z + ze^{xy} = C$

### Exercise 48, page 230

1. $\dfrac{y}{x} - z^2 = C$
2. $\dfrac{x^2y^2(1 + z)}{1 - z} = C$
3. $z(x + y) - x^2 - y^2 = C$
4. $(x^2 + y^2)z^2 = C$
5. $yz + \ln x = C$
6. $\dfrac{x}{y} - \ln z = C$
7. $xz - \cos yz = C$
8. $\text{Arc} \tan \dfrac{z}{x} - \text{Arc} \sin \dfrac{z}{y} = C$
9. $\dfrac{y(x + z)}{z + y} = C; \dfrac{1}{(y + z)^2}$
10. $y + z^2 + 2e^{-x^2}\displaystyle\int_0^x (1 + x^2)e^{x^2}\, dx = C; \; 1$
11. $\dfrac{x}{y} + \dfrac{y}{z} - \ln z = C; \dfrac{1}{y^2z^2}$
12. $z\sqrt{xy}e^{-xy} = C; \dfrac{e^{-xy}}{2\sqrt{xy}}$
13. Not integrable
14. $yz + zx + xy = C(x + y + z); \dfrac{1}{(x + y + z)^2}$

### Exercise 49, page 233

1. $z = \dfrac{x}{y} + Cx$
2. $z = Cx^2 - y^2$
3. $z = x \ln Cy$
4. $z = Ce^{\pm xy}$
5. $z = C\sqrt{x^2 + y^2}$
6. $z = \dfrac{C}{y - x}$
7. $z^2 = (x + C)^2 + y^2 - 1$
8. $z = Cx + y - 1$

### Exercise 50, pages 239–240

1. $z = xp + yq + pq$
2. $xp + yq = 0$
3. $xp + yq = 2z$
4. $xp + yq = z$
5. $q^2 - p^2 = (x + y)^2$
6. $z^2 - x^2 - y^2 = 2z(xp + yq)$
7. $zp^2 + q^2 = \frac{4}{9}$
8. $p = \sin qx$
9. $z = e^{\frac{px + qy}{z}}$
10. $pq = 4xy$

11. $pq = yz$

12. $z + x^2p + y^2q = 0$

13. $x_2 - x_1, \quad x_3 - x_1$

14. $x_2 - \ln x_1, \quad x_3 + \frac{1}{2}x_2^2$

15. $x_2x_3, \quad \dfrac{x_1}{x_2} e^{-x_2x_3}$

16. $x_2 - x_1, \quad 2\sqrt{x_3} + x_2$

17. $x_1^2 + x_2^2, \quad \text{Arc tan} \dfrac{x_2}{x_1} - \text{Arc tan } x_3$

18. $z = x + c_1, \quad z = c_2y + c_1$

19. $z = \sqrt{x^2 + c_1^2}, \quad z = \sqrt{y^2 + c_2^2}$

20. $z = c_1e^{\frac{2}{x}}, \quad z = c_2e^{-\frac{2}{y}}$

21. $z = y + c_1, \quad z = c_2e^{-\frac{1}{x}}$

22. $z = \frac{1}{2}x^2 + c_1, \quad z = c_2e^{-y}$

## Exercise 51, page 241

1. $z = b(ax + y)^2$

2. $bxy = e^{\frac{z}{a}}$

3. $z = ax + \dfrac{b}{y}$

4. $z = ax \pm \sqrt{a^2 - y^2}$

5. $z = x(b + ay - a \ln x)$

6. $z = ax + by + ab$

7. $z = ay + b \pm \dfrac{x}{2}\sqrt{x^2 - a^2} - \dfrac{a^2}{2}\ln(x \pm \sqrt{x^2 - a^2})$

8. $z = -xy + ay + a + (a - x)\ln(a - x) + b$

9. $z = \pm 2\sqrt{ax} \pm \sqrt{(1 - a)y} + b$

10. $2az = 2xy + 2a^2y - x^2 - y^2 + b$

11. $4z = (y + b)^2 - (x - 2a)^2$

12. $z = [b + ay + \frac{1}{3}(x - 4a^2)^{\frac{3}{2}}]^2$

## Exercise 52, pages 244–245

1. $y^3 - 5; \quad xy(y^3 - 5)^2 + \frac{1}{7}y^5 - \frac{5}{2}y^2 = C$

2. $x^{-3}; \quad \ln x + \dfrac{y}{x} - \dfrac{y^2}{2x^2} = C$

3. $e^{6x}; \quad \left(x^2y + \dfrac{y^2}{2}\right)e^{6x} = C$

4. $\dfrac{1}{xy(y^2 - x^2)}; \quad \ln \dfrac{xy^2}{y^2 - x^2} = C$

5. $\dfrac{-1}{xy(x^3 + y^3)}; \quad \ln \dfrac{x^3 + y^3}{xy} = C$

6. $x - 2; \quad y(x - 2)^2(x - 3) + \frac{1}{12}x^3(3x - 8) = C$

7. $e^{\frac{x^3}{3}}; \quad e^{\frac{x^3}{3}}(xy^3 - 2y) + \displaystyle\int_0^x xe^{\frac{x^3}{3}} dx = C$

8. $e^{\frac{y^2}{2}}; \quad (x^2y^2 + 3xy - x)e^{\frac{y^2}{2}} = C$

10. $-\dfrac{1}{2xy}$

11. $\dfrac{1}{x^2y^2(2 + xy - x^2y^2)}$

12. $\dfrac{1}{xy(1 - x^{\frac{1}{2}}y^{\frac{1}{2}})}$

13. $\dfrac{1}{xy(\cos xy - \sin xy)}$

14. $\dfrac{1}{xy(e^{xy} - \ln xy)}$

## Exercise 53, page 249

1. $z = \dfrac{y^2 - x^2}{y}$

2. $z = x$

3. $z = \pm(\sqrt{2x} - \sqrt{2y})$

4. $z = x + y + 1$

## Exercise 54, page 251

1. $\dfrac{k}{p}$

2. $\dfrac{a}{p^2} + \dfrac{b}{p}$

3. $\dfrac{2a}{p^3} + \dfrac{b}{p^2} + \dfrac{c}{p}$

4. $\dfrac{a}{p^2 + a^2}$

5. $\dfrac{p}{p^2 + a^2}$

6. $\dfrac{b}{p^2 - b^2}$

7. $\dfrac{p}{p^2 - b^2}$

8. $\dfrac{ab}{p} - \dfrac{a + b}{p^2} + \dfrac{2}{p^3}$

9. $\dfrac{1}{(p + a)(p + b)}$

10. $\dfrac{1}{(p - 1)^2}$

11. $\dfrac{2ap}{(p^2 - a^2)^2}$

12. $\dfrac{(p^2 + a^2)}{(p^2 - a^2)^2}$

13. $\dfrac{2ap}{(p^2 + a^2)^2}$

14. $\dfrac{p^2 - a^2}{(p^2 + a^2)^2}$

## Exercise 55, page 257

10. $\dfrac{p + a}{(p + a)^2 + b^2}$

11. $\dfrac{b}{(p - a)^2 - b^2}$

12. $\dfrac{p + a}{(p + a)^2 - b^2}$

13. $\dfrac{2p(p^2 - 3b^2)}{(p^2 + b^2)^3}$

14. $\ln\left(\dfrac{p^2 + b^2}{p^2}\right)$

## Exercise 56, page 258

1. $\frac{1}{6}(e^x + 5e^{-5x})$

2. $1 - e^{-x} - xe^{-x}$

3. $-\frac{1}{2}e^{-x} + 2e^{-2x} - \frac{3}{2}e^{0x}$

4. $e^{-x} - 2e^{-3x}$

5. $e^{2x}(1 + x)$

6. $\frac{1}{2}(\sinh x + x \cosh x)$

7. $4e^{-2x} - \frac{7}{4}e^{-x} - \frac{9}{4}e^{-3x} + \frac{1}{2}xe^{-x}$

8. $\frac{1}{2}xe^x - \frac{1}{2}\sin x$

9. $e^{-x}(1 - \cos x\sqrt{2})$

10. $e^{-x}(\cos x\sqrt{2} + \frac{1}{2}\sqrt{2}\sin x\sqrt{2})$

11. $\frac{1}{3}e^x - \frac{1}{3}e^{-\frac{1}{2}x}(\cos \frac{1}{2}x\sqrt{3} - \frac{27}{2}\sqrt{3}\sin \frac{1}{2}x\sqrt{3})$

12. $3e^{-x} + \frac{2}{3}e^{-2x} - \frac{2}{3}e^x$

## Exercise 57, page 261

1. $\frac{1}{2}\sinh 2x + \frac{8}{5}\cosh 2x - \frac{3}{5}\cos 2x$

2. $\cos x + \frac{5}{3}\sin x - \frac{1}{3}\sin 2x$

3. $\frac{1}{9}e^x(3x + 8) + \frac{1}{9}e^{-2x}$

4. $4e^{-x} - e^{-2x}(x + 3)$

5. $e^{-\frac{1}{2}x}\left(2 \cos\dfrac{x\sqrt{3}}{2} + \sqrt{3} \sin\dfrac{x\sqrt{3}}{2}\right) - \cos x$

6. $e^{-\frac{1}{2}x}\left(\cos\dfrac{x\sqrt{3}}{2} + \dfrac{7}{\sqrt{3}} \sin\dfrac{x\sqrt{3}}{2}\right) + x^2 - 2x$

7. $e^{-x}(x + 2) - e^{-2x}(\frac{1}{2}x^2 + 1)$

8. $\frac{1}{4}[e^{2x}(x + 1) + 3e^{-2x} - x]$

9. $\frac{1}{6}e^{3x}(x + 2) + \frac{2}{3}e^{-3x} - \frac{1}{18}\sin 3x$

10. $\dfrac{29}{40} e^{-2x} + \dfrac{29}{135} e^{3x} - \dfrac{x^3}{6} + \dfrac{x^2}{12} - \dfrac{7x}{36} + \dfrac{13}{216}$

11. $-2\sqrt{3}e^{\frac{3}{2}x} \sin\dfrac{x\sqrt{3}}{2} + e^x(x + 1)$

12. $\dfrac{1}{3}\left(xe^x - \dfrac{2}{\sqrt{3}} e^{-\frac{1}{2}x} \sin\dfrac{x\sqrt{3}}{2}\right)$

13. $-x^2 + e^x - e^{-\frac{1}{2}x}\left(\cos\dfrac{x\sqrt{3}}{2} + \sqrt{3} \sin\dfrac{x\sqrt{3}}{2}\right)$

14. $\frac{3}{2}e^{3x} - \frac{1}{2}e^x - e^{2x}(\frac{1}{3}x^3 + 2x + 1)$

## Exercise 58, page 267

1. $\dfrac{1}{a}(e^{ax} - 1)$

2. $\dfrac{1}{a}(1 - e^{-ax})$

3. $2\sqrt{\dfrac{x}{\pi}}$

4. $\dfrac{4}{3}x\sqrt{\dfrac{x}{\pi}}$

5. $a^{-(n+1)}e^{-ax}[n!e^{ax} - (ax)^n - n(ax)^{n-1} - n(n - 1)(ax)^{n-2} - \cdots - n!]$

343

6. $\dfrac{1}{k^2}(1 - \cos kx)$  

7. $\dfrac{1}{k^2}(\cosh kx - 1)$

8. $\dfrac{1}{k^4}(2 - 2\cos kx - kx\sin kx)$  

9. $\dfrac{1}{k^3}(kx - \sin kx)$

10. $\dfrac{1}{k^3}(\sinh kx - kx)$  

11. $\dfrac{1}{2k^5}(2kx - 3\sin kx + kx\cos kx)$

12. $\frac{1}{6}(2\sin x - \cos 2x)$  

13. $\frac{1}{3}(\cos x - \cos 2x)$  

14. $\frac{1}{3}(2\sin 2x - \sin x)$

## Exercise 59, page 271

1. $\dfrac{p}{p^2 + b^2}$  

2. $\dfrac{b}{p^2 + b^2}$

3. $\dfrac{pe^{\frac{1}{2}p\pi}}{(p^2 + 4)(e^{\frac{1}{2}p\pi} - 1)}$  

4. $\dfrac{2e^{3p}}{p(e^{3p} + 1)}$

5. $\dfrac{1 + 2ap}{p^2(1 - e^{2ap})}$  

6. $\dfrac{p^2 + 8(e^{\frac{1}{2}p\pi} + 1)}{p(1 + e^{\frac{1}{2}p\pi})(p^2 + 16)}$

7. $\dfrac{2k^2}{p(p^2 + 16k^2)}$  

8. $\dfrac{(e^{\frac{1}{2}p} - 1)^2}{p^2(1 + e^p)}$

9. $\dfrac{(1 - e^{-\frac{1}{2}p})^2}{p^2(1 - e^{-2p})}, \ \dfrac{e^{\frac{1}{2}p} - 1}{p^2(1 + e^{\frac{1}{2}p})}$

10. $\dfrac{e^p - pe^{\frac{1}{2}p} - 1}{p^2(e^p - 1)}, \ \dfrac{e^p - pe^{\frac{1}{2}p} - 1}{p^2(e^p - 1)(1 - e^{-\frac{1}{2}p})}, \ \dfrac{e^p - pe^{\frac{1}{2}p} - 1}{p^2(e^{\frac{1}{2}p} - 1)^2}$

## Exercise 60, page 274

1. $x = t^2 + t - 5, \ y = \frac{1}{3}t^3 - t^2 + 2$  

2. $x = e^t + t, \ y = e^t - e^{-t}$

3. $x = \sin t + t^2, \ y = \cos t + t - 1$

4. $x = 3 + \sin 2t - \frac{3}{2}e^{-t} - \frac{1}{2}e^{2t}, \ y = -3 + \cos 2t + \frac{9}{2}e^{-t} + \frac{3}{2}e^{2t}$

5. $x = 2 + t + e^t - 2\cos t - 3\sin t, \ y = 2 + e^t - \cos t - 2\sin t$

6. $x = t^3 - t^2, \ y = 3t^2 - 2t$  

7. $x = e^{2t} + t^2, \ y = 5 - t - 5e^{2t}$

8. $x = \sin t + t^2, \ y = \cos t - t^3$

9. $x = \sin 2t + e^t - 1, \ y = 2\cos 2t - t^2 - 2$

10. $x = e^t\sin 2t, \ y = e^t\cos 2t$

## Exercise 61, page 280

1. $\sin 5x$  

2. $\cos x + \dfrac{2}{\pi}\displaystyle\sum_{n=1}^{\infty}\left[1 + (-1)^n\right]\dfrac{n}{n^2 + 1}\sin nx$

3. $\frac{1}{2} + \frac{1}{2}\cos 2x$  

4. $\dfrac{\pi^2}{3} + 4\displaystyle\sum_{n=1}^{\infty}\dfrac{(-1)}{n^2}\cos nx$

5. $-\dfrac{1}{2}\sin x + \displaystyle\sum_{n=2}^{\infty}\dfrac{2n(-1)^n}{n^2 - 1}\sin nx$

6. $\dfrac{\pi}{4} + \displaystyle\sum_{n=1}^{\infty}\left[\dfrac{1 - (-1)^n}{n^2\pi}\cos nx + \dfrac{(-1)^n}{n}\sin nx\right]$

7. $\dfrac{2}{\pi}\displaystyle\sum_{n=1}^{\infty}\dfrac{(-1)^n}{1 - 4n^2}\sin 2nx$  

8. $-\dfrac{\pi}{2} + 2\displaystyle\sum_{n=1}^{\infty}\dfrac{(-1)^n}{n}\sin nx$

9. $-\dfrac{\pi}{4}+\dfrac{1}{\pi}\sum\limits_{n=1}^{\infty}\left[\dfrac{1}{n}\left(1+\cos\dfrac{n\pi}{2}-2\cos n\pi\right)\sin nx-\dfrac{1}{n}\sin\dfrac{n\pi}{2}\cos nx\right]$

10. $\dfrac{2}{\pi}\sum\limits_{n=1}^{\infty}\dfrac{2-(-1)^n}{n}\sin nx$

### Exercise 62, page 284

1. $\dfrac{13}{3}+\dfrac{(-1)^n 4}{\pi^2}\sum\limits_{n=1}^{\infty}\left(\dfrac{1}{n^2}\cos n\pi x-\dfrac{2\pi}{n}\sin n\pi x\right)$

2. $1-\dfrac{2}{\pi}\sum\limits_{n=1}^{\infty}\dfrac{1}{n}\sin n\pi x$ 
3. $\pi+3-2\sum\limits_{n=1}^{\infty}\dfrac{1}{n}\sin 2nx$

4. $-\dfrac{1}{3}(\pi^2+3)+\sum\limits_{n=1}^{\infty}\dfrac{1}{n^2}\cos 2nx$

5. $5-10\sum\limits_{n=1}^{\infty}\left[\dfrac{1-(-1)^n}{n^2\pi^2}\cos\dfrac{n\pi x}{5}+\dfrac{(-1)^n}{n\pi}\sin\dfrac{n\pi x}{5}\right]$

6. $\dfrac{3}{4}+\sum\limits_{n=1}^{\infty}\left[\dfrac{1-(-1)^n}{n^2\pi^2}\cos n\pi x-\dfrac{1}{n\pi}\sin n\pi x\right]$

7. $3+\dfrac{2}{n\pi}\sum\limits_{n=1}^{\infty}[(-1)^n-1]\sin\dfrac{n\pi x}{2}$

8. $-\dfrac{1}{2}+\dfrac{1}{\pi^2}\sum\limits_{n=1}^{\infty}\left[\dfrac{1+(-1)^n}{n^2}\cos n\pi x-\dfrac{2}{n^3\pi}(1+n^2\pi^2\cos n\pi)\sin n\pi x\right]$

### Exercise 63, page 289

1. $\dfrac{4}{\pi}\sum\limits_{n=1}^{\infty}\dfrac{1-(-1)^n}{\pi}\sin nx$ 
2. $\dfrac{1}{\pi}\sum\limits_{n=1}^{\infty}\dfrac{(-1)^n-1}{n^3-4n}(n^2+4)\sin nx$

3. $\dfrac{1}{4}(1-2\pi^2)+\dfrac{1}{2}\sum\limits_{n=1}^{\infty}\dfrac{1+(-1)^n}{(n^2-1)^2}(n^2+1)\sin nx$

4. $\sin x$ 
5. $\dfrac{8}{\pi^2}\sum\limits_{n=1}^{\infty}\left(\sin\dfrac{n\pi}{2}-\sin n\pi\right)\dfrac{\sin nx}{n^2}$

6. $\dfrac{3\pi}{8}+\dfrac{2}{\pi}\sum\limits_{n=1}^{\infty}\dfrac{1}{n^2}\left(\cos n\pi-\cos\tfrac{1}{2}n\pi-n\pi\sin\tfrac{1}{2}n\pi\right)\cos nx$

7. $\dfrac{2}{3\pi}+\dfrac{12}{\pi}\sum\limits_{n=1}^{\infty}\dfrac{1+(-1)^n}{9-n^2}\cos nx$

8. $\dfrac{1}{\pi}(1+e^{-\pi})+\dfrac{2}{\pi}\sum\limits_{n=1}^{\infty}\dfrac{1-(-1)^n}{1+n^2}\cos nx$

# ANSWERS TO EXERCISES

9. $1 + \dfrac{8}{\pi^2} \displaystyle\sum_{n=1}^{\infty} \dfrac{1}{n^2} \left(2 \cos \tfrac{1}{2} n\pi - \cos n\pi - 1\right) \cos nx$

10. $\dfrac{1}{3} + \dfrac{8}{\pi^2} \displaystyle\sum_{n=1}^{\infty} \dfrac{1 - (-1)^n}{n^2} \cos nx$

## Exercise 64, page 296

1. $\dfrac{2}{\pi} \displaystyle\sum_{n=1}^{\infty} \dfrac{(-1)^n n}{n^2 - 4} \sin \dfrac{n\pi x}{6} \cos \dfrac{n\pi t \sqrt{30g}}{6}$

2. $72e^3 \displaystyle\sum_{n=1}^{\infty} \dfrac{1}{n^2 \pi^2 + 36} \sin \tfrac{1}{2} n\pi \sin \dfrac{n\pi x}{6} \cos \dfrac{n\pi t \sqrt{30g}}{6}$

3. $\dfrac{1}{2} \displaystyle\sum_{n=1}^{\infty} \sin \dfrac{n\pi x}{6} \cos \dfrac{n\pi t \sqrt{30g}}{6}$

4. $\displaystyle\sum_{n=1}^{\infty} \dfrac{24}{5n^2 \pi^2} \sin \tfrac{1}{2} n\pi \sin \dfrac{n\pi x}{6} \cos \dfrac{n\pi t \sqrt{30g}}{6}$

5. $\dfrac{1}{\pi} \displaystyle\sum_{n=1}^{\infty} \left[ \dfrac{n \sin \tfrac{1}{2} n\pi}{n^2 - 4} + \dfrac{n \cos \tfrac{1}{2} n\pi - 6}{36 - n^2} + \dfrac{1}{n} \left(1 - \cos \tfrac{1}{2} n\pi\right) \right] \cdot \sin \dfrac{n\pi x}{6} \cos \dfrac{n\pi t \sqrt{30g}}{6}$